CW00549946

THE abc OF
BRITISH RAILWAYS
LOCOMOTIVES

COMBINED VOLUME
PARTS 1—4
Nos. 1-99999

**ALSO DIESEL AND ELECTRIC LOCOMOTIVES
AND MULTIPLE UNITS**

WINTER
1960/1
EDITION

LONDON :

Ian Allan Ltd

NOTES ON THE USE OF THIS BOOK

THE following notes are a guide to the system of reference marks and other details given in the lists of dimensions shown for each class.

1. Many of the classes listed are sub-divided by reason of mechanical or constructional differences (on the Eastern and North Eastern Regions the sub-divisions are denoted in some cases by " Parts," shown thus : D16/3). At the head of each class will be found a list of such sub-divisions, if any, usually arranged in order of introduction. Each part is given there a reference mark by which its relevant dimensions, if differing from those of other parts, and the locomotives included in this sub-division, or part, may be indentified. Any other differences between locomotives are also indicated, with reference marks, below the details of the class's introduction.

2. The lists of dimensions at the head of each class show locomotives fitted with two inside cylinders, Stephenson valve gear and slide valves, unless otherwise stated, e.g. (O) = two outside cylinders, P.V. = piston valves.

3. The following method is used to denote superheated locomotives, the letters being inserted, where applicable, after the boiler pressure details : Su = All engines superheated.
SS = Some engines superheated.

4. The date on which the first locomotive of a class was built or modified is denoted by " Introduced."

5. S. denotes Service (Departmental) locomotive still carrying B.R. number. This reference letter is introduced only for the reader's guidance and is not borne by the locomotive concerned.

Note :

On the Southern Region the letters " DS " preceding a number indicate a Service Locomotive. On the S.R. (only) this marking appears on the locomotive.

BRITISH RAILWAYS LOCOMOTIVE
SHEDS AND SHED CODES
AND PRINCIPAL SIGNING-ON POINTS

**ALL B.R. LOCOMOTIVES CARRY THE CODE OF THEIR HOME DEPOT
ON A SMALL PLATE AFFIXED TO THE SMOKEBOX DOOR.**

LONDON MIDLAND REGION

1A	**Willesden**	9A	**Longsight (Manchester)**
1B	Camden	9B	Stockport (Edgeley)
1C	Watford	9C	Macclesfield
1D	Devons Road (Bow)	9D	Buxton
1E	Bletchley	9E	Trafford Park
	Leighton Buzzard		Glazebrook
		9F	Heaton Mersey
			Gowhole
		9G	Gorton
2A	**Rugby**		Dinting
2B	Nuneaton		Reddish
2E	Northampton		
2F	Woodford Halse		
		12A	**Carlisle (Kingmoor)**
		12B	Carlisle (Upperby)
			Penrith
5A	**Crewe North**	12C	Carlisle (Canal)
5B	Crewe South	12D	Kirkby Stephen
5C	Stafford	12E	Barrow
5D	Stoke	12F	Workington
5E	Alsager	12G	Oxenholme
5F	Uttoxeter	12H	Tebay
6A	**Chester (Midland)**	14A	**Cricklewood**
6B	Mold Junction	14B	Kentish Town
6C	Birkenhead	14D	Neasden
6F	Bidston		Aylesbury
6G	Llandudno Junction	14E	Bedford
6H	Bangor		
6J	Holyhead		
6K	Rhyl	15A	**Wellingborough**
		15B	Kettering
		15C	Leicester (Midland)
		15D	Coalville
8A	**Edge Hill**	15E	Leicester (Central)
8B	Warrington (Dallam)	15F	Market Harborough
8C	Speke Junction		
8D	Widnes		
8E	Northwich	16A	**Nottingham**
8F	Springs Branch (Wigan)	16B	Kirkby-in-Ashfield
8G	Sutton Oak	16D	Annesley

17A	**Derby**		24D	Lower Darwen
17B	Burton		24E	Blackpool
	Horninglow		24F	Fleetwood
	Overseal		24G	Skipton
17C	Rowsley		24H	Hellifield
	Cromford		24J	Lancaster (Green Ayre)
	Middleton		24K	Preston
	Sheep Pasture		24L	Carnforth
18A	**Toton (Stapleford &**		26A	**Newton Heath**
	Sandiacre)		26B	Agecroft
18B	Westhouses		26C	Bolton
18C	Hasland		26D	Bury
			26E	Lees (Oldham)
21A	**Saltley**		26F	Patricroft
21B	Bescot			
21C	Bushbury			
21D	Aston		27A	**Bank Hall**
21E	Monument Lane		27B	Aintree
21F	Walsall		27C	Southport
			27D	Wigan
24A	**Accrington**		27E	Walton-on-the-Hill
24B	Rose Grove		27F	Brunswick (Liverpool)
24C	Lostock Hall			Warrington (Central)

EASTERN REGION

FP	**Finsbury Park Diesel**		34A	**Kings Cross**
	Depot		34B	Hornsey
			34C	Hatfield
30A	**Stratford**		34D	Hitchin
	Bishops Stortford		34E	New England
	Chelmsford		34F	Grantham
	Enfield Town			
	Hertford East			
	Southend (Victoria)			
	Wood St. (Walthamstow)			
30E	Colchester		36A	**Doncaster**
	Clacton		36C	Frodingham
	Maldon		36E	Retford
	Walton-on-Naze			
30F	Parkeston			
			40A	**Lincoln**
31A	**Cambridge**		40B	Immingham
	Ely			Grimsby
31B	March			New Holland
31C	Kings Lynn		40E	Colwick
			40F	Boston
				Sleaford
32A	**Norwich (Thorpe)**			
	Cromer Beach			
32B	Ipswich		41A	**Sheffield (Darnall)**
32C	Lowestoft Central		41B	Sheffield (Grimesthorpe)
32D	Yarmouth South Town		41C	Millhouses
			41D	Canklow
			41E	Staveley (Barrow Hill)
			41F	Mexborough
33B	Tilbury		41H	Staveley (ex-G.C.)
33C	Shoeburyness		41J	Langwith

NORTH EASTERN REGION

50A	**York**
50B	Hull (Dairycoates)
	Hull (Alexandra Dock)
50C	Hull (Botanic Gardens)
50D	Goole
50E	Scarborough
50F	Malton
51A	**Darlington**
51C	West Hartlepool
51F	West Auckland
51J	Northallerton
51L	Thornaby
52A	**Gateshead**
	Bowes Bridge
52B	Heaton
52C	Blaydon
	Alston
52D	Tweedmouth
	Alnmouth
52E	Percy Main
52F	North and South Blyth
52G	Sunderland

52H	Tyne Dock
	Pelton Level
52K	Consett
55A	**Leeds (Holbeck)**
55B	Stourton
55C	Farnley
55D	Royston
55E	Normanton
55F	Bradford (Manningham)
	Keighley
55G	Huddersfield
55H	Leeds (Neville Hill)
56A	**Wakefield**
	Knottingley
56B	Ardsley
56C	Copley Hill
56D	Mirfield
56E	Sowerby Bridge
56F	Low Moor
56G	Bradford (Hammerton St.

SCOTTISH REGION

60A	**Inverness**
	Dingwall
	Kyle of Lochalsh
60B	Aviemore
	Boat of Garten
60C	Helmsdale
	Tain
60D	Wick
	Thurso
61A	**Kittybrewster**
	Ballater
	Fraserburgh
	Inverurie
	Peterhead
61B	Aberdeen (Ferryhill)
61C	Keith
	Banff
	Elgin
62A	**Thornton**
	Anstruther
	Burntisland
	Kirkcaldy
	Ladybank
	Methil

62B	Dundee (Tay Bridge)
	Arbroath
	Montrose
	St. Andrews
62C	Dunfermline
	Alloa
	Kelty
63A	**Perth**
	Aberfeldy
	Blair Atholl
	Crieff
	Forfar
63B	Fort William
	Mallaig
63C	Oban
	Ballachulish
64A	**St. Margarets**
	(Edinburgh)
	Dunbar
	Galashiels
	Hardengreen
	Longniddry
	North Berwick
	Seafield
	South Leith
64B	Haymarket
64C	Dalry Road
64F	Bathgate

64G	Hawick
64H	Leith Central

65A	**Eastfield (Glasgow)**
	Arrochar
65B	St. Rollox
65C	Parkhead
65D	Dawsholm
	Dumbarton
65E	Kipps
65F	Grangemouth
65G	Yoker
65H	Helensburgh
65I	Balloch
65J	Stirling
	Killin
65K	Polmont

66A	**Polmadie (Glasgow)**
66B	Motherwell
66C	Hamilton
66D	Greenock (Ladyburn)
66E	Carstair

67A	**Corkerhill (Glasgow)**
67B	Hurlford
	Beith
	Muirkirk
67C	Ayr
67D	Ardrossan

68B	Dumfries
68C	Stranraer
68D	Beattock

SOUTHERN REGION

70A	**Nine Elms**
70B	Feltham
70C	Guildford
	Reading South
70D	Basingstoke
70H	Ryde (I.O.W.)

71A	**Eastleigh**
	Andover Junction
	Lymington
	Southampton Terminus
	Winchester
71B	Bournemouth
	Branksome
71G	Weymouth
	Bridport
71I	Southampton Docks

72A	**Exmouth Junction**
	Bude
	Callington
	Exmouth
	Lyme Regis
	Okehampton
	Seaton

72B	Salisbury
72C	Yeovil
72E	Barnstaple Junction
	Ilfracombe
	Torrington
72F	Wadebridge

73A	**Stewarts Lane**
73B	Bricklayers Arms
73C	Hither Green
73E	Faversham
73F	Ashford (Kent)
	Gillingham (Kent)
	Ramsgate
73H	Dover
	Folkestone
73J	Tonbridge

75A	**Brighton**
75B	Redhill
75C	Norwood Junction
75E	Three Bridges
	Horsham
75F	Tunbridge Wells West

WESTERN REGION

81A	**Old Oak Common**
81B	Slough
	Marlow
81C	Southall
81D	Reading
81E	Didcot
81F	Oxford
	Fairford

82A	**Bristol (Bath Road)**
	Bath
	Wells
	Weston-super-Mare
	Yatton
82B	St. Philip's Marsh
82C	Swindon
	Chippenham

82D	Westbury	
	Frome	
82E	Bristol (Barrow Road)	
82F	Bath (Green Park)	
	Radstock West	
82G	Templecombe	

83A	**Newton Abbot**	
	Kingsbridge	
83B	Taunton	
	Bridgwater	
83C	Exeter	
	Tiverton Junction	
83D	Laira (Plymouth)	
	Launceston	
83E	St. Blazey	
	Bodmin	
	Moorswater	
83F	Truro	
83G	Penzance	
	Helston	
	St. Ives	
83H	Plymouth (Friary)	

84A	**Wolverhampton**	
	(Stafford Road)	
84B	Oxley	
84C	Banbury	
84D	Leamington Spa	
84E	Tyseley	
	Stratford-on-Avon	
84F	Stourbridge Junction	
84G	Shrewsbury	
	Craven Arms	
	Knighton	
	Builth Road	
84H	Wellington (Salop)	
84J	Croes Newydd	
	Bala	
	Penmaenpool	
	Trawsfynydd	

85A	**Worcester**	
	Evesham	
	Kingham	
85B	Gloucester	
	Brimscombe	
	Cheltenham (Malvern Rd.	
	Lydney	
85C	Hereford	
	Leominster	
	Ross	
85D	Kidderminster	
85E	Gloucester (Barnwood)	
	Dursley	
	Tewkesbury	

85F	Bromsgrove	
	Redditch	

86A	**Newport**	
	(Ebbw Junction)	
86B	Newport (Pill)	
86C	Cardiff (Canton)	
86D	Llantrisant	
86E	Severn Tunnel Junction	
86F	Tondu	
86G	Pontypool Road	
86H	Aberbeeg	
86J	Aberdare	

87A	**Neath**	
	Glyn Neath	
	Neath (N. & B.	
87B	Duffryn Yard	
87C	Danygraig	
87D	Swansea East Dock	
	Gurnos	
	Upper Bank	
87E	Landore	
87F	Llanelly	
	Burry Port	
	Llandovery	
	Pantyffynnon	
87G	Carmarthen	
87H	Neyland	
	Cardigan	
	Milford Haven	
	Pembroke Dock	
	Whitland	
87J	Goodwick	

88A	**Cardiff (Radyr)**	
	Cathays	
88B	Cardiff East Dock	
88C	Barry	
88D	Merthyr	
	Dowlais Cae Harris	
	Dowlais Central	
	Rhymney	
88E	Abercynon	
88F	Treherbert	
	Ferndale	

89A	**Oswestry**	
	Llanidloes	
	Moat Lane	
89B	Brecon	
89C	Machynlleth	
	Aberystwyth	
	Aberystwyth (V. of R.	
	Portmadoc	
	Pwllheli	

SUMMARY OF WESTERN REGION
STEAM LOCOMOTIVE CLASSES
WITH HISTORICAL NOTES AND DIMENSIONS

The code given in smaller bold type at the head of each Class,
e.g. " 6MT " denotes its British Railways power classification.

The numbers of locomotives in service have been checked in the W.R. to July 16th,
1960, L.M.R. to July 16th, Sc.R. to July 30th, and S.R. to July 8th.

4-6-0   6MT   1000 Class
" County "

Introduced 1945. Hawksworth design
with 280 lb. boiler pressure since
reduced to 250 lb. per sq. in.
Fitted with double chimney.
Weight: Loco.   76 tons 17 cwt.
         Tender 49 tons 0 cwt.
Pressure: 250 lb. Su.
Cyls.: (O) 18½″ × 30″.
Driving Wheels: 6′ 3″.
T.E.: 28,241 lb. P.V.

1000–29   **Total 30**

4-6-0   7P   4073 Class
" Castle "

*Introduced 1923. Collett design,
developed from " Star " (4037,
5083–92 converted from " Star ").
†Introduced 1946. Fitted with 3-row
superheater.
‡Introduced 1947. Fitted with 4-row
superheater.
¶Introduced 1956. Fitted with double
chimney.
Weight: Loco.   79 tons 17 cwt.
         Tender 46 tons 14 cwt.
Pressure: 225 lb. Su.
Cyls.: (4) 16″ × 26″.
Driving Wheels: 6′ 8½″.
T.E.: 31,625 lb.
Inside Walschaerts valve gear and
rocking shafts. P.V.

*4037/75–7/9/81–6/9/92/4–6/8/9,
5001–4/6–9/11–25/7/9–32/4/
5/8–42/4–8/51–6/8–60/2/6–70/
6/80/4/5/7/9–92
†5000/37/50/63/5/72/4/5/7/8/81/
2/93/6–9, 7000–2/5/7–12/5–7/
20/1/5–8/31–3/5/7

‡4074/8, 5026/33/6/49/71/3/94/5,
7019/24/9/30/4/6
†¶7003/6/14/23
‡¶4080/7/8/90/3, 5043/57/61/
4/88, 7004/13/8/22 **Total 157**

4-6-0   5MT   4900 Class
" Hall "

Introduced 1928. Modified design of
Collett rebuild with 6′ 0″ driving
wheels of " Saint " (built 1907) for
new construction, with higher-
pitched boiler, modified foot-
plating and detail differences.
Weight: Loco.   75 tons 0 cwt.
         Tender 46 tons 14 cwt.
Pressure: 225 lb. Su.
Cyls.: (O) 18½″ × 30″.
Driving Wheels: 6′ 0″.
T.E.: 27,275 lb.
P.V.

4901–10/2–39/41–99, 5900–14/6–
99, 6900–58   **Total 255**

4-6-0   8P   6000 Class
" King "

Introduced 1927. Collett design.
All engines modified since 1947 with
4-row superheater and since 1955
with double chimney.
Weight: Loco.   89 tons 0 cwt.
         Tender 46 tons 14 cwt.
Pressure: 250 lb. Su.
Cyls.: (4) 16¼″ × 28″.
Driving Wheels: 6′ 6″.
T.E.: 40,285 lb.
Inside Walschaerts valve gear and
rocking shafts. P.V.
6000–29   **Total 30**

4-6-0   5MT   6800 Class
"Grange"

Introduced 1936. Collett design, variation of "Hall" with smaller wheels, incorporating certain parts of withdrawn 4300 2-6-0 locos.
Weight: Loco.   74 tons 0 cwt.
         Tender 40 tons 0 cwt.
Pressure: 225 lb. Su.
Cyls.: (O) $18\frac{1}{2}'' \times 30''$.
Driving Wheels: 5' 8".
T.E.: 28,875 lb.
P.V.

6800–79   **Total 80**

4-6-0   5MT   6959 Class
"Modified Hall"

Introduced 1944. Hawksworth development of "Hall," with larger superheater, "one-piece" main frames and plate-framed bogie.
Weight: Loco. 75 tons 16 cwt.
         Tender 46 tons 14 cwt.
Pressure: 225 lb. Su.
Cyls.: (O) $18\frac{1}{2}'' \times 30''$.
Driving Wheels: 6' 0".
T.E.: 27,275 lb.
P.V

6959–99, 7900–29   **Total 71**

4-6-0   5MT   7800 Class
"Manor"

Introduced 1938. Collett design for secondary lines, incorporating certain parts of withdrawn 4300 2-6-0 locos.
Weight: Loco.   68 tons 18 cwt.
         Tender 40 tons 0 cwt.
Pressure: 225 lb. Su.
Cyls.: (O) $18'' \times 30''$.
Driving Wheels: 5' 8".
T.E.: 27,340 lb.
P.V

7800–29   **Total 30**

4-4-0   "City" Class

Introduced 1903. Churchward design.
Weight: Loco.   55 tons 6 cwt.
         Tender 36 tons 15 cwt.
Pressure: 200 lb. Su.
Cyls.: $18'' \times 26''$.
Driving Wheels: 6' $8\frac{1}{2}''$.
T.E.: 17,790 lb.

3440
Withdrawn 1931 and preserved in York Museum. Returned to service 1957.

                  Total 1

4-4-0   2P   9000 Class

Introduced 1936. Collett rebuild, incorporating "Duke" type boiler and "Bulldog" frames for light lines.
Weight: Loco.   49 tons 0 cwt.
         Tender $\begin{cases} 40 \text{ tons } & 0 \text{ cwt.} \\ 36 \text{ tons } & 15 \text{ cwt.} \end{cases}$
Pressure: 180 lb. SS.
Cyls.: $18'' \times 26''$.
Driving Wheels: 5' 8".
T.E.: 18,955 lb.

9014/7   **Total 2**

2-8-0   8F   2800 Class

*Introduced 1903. Churchward design, earlier locos. subsequently fitted with new boiler and superheater.
†Introduced 1938. Collett locos., with side-window cab and detail alterations.
Weight: Loco. $\begin{cases} 75 \text{ tons } 10 \text{ cwt.*} \\ 76 \text{ tons } 5 \text{ cwt.†} \end{cases}$
         Tender 40 tons 0 cwt.
Pressure: 225 lb. Su.
Cyls.: (O) $18\frac{1}{2}'' \times 30''$.
Driving Wheels: 4' $7\frac{1}{2}''$.
T.E.: 35,380 lb.
P.V.

*2807/13/8/9/21/2/34/6/9/41/2/
    5/6/9/51–62/5–7/71–6/9/82/3
†2884–99, 3800–66   **Total 121**

2-8-0   7F   **4700 Class**

Introduced 1919. Churchward mixed
traffic design (4700 built with smaller
boiler and later rebuilt).
Weight: Loco.   82 tons 0 cwt.
           Tender 46 tons 14 cwt.
Pressure: 225 lb. Su.
Cyls.: (O) 19″ × 30″.
Driving Wheels: 5′ 8″.
T.E.: 30,460 lb.
P.V.

4700–8   **Total 9**

2-6-0   4MT   **4300 Class**

*Introduced 1911. Churchward design.
†Introduced 1925. Locos. with detail
alteration affecting boiler.
‡Introduced 1932. Locos. with side
window cab and detail alterations.

Weight: Loco. $\begin{cases} 62 \text{ tons } 0 \text{ cwt.} \\ 64 \text{ tons } 0 \text{ cwt.†} \\ 65 \text{ tons } 6 \text{ cwt.‡} \end{cases}$
          Tender 40 tons 0 cwt.
Pressure: 200 lb. Su.
Cyls.: (O) 18½″ × 30″.
Driving Wheels: 5′ 8″.
T.E.: 25,670 lb.
P.V.

*5306/11/8/22/4/6/30–2/6/7/9/51/
7/8/69/70/6/80/4/5/99,   6301/2/
4/6/9/10/2–4/6/7/9/20/4/6/7/9/
30/2/3/5–53/6/7/60–82/4–92/4/
5/8, 7305–21

†7300–4

‡7322–41   **Total 140**

0-6-0   3MT   **2251 Class**

Introduced 1930. Collett design.
Weight:
   Loco.   43 tons 8 cwt.
   Tender $\begin{cases} 36 \text{ tons } 15 \text{ cwt.} \\ 47 \text{ tons } 6 \text{ cwt. (ex-R.O.D.} \\ \text{tender from 3000 Class} \\ \text{2-8-0).} \end{cases}$
Pressure: 200 lb. Su.
Cyls.: 17½″ × 24″.
Driving Wheels: 5′ 2″.
T.E.: 20,155 lb.

2200–2/4/6/7/9–24/7/9–34/6/9–
51/3/5–7/60/1/7/8/71/3/6/7/83/
6–9/91/2/4/5/8, 3200/1/3–19
                  Total 84

2-8-2T   8F   **7200 Class**

Introduced 1934. Collett rebuild, with
extended bunker and trailing wheels,
of Churchward 4200 class 2-8-0T.
Weight: 92 tons 2 cwt.
Pressure: 200 lb. Su.
Cyls.: (O) 19″ × 30″.
Driving Wheels: 4′ 7½″.
T.E.: 33,170 lb.
P.V.

7200–53   **Total 54**

2-8-0T $\left\{ {}^{7F*}_{8F†} \right\}$ **4200 Class**

*Introduced 1910. Churchward design.
†5205 class. Introduced 1923. With
enlarged cyls. and detail alterations.
Weight: $\begin{cases} 81 \text{ tons } 12 \text{ cwt.*} \\ 82 \text{ tons } 2 \text{ cwt.†} \end{cases}$
Pressure: 200 lb. Su.
Cyls.: $\begin{cases} \text{(O) } 18½″ × 30″*. \\ \text{(O) } 19″ × 30″†. \end{cases}$
Driving Wheels: 4′ 7½″.
T.E.: $\begin{cases} 31,450 \text{ lb.*} \\ 33,170 \text{ lb.†} \end{cases}$
P.V.

*4203/7/13/4/8/22/5/7–30/2/3/
5–8/41–3/6–8/50–9/62–99,
5200–4

†5205–64   **Total 136**

2-6-2T   4MT   **4500 Class**

*Introduced 1906. Churchward design
for light branches, developed from
4400 class with larger wheels, earlier
locos. subsequently fitted with superheater.
†4575 class. Introduced 1927. With
detail alterations and increased
weight.
‡Introduced 1953. Push-and-pull fitted.
Weight: $\begin{cases} 57 \text{ tons } 0 \text{ cwt.*} \\ 61 \text{ tons } 0 \text{ cwt.††} \end{cases}$
Pressure: 200 lb. Su.
Cyls.: (O) 17″ × 24″.
Driving Wheels: 4′ 7½″.
T.E.: 21,250 lb.
P.V.

*4507/49/50/2/5/7–9/61/3–7/9–
71/3/4

†4575/87/8/91/3/4, 5503/4/8–10/
4–6/8/20/1/5/6/31/2/6–42/4/6–
50/2–4/7/8/62–5/9–71/3

‡4589, 5511/29/34/45/55/60/8/72

Total 75

2-6-2T 4MT 5101 & 6100 Classes

***5101 class.** Introduced 1929. Modified
design for new construction of Collett
rebuild, with detail alterations and
increased weight, of Churchward 3100
class (introduced 1903 and subsequently fitted with superheater).

†**6100 class.** Introduced 1931. Locos.
for London suburban area with
increased boiler pressure.
Weight: 78 tons 9 cwt.
Pressure: { 200 lb. Su.*
{ 225 lb. Su.†
Cyls.: (O) 18″ × 30″.
Driving Wheels: 5′ 8″.
T.E.: { 24,300 lb.*
{ 27,340 lb.†
P.V.

*4100–37/40–61/3/5–79, 5101/3/
4/10/50–4/8/64/6/7/9/73–7/80–
4/7/8/90–5/8/9

†6101/3/6–20/2–69   **Total 175**

2-6-2T 4MT 8100 Class

Introduced 1938. Collett rebuild, with
higher pressure and smaller wheels, of
Churchward locos. in 5100 class.
Weight: 76 tons 11 cwt.
Pressure: 225 lb. Su.
Cyls.: (O) 18″ × 30″.
Driving Wheels: 5′ 6″.
T.E.: 28,165 lb.
P.V.

8100–4/6–9   **Total 9**

2-6-2T unclass. V. of R.

*Introduced 1902. Davies and Metcalfe
design for V. of R. 1′ 11¼″ gauge.
†Introduced 1923. G.W. development
of V. of R. design.
Weight: 25 tons 0 cwt.
Gauge: 1′ 11½″.
Pressure: 165 lb.
Cyls.: (O) { 11″ × 17″.*
{ 11½″ × 17″.†
Driving Wheels: 2′ 6″.
T.E.: { 9,615 lb.*
{ 10,510 lb.†
Walschaerts valve gear.

*9   †7/8   **Total 3**

0-6-2T 5MT 5600 Class

*Introduced 1924. Collett design for
service in Welsh valleys.
†Introduced 1927. Locos. with detail
alterations.
Weight: { 68 tons 12 cwt.*
{ 69 tons 7 cwt.†
Pressure: 200 lb. Su.
Cyls.: 18″ × 26″.
Driving Wheels: 4′ 7½″.
T.E.: 25,800 lb.
P.V

*5600–99
†6600–99   **Total 200**

0-6-0ST 0F 1361 Class

Introduced 1910. Churchward design for dock shunting.

Weight: 35 tons 4 cwt.
Pressure: 150 lb.
Cyls.: (O) 16″ × 20″.
Driving Wheels: 3′ 8″
T.E.: 14,835 lb.

1361–5 **Total 5**

0-6-0PT 1F 1366 Class

Introduced 1934. Collett development of 1361 class, with pannier tanks.

Weight: 35 tons 15 cwt.
Pressure: 165 lb.
Cyls.: (O) 16″ × 20″.
Driving Wheels: 3′ 8″.
T.E.: 16,320 lb.

1366–9/71 **Total 5**

0-6-0PT 4F 1500 Class

Introduced 1949. Hawksworth short-wheelbase heavy shunting design.

Weight: 58 tons 4 cwt.
Pressure: 200 lb.
Cyls.: (O) 17½″ × 24″.
Driving Wheels: 4′ 7½″.
T.E.: 22,515 lb.
Walschaerts valve gear. P.V.

1500–8 **Total 9**

0-6-0PT 2F 1600 Class

Introduced 1949. Hawksworth light branch line and shunting design.

Weight: 41 tons 12 cwt.
Pressure: 165 lb.
Cyls.: 16½″ × 24″.
Driving Wheels: 4′ 1½″.
T.E.: 18,515 lb.

1601/2/5–9/11–5/7–9/21–4/6–8/
30–4/6/8–43/5–51/3–69

Total 58

0-6-0PT 1P 5400 Class

Introduced 1931. Collett design for light passenger work, push-and-pull fitted.

Weight: 46 tons 12 cwt.
Pressure: 165 lb.
Cyls.: 16½″ × 24″.
Driving Wheels: 5′ 2″.
T.E.: 14,780 lb.

5410/2/6/7/20/1 **Total 6**

0-6-0PT 3F 5700 Class

*Introduced 1929. Collett design for shunting and light goods work developed from 2021 class.
†Introduced 1930. Locos. with steam brake and no A.T.C. fittings, for shunting only.
§Introduced 1933. Locos. with detail alterations, modified cab (except 8700) and increased weight.
‡Introduced 1933. Locos. with condensing apparatus for working over L.T. Metropolitan line.
¶Introduced 1948. Steam brake locos. with increased weight.

Weight: { 47 tons 10 cwt.*†
{ 50 tons 15 cwt.‡
{ 49 tons 0 cwt.§¶
Pressure: 200 lb.
Cyls.: 17½″ × 24″.
Driving Wheels: 4′ 7½″.
T.E.: 22,515 lb.

*5706/20/8/44/6/8/9/56–9/61/6/8
/70/1/3–5/8–80/3/7/9/91/3/8,
7700/2/4/7/9/13/5/8–26/9/32
/6/9–41/4/5/7–9/53/5–7/60–
2/4–6/71/2/5–7/80/2–8/90/4/
6/8/9, 8701/2/5–7/9–49

†6700/14/20/4/38/9/41/2/9

§3600–3739/41–92/4–9, 4600–85/
7–99, 8700/50–4/6/7/9–99,
9600–72/4–82, 9711–71/3–99

‡9700–7/9/10

¶6751–5/7/60–70/2/5–8

Total 686

0-6-0PT 2P* 2F†
6400 & 7400 Classes

*6400 class. Introduced 1932. Collett design for light passenger work, variation of 5400 class with smaller wheels, push-and-pull fitted.

12

†7400 class. Introduced 1936. Non-push-and-pull fitted locos.
Weight: { 45 tons 12 cwt.*
{ 45 tons 9 cwt.†
Pressure: 180 lb.
Cyls.: 16½″ × 24″.
Driving Wheels: 4′ 7½″.
T.E.: 18,010 lb.

*6400/3/8/10–3/5/6/8/9/21/2/4–6/9–31/3–8

†7402–10/2–4/7/8/21–37/9–46/8/9

Total : 6400 Class 25
7400 Class 41

0-6-0PT 4F 9400 Class

*Introduced 1947. Hawksworth taper boiler design for heavy shunting.
†Introduced 1949. Locos. with non-superheated boiler.
Weight: 55 tons 7 cwt.
Pressure: 200 lb. SS.
Cyls.: 17½″ × 24″.
Driving Wheels: 4′ 7½″.
T.E.: 22,515 lb.

*9401/4–9

†3400–9, 8400–7/9/13–6/8/20/2/4–8/30/1/3/5–41/4–6/9/51–4/6–61/4–7/9–84/6–91/3–9, 9410–6/8–26/9–31/3/5–4/6—7/40–2/4/6–8/50–8/60–90/3–5/7/8

Total 169

0-6-0T Unclass. W. & L.

(Line closed: locos. stored.)
Introduced 1902. Beyer Peacock design for 2′ 6″ gauge W. & L. Section, Cambrian Railways.
Weight: 19 tons 18 cwt.
Gauge: 2′ 6″.
Pressure: 150 lb.
Cyls.: (O) 11½″ × 16″.
Driving Wheels: 2′ 9″.
T.E.: 8,175 lb.
Walschaerts valve gear.

822/3   Total 2

0-4-2T IP
1400 & 5800 Classes

*1400 class introduced 1932. Collett design for light branch work (originally designated 4800 class). Push-and-pull fitted.
†5800 class introduced 1933. Non-push-and-pull fitted locos.
Weight: 41 tons 6 cwt.
Pressure: 165 lb.
Cyls.: 16″ × 24″.
Driving Wheels: 5′ 2″.
T.E.: 13,900 lb.

*1409/10/9–21/4/6/31–5/8/40/2/4/5/7/50/1/3–5/8/62/3/6/8/70–4

†5815

Total 34

0-4-0ST OF Cardiff Rly.

Introduced 1893. Kitson design for Cardiff Railway.
Weight: 25 tons 10 cwt.
Pressure: 160 lb.
Cyls.: (O) 14″ × 21″.
Driving Wheels: 3′ 2½″.
T.E.: 14,540 lb.
Hawthorn Kitson valve gear.

1338   Total 1

0-4-0ST OF P. & M.

Introduced 1907. Peckett design for P. & M.
Weight: 33 tons 10 cwt.
Pressure: 150 lb.
Cyls.: (O) 15″ × 21″.
Driving Wheels: 3′ 7″.
T.E.: 14,010 lb.

1151/2   Total 2

0-4-0ST S.H.T.

Introduced 1906. Peckett design for S.H.T. (similar to 1151/2).
Weight: 33 tons 10 cwt.
Pressure: 150 lb.
Cyls.: (O) 15″ × 21″.
Driving Wheels: 3′ 7″
T.E.: 14,010 lb.

1143   Total 1

NUMERICAL LIST OF WESTERN REGION STEAM LOCOMOTIVES

Locomotives are of G.W. origin except where indicated by other initials

2-6-2T   V. of R.

7	Owain Glyndŵr
8	Llywelyn
9	Prince of Wales

0-6-0T   W. & L.

822   823

(Line closed : locos. stored.)

4-6-0   1000 Class
" County "

1000	County of Middlesex
1001	County of Bucks
1002	County of Berks
1003	County of Wilts
1004	County of Somerset
1005	County of Devon
1006	County of Cornwall
1007	County of Brecknock
1008	County of Cardigan
1009	County of Carmarthen
1010	County of Caernarvon
1011	County of Chester
1012	County of Denbigh
1013	County of Dorset
1014	County of Glamorgan
1015	County of Gloucester
1016	County of Hants
1017	County of Hereford
1018	County of Leicester
1019	County of Merioneth
1020	County of Monmouth
1021	County of Montgomery
1022	County of Northampton
1023	County of Oxford
1024	County of Pembroke
1025	County of Radnor
1026	County of Salop
1027	County of Stafford
1028	County of Warwick
1029	County of Worcester

0-4-0ST   S.H.T.

1143

0-4-0ST   P. & M.

1151   1152

0-4-0ST   Car. R.

1338

0-6-0ST   1361 Class

| 1361 | 1363 | 1365 |
| 1362 | 1364 | |

0-6-0PT   1366 Class

| 1366 | 1368 | 1371 |
| 1367 | 1369 | |

0-4-2T   1400 Class

1409	1421	1432	1438
1410	1424	1433	1440
1419	1426	1434	1442
1420	1431	1435	1444

1445	1454	1463	1471	2249	2260	2276	2289
1447	1455	1466	1472	2250	2261	2277	2291
1450	1458	1468	1473	2251	2267	2283	2292
1451	1462	1470	1474	2253	2268	2286	2294
1453				2255	2271	2287	2295
				2256	2273	2288	2298
				2257			

0-6-0PT   1500 Class

1500	1503	1505	1507
1501	1504	1506	1508
1502			

0-6-0PT   1600 Class

1601	1621	1640	1656
1602	1622	1641	1657
1605	1623	1642	1658
1606	1624	1643	1659
1607	1626	1645	1660
1608	1627	1646	1661
1609	1628	1647	1662
1611	1630	1648	1663
1612	1631	1649	1664
1613	1632	1650	1665
1614	1633	1651	1666
1615	1634	1653	1667
1617	1636	1654	1668
1618	1638	1655	1669
1619	1639		

0-6-0   2251 Class

2200	2213	2223	2239
2201	2214	2224	2240
2202	2215	2227	2241
2204	2216	2229	2242
2206	2217	2230	2243
2207	2218	2231	2244
2209	2219	2232	2245
2210	2220	2233	2246
2211	2221	2234	2247
2212	2222	2236	2248

2-8-0   2800 Class

2807	2851	2867	2887
2813	2852	2871	2888
2818	2853	2872	2889
2819	2854	2873	2890
2821	2855	2874	2891
2822	2856	2875	2892
2834	2857	2876	2893
2836	2858	2879	2894
2839	2859	2882	2895
2841	2860	2883	2896
2842	2861	2884	2897
2845	2862	2885	2898
2846	2865	2886	2899
2849	2866		

0-6-0   2251 Class

3200	3206	3211	3216
3201	3207	3212	3217
3203	3208	3213	3218
3204	3209	3214	3219
3205	3210	3215	

0-6-0PT   9400 Class

3400	3403	3406	3408
3401	3404	3407	3409
3402	3405		

4-4-0 "City" Class

3440 City of Truro

0-6-0PT 5700 Class

3600	3640	3680	3720
3601	3641	3681	3721
3602	3642	3682	3722
3603	3643	3683	3723
3604	3644	3684	3724
3605	3645	3685	3725
3606	3646	3686	3726
3607	3647	3687	3727
3608	3648	3688	3728
3609	3649	3689	3729
3610	3650	3690	3730
3611	3651	3691	3731
3612	3652	3692	3732
3613	3653	3693	3733
3614	3654	3694	3734
3615	3655	3695	3735
3616	3656	3696	3736
3617	3657	3697	3737
3618	3658	3698	3738
3619	3659	3699	3739
3620	3660	3700	3741
3621	3661	3701	3742
3622	3662	3702	3743
3623	3663	3703	3744
3624	3664	3704	3745
3625	3665	3705	3746
3626	3666	3706	3747
3627	3667	3707	3748
3628	3668	3708	3749
3629	3669	3709	3750
3630	3670	3710	3751
3631	3671	3711	3752
3632	3672	3712	3753
3633	3673	3713	3754
3634	3674	3714	3755
3635	3675	3715	3756
3636	3676	3716	3757
3637	3677	3717	3758
3638	3678	3718	3759
3639	3679	3719	3760

3761	3771	3781	3790
3762	3772	3782	3791
3763	3773	3783	3792
3764	3774	3784	3793
3765	3775	3785	3794
3766	3776	3786	3795
3767	3777	3787	3796
3768	3778	3788	3797
3769	3779	3789	3798
3770	3780		3799

2-8-0 2800 Class

3800	3817	3834	3851
3801	3818	3835	3852
3802	3819	3836	3853
3803	3820	3837	3854
3804	3821	3838	3855
3805	3822	3839	3856
3806	3823	3840	3857
3807	3824	3841	3858
3808	3825	3842	3859
3809	3826	3843	3860
3810	3827	3844	3861
3811	3828	3845	3862
3812	3829	3846	3863
3813	3830	3847	3864
3814	3831	3848	3865
3815	3832	3849	3866
3816	3833	3850	

4-6-0 4073 Class
"Castle"

4037	The South Wales Borderers
4074	Caldicot Castle
4075	Cardiff Castle
4076	Carmarthen Castle
4077	Chepstow Castle
4078	Pembroke Castle
4079	Pendennis Castle
4080	Powderham Castle
4081	Warwick Castle

4082	Windsor Castle	4233	4254	4271	4286
4083	Abbotsbury Castle	4235	4255	4272	4287
4084	Aberystwyth Castle	4236	4256	4273	4288
4085	Berkeley Castle	4237	4257	4274	4289
4086	Builth Castle	4238	4258	4275	4290
4087	Cardigan Castle	4241	4259	4276	4291
4088	Dartmouth Castle	4242	4262	4277	4292
4089	Donnington Castle	4243	4263	4278	4293
4090	Dorchester Castle	4246	4264	4279	4294
4092	Dunraven Castle	4247	4265	4280	4295
4093	Dunster Castle	4248	4266	4281	4296
4094	Dynevor Castle	4250	4267	4282	4297
4095	Harlech Castle	4251	4268	4283	4298
4096	Highclere Castle	4252	4269	4284	4299
4098	Kidwelly Castle	4253	4270	4285	
4099	Kilgerran Castle				

2-6-2T   5100 Class

4100	4119	4140	4159
4101	4120	4141	4160
4102	4121	4142	4161
4103	4122	4143	4163
4104	4123	4144	4165
4105	4124	4145	4166
4106	4125	4146	4167
4107	4126	4147	4168
4108	4127	4148	4169
4109	4128	4149	4170
4110	4129	4150	4171
4111	4130	4151	4172
4112	4131	4152	4173
4113	4132	4153	4174
4114	4133	4154	4175
4115	4134	4155	4176
4116	4135	4156	4177
4117	4136	4157	4178
4118	4137	4158	4179

2-6-2T   4500 Class

4507	4559	4569	4587
4549	4561	4570	4588
4550	4563	4571	4589
4552	4564	4573	4591
4555	4565	4574	4593
4557	4566	4575	4594
4558	4567		

0-6-0PT   5700 Class

4600	4615	4630	4645
4601	4616	4631	4646
4602	4617	4632	4647
4603	4618	4633	4648
4604	4619	4634	4649
4605	4620	4635	4650
4606	4621	4636	4651
4607	4622	4637	4652
4608	4623	4638	4653
4609	4624	4639	4654
4610	4625	4640	4655
4611	4626	4641	4656
4612	4627	4642	4657
4613	4628	4643	4658
4614	4629	4644	4659

2-8-0T   4200 Class

4203	4214	4225	4229
4207	4218	4227	4230
4213	4222	4228	4232

4660	4670	4680	4691
4661	4671	4681	4692
4662	4672	4682	4693
4663	4673	4683	4694
4664	4674	4684	4695
4665	4675	4685	4696
4666	4676	4687	4697
4667	4677	4688	4698
4668	4678	4689	4699
4669	4679	4690	

2-8-0   4700 Class

4700	4703	4705	4707
4701	4704	4706	4708
4702			

4-6-0 " Hall " 4900 Class

4901	Adderley Hall
4902	Aldenham Hall
4903	Astley Hall
4904	Binnegar Hall
4905	Barton Hall
4906	Bradfield Hall
4907	Broughton Hall
4908	Broome Hall
4909	Blakesley Hall
4910	Blaisdon Hall
4912	Berrington Hall
4913	Baglan Hall
4914	Cranmore Hall
4915	Condover Hall
4916	Crumlin Hall
4917	Crosswood Hall
4918	Dartington Hall
4919	Donnington Hall
4920	Dumbleton Hall
4921	Eaton Hall
4922	Enville Hall
4923	Evenley Hall
4924	Eydon Hall
4925	Eynsham Hall
4926	Fairleigh Hall
4927	Farnborough Hall
4928	Gatacre Hall
4929	Goytrey Hall
4930	Hagley Hall
4931	Hanbury Hall
4932	Hatherton Hall
4933	Himley Hall
4934	Hindlip Hall
4935	Ketley Hall
4936	Kinlet Hall
4937	Lanelay Hall
4938	Liddington Hall
4939	Littleton Hall
4941	Llangedwyn Hall
4942	Maindy Hall
4943	Marrington Hall
4944	Middleton Hall
4945	Milligan Hall
4946	Moseley Hall
4947	Nanhoran Hall
4948	Northwick Hall
4949	Packwood Hall
4950	Patshull Hall
4951	Pendeford Hall
4952	Peplow Hall
4953	Pitchford Hall
4954	Plaish Hall
4955	Plaspower Hall
4956	Plowden Hall
4957	Postlip Hall
4958	Priory Hall
4959	Purley Hall
4960	Pyle Hall
4961	Pyrland Hall
4962	Ragley Hall
4963	Rignall Hall
4964	Rodwell Hall
4965	Rood Ashton Hall
4966	Shakenhurst Hall
4967	Shirenewton Hall
4968	Shotton Hall
4969	Shrugborough Hall
4970	Sketty Hall
4971	Stanway Hall
4972	Saint Brides Hall
4973	Sweeney Hall
4974	Talgarth Hall
4975	Umberslade Hall
4976	Warfield Hall
4977	Watcombe Hall

4978	Westwood Hall	5018	St. Mawes Castle
4979	Wootton Hall	5019	Treago Castle
4980	Wrottesley Hall	5020	Trematon Castle
4981	Abberley Hall	5021	Whittington Castle
4982	Acton Hall	5022	Wigmore Castle
4983	Albert Hall	5023	Brecon Castle
4984	Albrighton Hall	5024	Carew Castle
4985	Allesley Hall	5025	Chirk Castle
4986	Aston Hall	5026	Criccieth Castle
4987	Brockley Hall	5027	Farleigh Castle
4988	Bulwell Hall	5029	Nunney Castle
4989	Cherwell Hall	5030	Shirburn Castle
4990	Clifton Hall	5031	Totnes Castle
4991	Cobham Hall	5032	Usk Castle
4992	Crosby Hall	5033	Broughton Castle
4993	Dalton Hall	5034	Corfe Castle
4994	Downton Hall	5035	Coity Castle
4995	Easton Hall	5036	Lyonshall Castle
4996	Eden Hall	5037	Monmouth Castle
4997	Elton Hall	5038	Morlais Castle
4998	Eyton Hall	5039	Rhuddlan Castle
4999	Gopsal Hall	5040	Stokesay Castle

4-6-0   4073 Class
"Castle"

5000	Launceston Castle	5041	Tiverton Castle
5001	Llandovery Castle	5042	Winchester Castle
5002	Ludlow Castle	5043	Earl of Mount Edgcumbe
5003	Lulworth Castle	5044	Earl of Dunraven
5004	Llanstephan Castle	5045	Earl of Dudley
5006	Tregenna Castle	5046	Earl Cawdor
5007	Rougemont Castle	5047	Earl of Dartmouth
5008	Raglan Castle	5048	Earl of Devon
5009	Shrewsbury Castle	5049	Earl of Plymouth
5011	Tintagel Castle	5050	Earl of St. Germans
5012	Berry Pomeroy Castle	5051	Earl Bathurst
5013	Abergavenny Castle	5052	Earl of Radnor
5014	Goodrich Castle	5053	Earl Cairns
5015	Kingswear Castle	5054	Earl of Ducie
5016	Montgomery Castle	5055	Earl of Eldon
5017	The Gloucestershire Regiment 28th, 61st	5056	Earl of Powis
		5057	Earl Waldegrave
		5058	Earl of Clancarty
		5059	Earl St. Aldwyn
		5060	Earl of Berkeley
		5061	Earl of Birkenhead
		5062	Earl of Shaftesbury
		5063	Earl Baldwin
		5064	Bishop's Castle
		5065	Newport Castle

19

5066	Sir Felix Pole
5067	St. Fagans Castle
5068	Beverston Castle
5069	Isambard Kingdom Brunel
5070	Sir Daniel Gooch
5071	Spitfire
5072	Hurricane
5073	Blenheim
5074	Hampden
5075	Wellington
5076	Gladiator
5077	Fairey Battle
5078	Beaufort
5080	Defiant
5081	Lockheed Hudson
5082	Swordfish
5084	Reading Abbey
5085	Evesham Abbey
5087	Tintern Abbey
5088	Llanthony Abbey
5089	Westminster Abbey
5090	Neath Abbey
5091	Cleeve Abbey
5092	Tresco Abbey
5093	Upton Castle
5094	Tretower Castle
5095	Barbury Castle
5096	Bridgwater Castle
5097	Sarum Castle
5098	Clifford Castle
5099	Compton Castle

2-8-0T   4200 Class

5200	5217	5233	5249
5201	5218	5234	5250
5202	5219	5235	5251
5203	5220	5236	5252
5204	5221	5237	5253
5205	5222	5238	5254
5206	5223	5239	5255
5207	5224	5240	5256
5208	5225	5241	5257
5209	5226	5242	5258
5210	5227	5243	5259
5211	5228	5244	5260
5212	5229	5245	5261
5213	5230	5246	5262
5214	5231	5247	5263
5215	5232	5248	5264
5216			

2-6-0   4300 Class

5306	5330	5351	5376
5311	5331	5357	5380
5318	5332	5358	5384
5322	5336	5369	5385
5324	5337	5370	5399
5326	5339		

0-6-0PT   5400 Class

5410	5416	5420	5421
5412	5417		

2-6-2T   5100 Class

5101	5158	5177	5191
5103	5164	5180	5192
5104	5166	5181	5193
5110	5167	5182	5194
5150	5169	5183	5195
5151	5173	5184	
5152	5174	5187	5198
5153	5175	5188	5199
5154	5176	5190	

2-6-2T   4500 Class

5503	5511	5520	5531
5504	5514	5521	5532
5508	5515	5525	5534
5509	5516	5526	5536
5510	5518	5529	5537

5538	5547	5555	5565	5766	5773	5779	5789
5539	5548	5557	5568	5768	5774	5780	5791
5540	5549	5558	5569	5770	5775	5783	5793
5541	5550	5560	5570	5771	5778	5787	5798
5542	5552	5562	5571				
5544	5553	5563	5572				
5545	5554	5564	5573				
5546							

0-4-2T   5800 Class

5815

0-6-2T   5600 Class

5600	5625	5650	5675
5601	5626	5651	5676
5602	5627	5652	5677
5603	5628	5653	5678
5604	5629	5654	5679
5605	5630	5655	5680
5606	5631	5656	5681
5607	5632	5657	5682
5608	5633	5658	5683
5609	5634	5659	5684
5610	5635	5660	5685
5611	5636	5661	5686
5612	5637	5662	5687
5613	5638	5663	5688
5614	5639	5664	5689
5615	5640	5665	5690
5616	5641	5666	5691
5617	5642	5667	5692
5618	5643	5668	5693
5619	5644	5669	5694
5620	5645	5670	5695
5621	5646	5671	5696
5622	5647	5672	5697
5623	5648	5673	5698
5624	5649	5674	5699

4-6-0   4900 Class
" Hall "

5900	Hinderton Hall
5901	Hazel Hall
5902	Howick Hall
5903	Keele Hall
5904	Kelham Hall
5905	Knowsley Hall
5906	Lawton Hall
5907	Marble Hall
5908	Moreton Hall
5909	Newton Hall
5910	Park Hall
5911	Preston Hall
5912	Queen's Hall
5913	Rushton Hall
5914	Ripon Hall
5916	Trinity Hall
5917	Westminster Hall
5918	Walton Hall
5919	Worsley Hall
5920	Wycliffe Hall
5921	Bingley Hall
5922	Caxton Hall
5923	Colston Hall
5924	Dinton Hall
5925	Eastcote Hall
5926	Grotrian Hall
5927	Guild Hall
5928	Haddon Hall

0-6-0PT   5700 Class

5706	5744	5749	5758
5720	5746	5756	5759
5728	5748	5757	5761

5929	Hanham Hall
5930	Hannington Hall
5931	Hatherley Hall
5932	Haydon Hall
5933	Kingsway Hall
5934	Kneller Hall
5935	Norton Hall
5936	Oakley Hall
5937	Stanford Hall
5938	Stanley Hall
5939	Tangley Hall
5940	Whitbourne Hall
5941	Campion Hall
5942	Doldowlod Hall
5943	Elmdon Hall
5944	Ickenham Hall
5945	Leckhampton Hall
5946	Marwell Hall
5947	Saint Benet's Hall
5948	Siddington Hall
5949	Trematon Hall
5950	Wardley Hall
5951	Clyffe Hall
5952	Cogan Hall
5953	Dunley Hall
5954	Faendre Hall
5955	Garth Hall
5956	Horsley Hall
5957	Hutton Hall
5958	Knolton Hall
5959	Mawley Hall
5960	Saint Edmund Hall
5961	Toynbee Hall
5962	Wantage Hall
5963	Wimpole Hall
5964	Wolseley Hall
5965	Woollas Hall
5966	Ashford Hall
5967	Bickmarsh Hall
5968	Cory Hall
5969	Honington Hall
5970	Hengrave Hall
5971	Merevale Hall
5972	Olton Hall
5973	Rolleston Hall
5974	Wallsworth Hall
5975	Winslow Hall

5976	Ashwicke Hall
5977	Beckford Hall
5978	Bodinnick Hall
5979	Cruckton Hall
5980	Dingley Hall
5981	Frensham Hall
5982	Harrington Hall
5983	Henley Hall
5984	Linden Hall
5985	Mostyn Hall
5986	Arbury Hall
5987	Brocket Hall
5988	Bostock Hall
5989	Cransley Hall
5990	Dorford Hall
5991	Gresham Hall
5992	Horton Hall
5993	Kirby Hall
5994	Roydon Hall
5995	Wick Hall
5996	Mytton Hall
5997	Sparkford Hall
5998	Trevor Hall
5999	Wollaton Hall

4-6-0   6000 Class
" King "

6000	King George V
6001	King Edward VII
6002	King William IV
6003	King George IV
6004	King George III
6005	King George II
6006	King George I
6007	King William III
6008	King James II
6009	King Charles II
6010	King Charles I
6011	King James I
6012	King Edward VI
6013	King Henry VIII
6014	King Henry VII
6015	King Richard III
6016	King Edward V
6017	King Edward IV

6018	King Henry VI
6019	King Henry V
6020	King Henry IV
6021	King Richard II
6022	King Edward III
6023	King Edward II
6024	King Edward I
6025	King Henry III
6026	King John
6027	King Richard I
6028	King George VI
6029	King Edward VIII

6357	6368	6377	6387
6360	6369	6378	6388
6361	6370	6379	6389
6362	6371	6380	6390
6363	6372	6381	6391
6364	6373	6382	6392
6365	6374	6384	6394
6366	6375	6385	6395
6367	6376	6386	6398

2-6-2T 6100 Class

6101	6122	6138	6154
6103	6123	6139	6155
6106	6124	6140	6156
6107	6125	6141	6157
6108	6126	6142	6158
6109	6127	6143	6159
6110	6128	6144	6160
6111	6129	6145	6161
6112	6130	6146	6162
6113	6131	6147	6163
6114	6132	6148	6164
6115	6133	6149	6165
6116	6134	6150	6166
6117	6135	6151	6167
6118	6136	6152	6168
6119	6137	6153	6169
6120			

0-6-0PT 6400 Class

6400	6415	6424	6433
6403	6416	6425	6434
6408	6418	6426	6435
6410	6419	6429	6436
6411	6421	6430	6437
6412	6422	6431	6438
6413			

2-6-0 4300 Class

6301	6317	6335	6345
6302	6319	6336	6346
6304	6320	6337	6347
6306	6324	6338	6348
6309	6326	6339	6349
6310	6327	6340	6350
6312	6329	6341	6351
6313	6330	6342	6352
6314	6332	6343	6353
6316	6333	6344	6356

0-6-2T 5600 Class

6600	6620	6640	6660
6601	6621	6641	6661
6602	6622	6642	6662
6603	6623	6643	6663
6604	6624	6644	6664
6605	6625	6645	6665
6606	6626	6646	6666
6607	6627	6647	6667
6608	6628	6648	6668
6609	6629	6649	6669
6610	6630	6650	6670
6611	6631	6651	6671
6612	6632	6652	6672
6613	6633	6653	6673
6614	6634	6654	6674
6615	6635	6655	6675
6616	6636	6656	6676
6617	6637	6657	6677
6618	6638	6658	6678
6619	6639	6659	6679

6680	6685	6690	6695
6681	6686	6691	6696
6682	6687	6692	6697
6683	6688	6693	6698
6684	6689	6694	6699

0-6-0PT   5700 Class

6700	6749	6760	6768
6714	6751	6761	6769
6720	6752	6762	6770
6724	6753	6763	6772
6738	6754	6764	6775
6739	6755	6765	6776
6741	6757	6766	6777
6742	6758	6767	6778

4-6-0   6800 Class
" Grange "

6800	Arlington Grange
6801	Aylburton Grange
6802	Bampton Grange
6803	Bucklebury Grange
6804	Brockington Grange
6805	Broughton Grange
6806	Blackwell Grange
6807	Birchwood Grange
6808	Beenham Grange
6809	Burghclere Grange
6810	Blakemere Grange
6811	Cranbourne Grange
6812	Chesford Grange
6813	Eastbury Grange
6814	Enborne Grange
6815	Frilford Grange
6816	Frankton Grange
6817	Gwenddwr Grange
6818	Hardwick Grange
6819	Highnam Grange
6820	Kingstone Grange
6821	Leaton Grange
6822	Manton Grange
6823	Oakley Grange
6824	Ashley Grange
6825	Llanvair Grange
6826	Nannerth Grange
6827	Llanfrechfa Grange
6828	Trellech Grange
6829	Burmington Grange
6830	Buckenhill Grange
6831	Bearley Grange
6832	Brockton Grange
6833	Calcot Grange
6834	Dummer Grange
6835	Eastham Grange
6836	Estevarney Grange
6837	Forthampton Grange
6838	Goodmoor Grange
6839	Hewell Grange
6840	Hazeley Grange
6841	Marlas Grange
6842	Nunhold Grange
6843	Poulton Grange
6844	Penhydd Grange
6845	Paviland Grange
6846	Ruckley Grange
6847	Tidmarsh Grange
6848	Toddington Grange
6849	Walton Grange
6850	Cleeve Grange
6851	Hurst Grange
6852	Headbourne Grange
6853	Morehampton Grange
6854	Roundhill Grange
6855	Saighton Grange
6856	Stowe Grange
6857	Tudor Grange
6858	Woolston Grange
6859	Yiewsley Grange
6860	Aberporth Grange
6861	Crynant Grange
6862	Derwent Grange
6863	Dolhywel Grange
6864	Dymock Grange

6865	Hopton Grange
6866	Morfa Grange
6867	Peterston Grange
6868	Penrhos Grange
6869	Resolven Grange
6870	Bodicote Grange
6871	Bourton Grange
6872	Crawley Grange
6873	Caradoc Grange
6874	Haughton Grange
6875	Hindford Grange
6876	Kingsland Grange
6877	Llanfair Grange
6878	Longford Grange
6879	Overton Grange

4-6-0	4900 Class
	" Hall "

6900	Abney Hall
6901	Arley Hall
6902	Butlers Hall
6903	Belmont Hall
6904	Charfield Hall
6905	Claughton Hall
6906	Chicheley Hall
6907	Davenham Hall
6908	Downham Hall
6909	Frewin Hall
6910	Gossington Hall
6911	Holker Hall
6912	Helmster Hall
6913	Levens Hall
6914	Langton Hall
6915	Mursley Hall
6916	Misterton Hall
6917	Oldlands Hall
6918	Sandon Hall
6919	Tylney Hall
6920	Barningham Hall
6921	Borwick Hall
6922	Burton Hall
6923	Croxteth Hall
6924	Grantley Hall
6925	Hackness Hall

6926	Holkham Hall
6927	Lilford Hall
6928	Underley Hall
6929	Whorlton Hall
6930	Aldersey Hall
6931	Aldborough Hall
6932	Burwarton Hall
6933	Birtles Hall
6934	Beachamwell Hall
6935	Browsholme Hall
6936	Breccles Hall
6937	Conyngham Hall
6938	Corndean Hall
6939	Calveley Hall
6940	Didlington Hall
6941	Fillongley Hall
6942	Eshton Hall
6943	Farnley Hall
6944	Fledborough Hall
6945	Glasfryn Hall
6946	Heatherden Hall
6947	Helmingham Hall
6948	Holbrooke Hall
6949	Haberfield Hall
6950	Kingsthorpe Hall
6951	Impney Hall
6952	Kimberley Hall
6953	Leighton Hall
6954	Lotherton Hall
6955	Lydcott Hall
6956	Mottram Hall
6957	Norcliffe Hall
6958	Oxburgh Hall

4-6-0	6959 Class
	" Modified Hall "

6959	Peatling Hall
6960	Raveningham Hall
6961	Stedham Hall
6962	Soughton Hall
6963	Throwley Hall
6964	Thornbridge Hall
6965	Thirlestaine Hall
6966	Witchingham Hall

6967	Willesley Hall	7009	Athelney Castle
6968	Woodcock Hall	7010	Avondale Castle
6969	Wraysbury Hall	7011	Banbury Castle
6970	Whaddon Hall	7012	Barry Castle
6971	Athelhampton Hall	7013	Bristol Castle
6972	Beningbrough Hall	7014	Caerhays Castle
6973	Bricklehampton Hall	7015	Carn Brea Castle
6974	Bryngwyn Hall	7016	Chester Castle
6975	Capesthorne Hall	7017	G. J. Churchward
6976	Graythwaite Hall	7018	Drysllwyn Castle
6977	Grundisburgh Hall	7019	Fowey Castle
6978	Haroldstone Hall	7020	Gloucester Castle
6979	Helperly Hall	7021	Haverfordwest Castle
6980	Llanrumney Hall	7022	Hereford Castle
6981	Marbury Hall	7023	Penrice Castle
6982	Melmerby Hall	7024	Powis Castle
6983	Otterington Hall	7025	Sudeley Castle
6984	Owsden Hall	7026	Tenby Castle
6985	Parwick Hall	7027	Thornbury Castle
6986	Rydal Hall	7028	Cadbury Castle
6987	Shervington Hall	7029	Clun Castle
6988	Swithland Hall	7030	Cranbrook Castle
6989	Wightwick Hall	7031	Cromwell's Castle
6990	Witherslack Hall	7032	Denbigh Castle
6991	Acton Burnell Hall	7033	Hartlebury Castle
6992	Arborfield Hall	7034	Ince Castle
6993	Arthog Hall	7035	Ogmore Castle
6994	Baggrave Hall	7036	Taunton Castle
6995	Benthall Hall	7037	Swindon
6996	Blackwell Hall		
6997	Bryn-Ivor Hall		
6998	Burton Agnes Hall		
6999	Capel Dewi Hall		

4-6-0　　　　　　4073 Class
" Castle "

7000	Viscount Portal
7001	Sir James Milne
7002	Devizes Castle
7003	Elmley Castle
7004	Eastnor Castle
7005	Sir Edward Elgar
7006	Lydford Castle
7007	Great Western
7008	Swansea Castle

2-8-2T　　　　　7200 Class

7200	7214	7228	7241
7201	7215	7229	7242
7202	7216	7230	7243
7203	7217	7231	7244
7204	7218	7232	7245
7205	7219	7233	7246
7206	7220	7234	7247
7207	7221	7235	7248
7208	7222	7236	7249
7209	7223	7237	7250
7210	7224	7238	7251
7211	7225	7239	7252
7212	7226	7240	7253
7213	7227		

2-6-0   4300 Class

7300	7311	7322	7333
7301	7312	7323	7334
7302	7313	7324	7335
7303	7314	7325	7336
7304	7315	7326	7337
7305	7316	7327	7338
7306	7317	7328	7339
7307	7318	7329	7340
7308	7319	7330	7341
7309	7320	7331	
7310	7321	7332	

0-6-0PT   7400 Class

7402	7414	7428	7439
7403	7417	7429	7440
7404	7418	7430	7441
7405	7421	7431	7442
7406	7422	7432	7443
7407	7423	7433	7444
7408	7424	7434	7445
7409	7425	7435	7446
7410	7426	7436	7448
7412	7427	7437	7449
7413			

0-6-0PT   5700 Class

7700	7722	7744	7762
7702	7723	7745	7764
7704	7724	7747	7765
7707	7725	7748	7766
7709	7726	7749	7771
7713	7729	7753	7772
7715	7732	7755	7775
7718	7736	7756	7776
7719	7739	7757	7777
7720	7740	7760	7780
7721	7741	7761	7782

7783	7786	7790	7798
7784	7787	7794	7799
7785	7788	7796	

4-6-0   7800 Class
" Manor "

7800	Torquay Manor
7801	Anthony Manor
7802	Bradley Manor
7803	Barcote Manor
7804	Baydon Manor
7805	Broome Manor
7806	Cockington Manor
7807	Compton Manor
7808	Cookham Manor
7809	Childrey Manor
7810	Draycott Manor
7811	Dunley Manor
7812	Erlestoke Manor
7813	Freshford Manor
7814	Fringford Manor
7815	Fritwell Manor
7816	Frilsham Manor
7817	Garsington Manor
7818	Granville Manor
7819	Hinton Manor
7820	Dinmore Manor
7821	Ditcheat Manor
7822	Foxcote Manor
7823	Hook Norton Manor
7824	Iford Manor
7825	Lechlade Manor
7826	Longworth Manor
7827	Lydham Manor
7828	Odney Manor
7829	Ramsbury Manor

4-6-0   6959 Class
" Modified Hall "

7900	Saint Peter's Hall
7901	Dodington Hall
7902	Eaton Mascot Hall
7903	Foremarke Hall
7904	Fountains Hall

7905	Fowey Hall
7906	Fron Hall
7907	Hart Hall
7908	Henshall Hall
7909	Heveningham Hall
7910	Hown Hall
7911	Lady Margaret Hall
7912	Little Linford Hall
7913	Little Wyrley Hall
7914	Lleweni Hall
7915	Mere Hall
7916	Mobberley Hall
7917	North Aston Hall
7918	Rhose Wood Hall
7919	Runter Hall
7920	Coney Hall
7921	Edstone Hall
7922	Salford Hall
7923	Speke Hall
7924	Thornycroft Hall
7925	Westol Hall
7926	Willey Hall
7927	Willington Hall
7928	Wolf Hall
7929	Wyke Hall

8457	8470	8480	8490
8458	8471	8481	8491
8459	8472	8482	8493
8460	8473	8483	8494
8461	8474	8484	8495
8464	8475	8486	8496
8465	8476	8487	8497
8466	8477	8488	8498
8467	8478	8489	8499
8469	8479		

2-6-2T 8100 Class

8100	8103	8106	8108
8101	8104	8107	8109
8102			

0-6-0PT 9400 Class

8400	8414	8428	8441
8401	8415	8430	8444
8402	8416	8431	8445
8403	8418	8433	8446
8404	8420	8435	8449
8405	8422	8436	8451
8406	8424	8437	8452
8407	8425	8438	8453
8409	8426	8439	8454
8413	8427	8440	8456

0-6-0PT 5700 Class

8700	8727	8751	8777
8701	8728	8752	8778
8702	8729	8753	8779
8705	8730	8754	8780
8706	8731	8756	8781
8707	8732	8757	8782
8709	8733	8759	8783
8710	8734	8760	8784
8711	8735	8761	8785
8712	8736	8762	8786
8713	8737	8763	8787
8714	8738	8764	8788
8715	8739	8765	8789
8716	8740	8766	8790
8717	8741	8767	8791
8718	8742	8768	8792
8719	8743	8769	8793
8720	8744	8770	8794
8721	8745	8771	8795
8722	8746	8772	8796
8723	8747	8773	8797
8724	8748	8774	8798
8725	8749	8775	8799
8726	8750	8776	

4-4-0 9000 Class

9014	9017

0-6-0PT   9400 Class

9401	9425	9455	9476
9404	9426	9456	9477
9405	9429	9457	9478
9406	9430	9458	9479
9407	9431	9460	9480
9408	9433	9461	9481
9409	9435	9462	9482
9410	9437	9463	9483
9411	9440	9464	9484
9412	9441	9465	9485
9413	9442	9466	9486
9414	9444	9467	9487
9415	9446	9468	9488
9416	9447	9469	9489
9418	9448	9470	9490
9419	9450	9471	9493
9420	9451	9472	9494
9421	9452	9473	9495
9422	9453	9474	9497
9423	9454	9475	9498
9424			

9664	9712	9741	9770
9665	9713	9742	9771
9666	9714	9743	9773
9667	9715	9744	9774
9668	9716	9745	9775
9669	9717	9746	9776
9670	9718	9747	9777
9671	9719	9748	9778
9672	9720	9749	9779
9674	9721	9750	9780
9675	9722	9751	9781
9676	9723	9752	9782
9677	9724	9753	9783
9678	9725	9754	9784
9679	9726	9755	9785
9680	9727	9756	9786
9681	9728	9757	9787
9682	9729	9758	9788
9700	9730	9759	9789
9701	9731	9760	9790
9702	9732	9761	9791
9703	9733	9762	9792
9704	9734	9763	9793
9705	9735	9764	9794
9706	9736	9765	9795
9707	9737	9766	9796
9709	9738	9767	9797
9710	9739	9768	9798
9711	9740	9769	9799

0-6-0PT   5700 Class

9600	9616	9632	9648
9601	9617	9633	9649
9602	9618	9634	9650
9603	9619	9635	9651
9604	9620	9636	9652
9605	9621	9637	9653
9606	9622	9638	9654
9607	9623	9639	9655
9608	9624	9640	9656
9609	9625	9641	9657
9610	9626	9642	9658
9611	9627	9643	9659
9612	9628	9644	9660
9613	9629	9645	9661
9614	9630	9646	9662
9615	9631	9647	9663

SERVICE LOCOMOTIVES

Diesel Mechanical

20	PWM 651	PWM 653
PWM 650	PWM 652	PWM 654

Total 6

Petrol

24   27

Total 2

LOCOMOTIVE SUPERINTENDENTS AND CHIEF MECHANICAL ENGINEERS OF THE G.W.R. & W.R.

Sir Daniel Gooch	... ...	1837–1864
Joseph Armstrong	... ...	{ 1854–1864* 1864–1877
George Armstrong (*Bro. of J. Armstrong*)	... ...	1864–1896*
William Dean ...	... ...	1877–1902
G. J. Churchward	... ...	1902–1921
Charles B. Collett	... ...	1922–1941
F. W. Hawksworth	... ...	1941–1949

* In charge of standard gauge locomotives at Stafford Road Works, Wolverhampton, with wide powers in design and construction.

HISTORIC LOCOMOTIVES PRESERVED IN STORE

Type	Originating Company	Pre-Grouping No.	G.W.R. No.	Name	Place of Preservation
0-6-0	G.W.R.	2513	2513	—	Swindon
4-6-0	G.W.R.	4003	4003	Lode Star	Swindon
4-6-0	G.W.R.	4073	4073	Caerphilly Castle	Swindon

SUMMARY OF SOUTHERN REGION STEAM LOCOMOTIVE CLASSES

IN ALPHABETICAL ORDER
WITH HISTORICAL NOTES AND DIMENSIONS

The Code given in smaller bold type at the head of each Class,
e.g. " 2F " denotes its British Railways power classification.

The number of locomotives in service has been checked in S.R. to July 8th, 1960
and W.R. to June 18th.

Classes

0-6-0T   0P   A1 & A1X

*A1. Introduced 1872. Stroudley L.B.S.C. " Terrier," later fitted with Marsh boiler, retaining original type smokebox.

†A1X. Introduced 1911. Rebuild of A1 with Marsh boiler and extended smokebox.

‡A1X. Loco. with increased cylinder diameter.

Weight: { 27 tons 10 cwt.*
{ 28 tons 5 cwt.‡‡
Pressure: 150 lb.
Cyls.: { 12″ × 20″.*†
{ 14 3/16″ × 20″.‡
Driving Wheels: 4′ 0″
T.E.: { 7,650 lb.*†
{ 10,695 lb.‡

*DS680
†DS681,   32635/40/6/50/61/2/70/8
‡32636   **Total   A1   1**
                                A1X 10

0-4-0T   1F   Class B4

Introduced 1891. Adams L.S.W. design for dock shunting.

Weight: 33 tons 9 cwt.
Pressure: 140 lb. Cyls. (O): 16″ × 22″
Driving Wheels: 3′ 9¾″.
T.E.: 14,650 lb.

30089/96, 30102   **Total 3**

0-6-0   2F   Class C

Introduced 1900. Wainwright S.E.C. design.

Weight: Loco. 43 tons 16 cwt.
Pressure: 160 lb.
Cyls.: 18½″ × 26″.
Driving Wheels: 5′ 2″.
T.E.: 19,520 lb.

31004/37/54/61/8/86,   31112/3/50,   31218/29/42/4/55/6/67/8/71/80/7/93/8,   31317, 31480/1/95/8,   31510/73/5/8/9/83/4/8–90/2,   31682/4/6/9–91/3–5, 31714–7/9–25   **Total 58**

0-6-0   2F   Class C2X

Introduced 1908. Marsh rebuild of R. J. Billinton L.B.S.C. C2 with larger C3-type boiler, extended smokebox, etc.

Weight: Loco. 45 tons 5 cwt.
Pressure: 170 lb.
Cyls.: 17½″ × 26″.
Driving Wheels: 5′ 0″.
T.E.: 19,175 lb.

32438/41/3/5/6/8–51, 32521–3/5/7/8/34–6/8/9/41/3–50/2/3
                        Total 31

4-4-0   3P   Class D1

Introduced 1921. Maunsell rebuild of Wainwright S.E.C. D, with larger superheated boiler, Belpaire firebox and long-travel piston valves.

Weight: Loco. 52 tons 4 cwt.
Pressure: 180 lb. Su.
Cyls.: 19″ × 26″.
Driving Wheels: 6′ 8″.
T.E.: 17,950 lb.

31145,   31246/7,   31487/9/94,
  31505/45,   31727/35/9/49

Total 12

4-4-0   3P   Class E1

Introduced 1919. Maunsell rebuild of
  Wainwright S.E.C. E, with larger
  superheated boiler, Belpaire firebox
  and long-travel piston valves.
Weight: Loco. 53 tons 9 cwt.
Pressure: 180 lb.
Cyls.: 19″ × 26″.
Driving Wheels: 6′ 6″.
T.E.: 18,410 lb.

31019/67, 31497, 31507

Total 4

0-6-0T   2F   Class E1

Introduced 1874. Stroudley L.B.S.C.
  design, reboilered by Marsh.
Weight: 44 tons 3 cwt.
Pressure: 170 lb.
Cyls.: 17″ × 24″.
Driving Wheels: 4′ 6″.
T.E.: 18,560 lb.

4, 32694

Total 2

0-6-0T   3F   Class E2

*Introduced 1913. L. B. Billinton
  L.B.S.C. design.
†Introduced 1915. Later locos. with
  tanks extended further forward.
Weight: { 52 tons 15 cwt.*
         { 53 tons 10 cwt.†
Pressure: 170 lb.
Cyls.: 17½″ × 26″.
Driving Wheels: 4′ 6″.
T.E.: 21,305 lb.

*32100–4
†32105–9

Total 10

0-6-2T   2P2F   Class E4

Introduced 1897. R. J. Billinton
  L.B.S.C. design, development of E3
  with larger wheels, reboilered with
  Marsh boiler and extended smokebox,
  cylinder diameter reduced from 18″
  by S.R.
Weight: 57 tons 10 cwt.
Pressure: 170 lb.
Cyls.: 17½″ × 26″.
Driving Wheels: 5′ 0″.
T.E.: 19,175 lb.

32468–70/2–5/9/84/7/91/5/8,
  32500/3–6/9/10/2/5/56/7/62–5/
  78/80/1

Total 31

0-6-2T   3F   Class E6

Introduced 1904. R. J. Billinton
  L.B.S.C. design, development of E5
  with smaller wheels, some with
  higher pressure.
Weight: 61 tons.
Pressure: 160 lb. or 175 lb.
Cyls.: 18″ × 26″.
Driving Wheels: 4′ 6″.
T.E.: 21,215 lb. or 23,205 lb.

32408/10/5–8

Total 6

0-6-0T   2F   Class G6

*Introduced 1894. Adams L.S.W.
  design, later additions by Drummond,
  but with Adams type boiler.
†Introduced 1925. Fitted with Drum-
  mond type boiler.
Weight: 47 tons 13 cwt.
Pressure: 160 lb.
Cyls.: 17½″ × 24″.
Driving Wheels: 4′ 10″.
T.E.: 17,235 lb.

*30238/58/66/77, 30349,
  DS3152
†30274

Total 7

5700 Class 0-6-0PT No. 5746   [*J. B. Bucknall*

5700 Class 0-6-0PT No. 6763   [*B. K. B. Green*

5700 Class 0-6-0PT No. 9704 (fitted with condensing apparatus)   [*C. P. Boocock*

Above:
1600 Class 0-6-0PT
No. 1647 [*P. J. Sharpe*

Left:
1600 Class 0-6-0PT
No. 1661 (fitted with
spark arrester)
[*P. J. Sharpe*

Below:
1500 Class 0-6-0PT
No. 1505 [*P. H. Wells*

9400 Class 0-6-0PT No. 8451   *[A. A. Delicata*

1366 Class 0-6-0PT No. 1369   *[B. E. Morrison*

1361 Class 0-6-0PT No. 1365   *[M. G. Martin*

1400 Class 0-4-2T No. 1420   *[P. H. Groom*

5800 Class 0-4-2T No. 5815   *[J. Wilkins*

5600 Class 0-6-2T No. 6621   *[J. Davenport*

2800 Class 2-8-0 No. 2865

[J. B. Bucknall

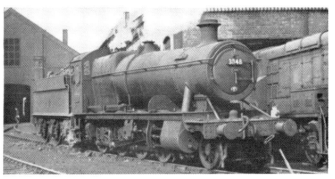

2800 Class 2-8-0 No. 3848 (with side-window cab)

[J. Davenport

4700 Class 2-8-0 No. 4700

[J. B. Bucknall

4073 Class 4-6-0 No. 7017 *G. J. Churchward* [R. C. Riley

4073 Class 4-6-0 No. 7014 *Caerhays Castle* (fitted with a double chimney) [Ivo Peters

6000 Class 4-6-0 No. 6028 *King George VI* [R. J. Buckley

Standard Class 5 4-6-0 No. 73092   [*J. E. Wilkinson*

1000 Class 4-6-0 No. 1019 *County of Merioneth*   [*R. A. Panting*

7800 Class 4-6-0 No. 7801 *Anthony Manor*   [*G. Wheeler*

4900 Class 4-6-0 No. 6954 *Lotherton Hall* [*R. K. Evans*

6959 Class 4-6-0 No. 6994 *Baggrave Hall* [*B. E. Morrison*

6800 Class 4-6-0 No. 6875 *Hindford Grange* [*G. Wheeler*

4-8-0T 8F Class G16

Introduced 1921. Urie L.S.W.
  "Hump" loco.
Weight: 95 tons 2 cwt.
Pressure: 180 lb. Su.
Cyls.: (O) 22″ × 28″.
Driving Wheels: 5′ 1″
T.E.: 33,990 lb.
Walschaerts valve gear. P.V.

30494/5   **Total 2**

0-4-4T 1P Class H

Introduced 1904. Wainwright S.E.C.
  design.
*Introduced 1949. Fitted for push-and-
  pull working.
Weight: 54 tons 8 cwt.
Pressure: 160 lb.
Cyls.: 18″ × 26″.
Driving Wheels: 5′ 6″
T.E.: 17,360 lb.

31261/5, 31305/7/24/6/8, 31542/
  50-2
*31005, 31161/2/77/93, 31263/6/
  76/8, 31306/8/22, 31500/12/
  7-22/30/3/43/4/53

                           Total 36

4-6-0 4P5F Class H15

*Introduced 1914. Urie L.S.W. design,
  fitted with Maunsell superheater
  from 1927, replacing earlier types.

†Introduced 1924. Maunsell locos.
  with N15-type boiler and smaller
  tender.

‡Introduced 1924. Maunsell rebuild of
  Drummond F13 4-cyl. 4-6-0 introduced 1905, with detail differences
  from rebuild of E14.

§Introduced 1927. Urie loco. (built
  1914 saturated), rebuilt with later
  N15-type boiler, with smaller firebox.

Weight: Loco.: { 81 tons 5 cwt.*
                 { 79 tons 19 cwt.†§
                 { 80 tons 11 cwt.‡
Pressure: { 180 lb. Su.*†§
                { 175 lb. Su.‡
Cyls.: (O) 21″ × 28″.
Driving Wheels: 6′ 0″.
T.E. { 26,240 lb.*†§
      { 25,510 lb.‡
Walschaerts valve gear.   P.V.

*30489   †30475/6, 30521-4
‡30331   §30491

                           Total 9

4-6-2T 6F Class H16

Introduced 1921. Urie L.S.W. design
  for heavy freight traffic.
Weight: 96 tons 8 cwt.
Pressure: 180 lb. Su.
Cyls.: (O) 21″ × 28″.
Driving Wheels: 5′ 7″.
T.E.: 28,200 lb.
Walschaerts valve gear.   P.V.

30516-20   **Total 5**

2-6-0 4P5F Class K

Introduced 1913. L. B. Billinton
  L.B.S.C. design.
Weight: Loco. 63 tons 15 cwt.
Pressure: 180 lb. Su.
Cyls.: (O) 21″ × 26″.
Driving Wheels: 5′ 6″
T.E.: 26,580 lb.
P.V.

32337-53   **Total 17**

4-4-0 3P Class L

Introduced 1914. Wainwright S.E.C.
  design, with detail alterations by
  Maunsell.

Weight: Loco. 57 tons 9 cwt.
Pressure: 160 lb. Su.
Cyls.: $20\frac{1}{2}'' \times 26''$.
Driving Wheels: 6′ 8″.
T.E.: 18,575 lb.
P.V.

31760/4–6/8/71/6/80

Total 8

4-4-0   3P   Class L1

Introduced 1926. Maunsell post-grouping development of L, with long-travel valves, side window cab and detail alterations.
Weight: Loco. 57 tons 16 cwt.
Pressure: 180 lb. Su.
Cyls : $19\frac{1}{2}'' \times 26''$.
Driving Wheels: 6′ 8″.
T.E.: 18,910 lb.
P.V.

31753/4/6/7/9/82/3/6/7/9

Total 10

4-6-0   7P   Class LN

*Introduced 1926. Maunsell design, cylinders and tender modified by Bulleid from 1938, and fitted with multiple-jet blastpipe and large-diameter chimney.
†Introduced 1929. Loco. fitted experimentally with smaller driving wheels.
‡Introduced 1929. Loco. fitted experimentally with longer boiler.
Weight: Loco. $\begin{cases} 83 \text{ tons } 10 \text{ cwt.*†} \\ 84 \text{ tons } 16 \text{ cwt.‡} \end{cases}$
Pressure: 220 lb. Su.
Cyls.: (4) $16\frac{1}{2}'' \times 26''$.
Driving Wheels: $\begin{cases} 6'7''.*‡ \\ 6'3''.† \end{cases}$
T.E.: $\begin{cases} 33,510 \text{ lb.*‡} \\ 35,300 \text{ lb.†} \end{cases}$
Walschaerts valve gear.   P.V.

*30850–8/61–5
†30859   ‡30860

Total 16

0-4-4T   2P   Class M7

*Introduced 1897. Drummond L.S.W. M7 design.

†Introduced 1903. Drummond X14 design, with increased front over-hang, steam reverser and detail alterations, now classified M7 (30254 originally M7).

‡Introduced 1925. X14 design fitted for push-and-pull working.

Weight: $\begin{cases} 60 \text{ tons } 4 \text{ cwt.*} \\ 60 \text{ tons } 3 \text{ cwt.†} \\ 62 \text{ tons } 0 \text{ cwt.‡} \end{cases}$

Pressure: 175 lb.

Cyls.: $18\frac{1}{2}'' \times 26''$.

Driving Wheels: 5′ 7″.

T.E.: 19,755 lb.

*30023–5/31–6/9/40/3/4, 30112, 30241/5–9/51/3/5, 30320/1/57, 30667–70/3/4/6

†30124/7/32, 30254, 30375/7/8, 30479

‡30021/8/9/45/8–53/5–60, 30104–11/25/8/9/31/3, 30328/79, 30480

Total 73

4-6-2   8P   Class MN

Introduced 1941. Bulleid design originally with 280 lb. pressure, multiple-jet blastpipe and Bulleid valve gear. Rebuilt since 1956 with Walschaerts valve gear, modified details and air-smoothed casing removed.

Weight: Loco. 97 tons 18 cwt.

Pressure: 250 lb.

Cyls: (3) $18'' \times 24''$.

Driving Wheels: 6′ 2″.

T.E.: 33,495 lb.

P.V.

35001–30

Total 30

Classes N & NI-Q

Classes N & NI

2-6-0 4P5F

*N. Introduced 1917. Maunsell S.E.C. mixed traffic design.
†NI. Introduced 1922. 3-cylinder development of N.
Weight: Loco. $\begin{cases} 61 \text{ tons } 4 \text{ cwt.*} \\ 64 \text{ tons } 5 \text{ cwt.†} \end{cases}$
Pressure: 200 lb. Su.
Cyls.: $\begin{cases} (O) \ 19'' \times 28''.* \\ (3) \ 16'' \times 28''.† \end{cases}$
Driving Wheels: 5' 6".
T.E.: $\begin{cases} 26,035 \text{ lb.*} \\ 27,695 \text{ lb.†} \end{cases}$
Walschaerts valve gear. P.V.

*31400–14, 31810–21/3–75
†31822/76–80

Total N 80
NI 6

4-6-0 5P Class N15

*Introduced 1925. Maunsell locos. with long-travel valves, increased boiler pressure, smaller fireboxes, and tenders from Drummond G14 4-6-0s.
†Introduced 1925. Later locos. with detail alterations and increased weight.
‡Introduced 1925. Locos. with modified cabs to suit Eastern Section, and new bogie tenders.
§Introduced 1926. Locos. with detail alterations and most with six-wheeled tenders for Central Section.
Weight: Loco. $\begin{cases} 79 \text{ tons } 18 \text{ cwt.*} \\ 80 \text{ tons } 19 \text{ cwt.†‡} \\ 81 \text{ tons } 17 \text{ cwt.§} \end{cases}$
Pressure: 200 lb. Su.
Cyls.: (O) $20\frac{1}{2}'' \times 28''$.
Driving Wheels: 6' 7".
T.E.: 25,320 lb.
Walschaerts valve gear. P.V.

*30453/7   †30448/50/1
‡30763–5/8/70–3/7/81–3/8/90
§30793–6/8–30800/2–4/6

Total 30

0-6-0 2F Class O1

*Introduced 1903. Wainwright rebuild with domed boiler and new cab of Stirling S.E. Class O 0-6-0 (introduced 1878).

†Introduced 1903. Loco. with smaller driving wheels.
Weight: Loco. 41 tons 1 cwt.
Pressure: 150 lb.
Cyls.: $18'' \times 26''$.
Driving Wheels: $\begin{cases} 5' \ 2''.* \\ 5' \ 1''.† \end{cases}$
T.E.: $\begin{cases} 17,325 \text{ lb.*} \\ 17,610 \text{ lb.†} \end{cases}$

*31065, 31258
†31048

Total 3

0-4-4T 0P Class O2

*Introduced 1889. Adams L.S.W. design.
†Introduced 1923. Fitted with Westinghouse brake for I.O.W. Bunkers enlarged from 1932.
‡Fitted with Drummond-type boiler.
§Fitted for push-and-pull working.
Weight: $\begin{cases} 46 \text{ tons } 18 \text{ cwt.*‡} \\ 48 \text{ tons } 8 \text{ cwt.†} \end{cases}$
Pressure: 160 lb.
Cyls.: $17\frac{1}{2}'' \times 24''$.
Driving Wheels: 4' 10".
T.E.: 17,235 lb.

*30192/3/9, 30200/25/9
†14/6–8/20–2/4–33
†35/6
‡30223   ‡§30183

Total 27

0-6-0T Unclass. Class P

Introduced 1909. Wainwright S.E.C. design for push-and-pull work, now used for shunting.
Weight: 28 tons 10 cwt.
Pressure: 160 lb.
Cyls.: $12'' \times 18''$.
Driving Wheels: 3' $9\frac{1}{2}''$.
T.E.: 7,810 lb.
31027, 31556

Total 2

0-6-0 4F Class Q

Introduced 1938. Maunsell design, later fitted with multiple-jet blastpipe and large-diameter chimney.
Weight: Loco. 49 tons 10 cwt.
Pressure 200 lb. Su.
Cyls.: $19'' \times 26''$.

Driving Wheels: 5' 1".
T.E.: 26,160 lb.
P.V.

30530–49   **Total 20**

0-6-0   5F   Class Q1

Introduced 1942. Bulleid " Austerity "
  design.
Weight: Loco. 51 tons 5 cwt.
Pressure: 230 lb. Su.
Cyls.: 19" × 26".
Driving Wheels: 5' 1"
T.E.: 30,080 lb.
P.V.

33001–40   **Total 40**

4-6-0   6F   Class S15

*Introduced 1920. Urie L.S.W. design,
  development of N15 for mixed traffic
  work.
†Introduced 1927. Maunsell design,
  with higher pressure, smaller grate,
  modified footplating and other detail
  differences. 30833–7 with 6-wheel
  tenders for Central Section.
‡Introduced 1936. Later locos, with
  detail differences and reduced weight.
Weight: Loco. { 79 tons 16 cwt.*
              80 tons 14 cwt.†
              79 tons 5 cwt.‡
Pressure: { 180 lb. Su.*
          200 lb. Su.†‡
Cyls.: { (O) 21" × 28".*
      { (O)20½" × 28".†‡
Driving Wheels: 5' 7".
T.E. { 28,200 lb.*
     29,855 lb.†‡
Walschaerts valve gear. P.V.

*30496–30515   †30823–37
‡30838–47

                 Total 45

4-4-0   3P   Class T9

*Introduced 1899. Drummond L.S.W.
  design, fitted with superheater and
  larger cylinders by Urie from 1922.
†Introduced 1899. Locos. with detail
  differences (originally fitted with
  firebox watertubes).
‡Introduced 1900. Locos. with wider
  cab and splashers, without coupling
  rod splashers and originally fitted
  with firebox watertubes.

Weight: Loco. { 51 tons 18 cwt.*
              51 tons 16 cwt.†
              51 tons 7 cwt.‡
Pressure: 175 lb. Su.
Cyls.: 19" × 26".
Driving Wheels: 6' 7".
T.E.: 17,675 lb.

*30117/20, 30287/8
†30707/9/15/7–9/29
‡30300/13/38

                 Total 14

Classes
2-6-0   4P3F   U & U1

*U. Introduced 1928. Rebuild of
  Maunsell S.E.C. Class K (" River ")
  2-6-4T (introduced 1917).
†U. Introduced 1928. Locos. built as
  Class U, with smaller splashers and
  detail alterations.
‡U1. Introduced 1928. 3-cylinder
  development of Class U (prototype
  31890, rebuilt from 2-6-4T, originally
  built 1925).
Weight: Loco. { 63 tons.*
              62 tons 6 cwt.†
              65 tons 6 cwt.‡
Pressure: 200 lb. Su.
Cyls.: { (O) 19" × 28".*†
      { (3) 16" × 28".‡
Driving Wheels: 6' 0".
T.E.: { 23,865 lb.*†
      25,385 lb.‡
Walschaerts valve gear. P.V.

*31790–31809   †31610–39
‡31890–31910

        Total Class U 50
            Class U1 21

0-6-0T   3F   Class USA

Introduced 1942. U.S. Army Trans-
  portation Corps design, purchased by
  S.R. 1946, and fitted with modified cab
  and bunker and other detail altera-
  tions.
Weight: 46 tons 10 cwt.
Pressure: 210 lb.
Cyls.: (O) 16½" × 24".
Driving Wheels: 4' 6".
T.E.: 21,600 lb.
Walschaerts valve gear. P.V.

30061–74   **Total 14**

4-4-0   5P   Class V

*Introduced 1930. Maunsell design.
†Introduced 1938. Fitted with multiple-jet blastpipe and large-diameter chimney by Bulleid.
Weight: Loco. 67 tons 2 cwt.
Pressure: 220 lb. Su.
Cyls.: (3) $16\frac{1}{2}'' \times 26''$.
Driving Wheels: 6' 7".
T.E.: 25,135 lb.
Walschaerts valve gear. P.V.

*30902-6/8/10-2/6/22/3/5-8/
32/5/6

†30900/1/7/9/13 – 5/7 – 21/4/29 –
31/3/4/7-9   **Total 40**

2-6-4T   6F   Class W

Introduced 1931. Maunsell design, developed from Class N1 2-6-0.
Weight: 90 tons 14 cwt.
Pressure: 200 lb. Su.
Cyls.: (3) $16\frac{1}{2}'' \times 28''$.
Driving Wheels: 5' 6".
T.E.: 29,450 lb.
Walschaerts valve gear. P.V.

31911–25   **Total 15**

Classes
4-6-2   7P5F   WC & BB

*Introduced 1945. Bulleid "West Country" Class, with Bulleid valve gear.
†Introduced 1946. Bulleid "Battle of Britain" Class, with Bulleid valve gear.
‡Introduced 1957. Rebuilt with Walschaerts valve gear, modified details and air-smoothed casing removed.
Weight: Loco. $\begin{cases} 86 \text{ tons } 0 \text{ cwt.}^{*\dagger} \\ 90 \text{ tons } 1 \text{ cwt.}\ddagger \end{cases}$
Pressure: 250 lb. Su.
Cyls.: (3) $16\frac{3}{8}'' \times 24''$.
Driving Wheels: 6' 2".
T.E.: 27,715 lb.
Bulleid valve gear. P.V.

*34002/6/7/9/11/5/9/20/3/4/ 30/2/
3/5/6/8/40/1/3/91/2/4-9,
34100-8

†34049/51/4-8/60/1/3-70/2-6/8-
81/3/4/6/7/9, 34109/10

*‡34001/3-5/8/10/2-4/6- 8/21/2/
5-9/31/4/7/9/42/4-8/93
†‡34050/2/3/9/62/71/7/82/5/8/90
     Total 110

0-8-0T   6F   Class Z

Introduced 1929. Maunsell design for heavy shunting.
Weight: 71 tons 12 cwt.
Pressure: 180 lb.
Cyls.: (3) $16'' \times 28''$.
Driving Wheels: 4' 8".
T.E.: 29,375 lb.
Walschaerts valve gear. P.V.

30950-7   **Total 8**

0-6-0   3F   Class 700

Introduced 1897. Drummond L.S.W. design, superheated from 1921.
Weight: Loco. 46 tons 14 cwt.
Pressure: 180 lb. Su.
Cyls.: $19'' \times 26''$.
Driving Wheels: 5' 1".
T.E.: 23,540 lb.

30306/8/9/15-7/25-7/39/46/50/5/
68, 30687/9-30701
     Total 28

2-4-0WT   0P   Class 0298

Introduced 1874. Beattie L.S.W. design, rebuilt by Adams (1884–92). Urie (1921–2) and Maunsell (1931–5).
Weight: 37 tons 16 cwt.
Pressure: 160 lb.
Cyls.: (O) $16\frac{1}{2}'' \times 20''$.
Driving Wheels: 5' 7".
T.E.: 11,050 lb.

30585-7   **Total 3**

4-4-2T   1P   Class 0415

Introduced 1882. Adams L.S.W. design, later reboilered.
Weight: 55 tons 2 cwt.
Pressure: 160 lb.
Cyls.: (O) $17\frac{1}{2}'' \times 24''$.
Driving Wheels: 5' 7".
T.E.: 14,920 lb.

30582-4   **Total 3**

BRITISH RAILWAYS LOCOMOTIVES
Nos. 30021-35030

Named Engines are indicated by an asterisk (*)

No.	Class	No.	Class	No.	Class	No.	Class
30021	M7	30068	U.S.A.	30238	G6	30350	700
30023	M7	30069	U.S.A.	30241	M7	30355	700
30024	M7	30070	U.S.A.	30245	M7	30357	M7
30025	M7	30071	U.S.A.	30246	M7	30368	700
30028	M7	30072	U.S.A.	30247	M7	30375	M7
30029	M7	30073	U.S.A.	30248	M7	30377	M7
30031	M7	30074	U.S.A.	30249	M7	30378	M7
30032	M7	30089	B4	30251	M7	30379	M7
30033	M7	30096	B4	30253	M7	30448*	N15
30034	M7	30102	B4	30254	M7	30450*	N15
30035	M7	30104	M7	30255	M7	30451*	N15
30036	M7	30105	M7	30258	G6	30453*	N15
30039	M7	30106	M7	30266	G6	30457*	N15
30040	M7	30107	M7	30274	G6	30475	H15
30043	M7	30108	M7	30277	G6	30476	H15
30044	M7	30109	M7	30287	T9	30479	M7
30045	M7	30110	M7	30288	T9	30480	M7
30048	M7	30111	M7	30300	T9	30489	H15
30049	M7	30112	M7	30306	700	30491	H15
30050	M7	30117	T9	30308	700	30494	G16
30051	M7	30120	T9	30309	700	30495	G16
30052	M7	30124	M7	30313	T9	30496	S15
30053	M7	30125	M7	30315	700	30497	S15
30055	M7	30127	M7	30316	700	30498	S15
30056	M7	30128	M7	30317	700	30499	S15
30057	M7	30129	M7	30320	M7	30500	S15
30058	M7	30131	M7	30321	M7	30501	S15
30059	M7	30132	M7	30325	700	30502	S15
30060	M7	30133	M7	30326	700	30503	S15
30061	U.S.A.	30183	O2	30327	700	30504	S15
30062	U.S.A.	30192	O2	30328	M7	30505	S15
30063	U.S.A.	30193	O2	30331	H15	30506	S15
30064	U.S.A.	30199	O2	30338	T9	30507	S15
30065	U.S.A.	30200	O2	30339	700	30508	S15
30066	U.S.A.	30223	O2	30346	700		
30067	U.S.A.	30225	O2	30349	G6		
		30229	O2				

No.	Class	No.	Class	No.	Class	No.	Class
30509	S15	30670	M7	30799*	N15	30864*	LN
30510	S15	30673	M7	30800*	N15	30865*	LN
30511	S15	30674	M7	30802*	N15	30900*	V
30512	S15	30676	M7	30803*	N15	30901*	V
30513	S15	30687	700	30804*	N15	30902*	V
30514	S15	30689	700	30806*	N15	30903*	V
30515	S15	30690	700	30823	S15	30904*	V
30516	H16	30691	700	30824	S15	30905*	V
30517	H16	30692	700	30825	S15	30906*	V
30518	H16	30693	700	30826	S15	30907*	V
30519	H16	30694	700	30827	S15	30908*	V
30520	H16	30695	700	30828	S15	30909*	V
30521	H15	30696	700	30829	S15	30910*	V
30522	H15	30697	700	30830	S15	30911*	V
30523	H15	30698	700	30831	S15	30912*	V
30524	H15	30699	700	30832	S15	30913*	V
30530	Q	30700	700	30833	S15	30914*	V
30531	Q	30701	700	30834	S15	30915*	V
30532	Q	30707	T9	30835	S15	30916*	V
30533	Q	30709	T9	30836	S15	30917*	V
30534	Q	30715	T9	30837	S15	30918*	V
30535	Q	30717	T9	30838	S15	30919*	V
30536	Q	30718	T9	30839	S15	30920*	V
30537	Q	30719	T9	30840	S15	30921*	V
30538	Q	30729	T9	30841	S15	30922*	V
30539	Q	30763*	N15	30842	S15	30923*	V
30540	Q	30764*	N15	30843	S15	30924*	V
30541	Q	30765*	N15	30844	S15	30925*	V
30542	Q	30768*	N15	30845	S15	30926*	V
30543	Q	30770*	N15	30846	S15	30927*	V
30544	Q	30771*	N15	30847	S15	30928*	V
30545	Q	30772*	N15	30850*	LN	30929*	V
30546	Q	30773*	N15	30851*	LN	30930*	V
30547	Q	30777*	N15	30852*	LN	30931*	V
30548	Q	30781*	N15	30853*	LN	30932*	V
30549	Q	30782*	N15	30854*	LN	30933*	V
30582	0415	30783*	N15	30855*	LN	30934*	V
30583	0415	30788*	N15	30856*	LN	30935*	V
30584	0415	30790*	N15	30857*	LN	30936*	V
30585	0298	30793*	N15	30858*	LN	30937*	V
30586	0298	30794*	N15	30859*	LN	30938*	V
30587	0298	30795*	N15	30860*	LN	30939*	V
30667	M7	30796*	N15	30861*	LN	30950	Z
30668	M7	30798*	N15	30862*	LN	30951	Z
30669	M7	30798*	N15	30863*	LN	30952	Z

No.	Class	No.	Class	No.	Class	No.	Class
30953	Z	31287	C	31520	H	31631	U
30954	Z	31293	C	31521	H	31632	U
30955	Z	31298	C	31522	H	31633	U
30956	Z	31305	H	31530	H	31634	U
30957	Z	31306	H	31533	H	31635	U
31004	C	31307	H	31542	H	31636	U
31005	H	31308	H	31543	H	31637	U
31019	EI	31317	C	31544	H	31638	U
31027	P	31322	H	31545	DI	31639	U
31037	C	31324	H	31550	H	31682	C
31048	OI	31326	H	31551	H	31684	C
31054	C	31328	H	31552	H	31686	C
31061	C	31400	N	31553	H	31689	C
31065	OI	31401	N	31556	P	31690	C
31067	EI	31402	N	31573	C	31691	C
31068	C	31403	N	31575	C	31693	C
31086	C	31404	N	31578	C	31694	C
31112	C	31405	N	31579	C	31695	C
31113	C	31406	N	31583	C	31714	C
31145	DI	31407	N	31584	C	31715	C
31150	C	31408	N	31588	C	31716	C
31161	H	31409	N	31589	C	31717	C
31162	H	31410	N	31590	C	31719	C
31177	H	31411	N	31592	C	31720	C
31193	H	31412	N	31610	U	31721	C
31218	C	31413	N	31611	U	31722	C
31229	C	31414	N	31612	U	31723	C
31242	C	31480	C	31613	U	31724	C
31244	C	31481	C	31614	N	31725	C
31246	DI	31487	DI	31615	U	31727	DI
31247	DI	31489	DI	31616	U	31735	DI
31255	C	31494	DI	31617	U	31739	DI
31256	C	31495	C	31618	U	31749	DI
31258	OI	31497	EI	31619	U	31753	LI
31261	H	31498	C	31620	U	31754	LI
31263	H	31500	H	31621	U	31756	LI
31265	H	31505	DI	31622	U	31757	LI
31266	H	31507	EI	31623	U	31759	LI
31267	C	31510	C	31624	U	31760	L
31268	C	31512	H	31625	U	31764	L
31271	C	31517	H	31626	U	31765	L
31276	H	31518	H	31627	U	31766	L
31278	H	31519	H	31628	U	31768	L
31280	**C**			31629	U	31771	L
				31630	U		

No.	Class	No.	Class	No.	Class	No.	Class
31776	L	31828	N	31873	N	32101	E2
31780	L	31829	N	31874	N	32102	E2
31782	LI	31830	N	31875	N	32103	E2
31783	LI	31831	N	31876	NI	32104	E2
31786	LI	31832	N	31877	NI	32105	E2
31787	LI	31833	N	31878	NI	32106	E2
31789	LI	31834	N	31879	NI	32107	E2
31790	U	31835	N	31880	NI	32108	E2
31791	U	31836	N	31890	UI	32109	E2
31792	U	31837	N	31891	UI	32337	K
31793	U	31838	N	31892	UI	32338	K
31794	U	31839	N	31893	UI	32339	K
31795	U	31840	N	31894	UI	32340	K
31796	U	31841	N	31895	UI	32341	K
31797	U	31842	N	31896	UI	32342	K
31798	U	31843	N	31897	UI	32343	K
31799	U	31844	N	31898	UI	32344	K
31800	U	31845	N	31899	UI	32345	K
31801	U	31846	N	31900	UI	32346	K
31802	U	31847	N	31901	UI	32347	K
31803	U	31848	N	31902	UI	32348	K
31804	U	31849	N	31903	UI	32349	K
31805	U	31850	N	31904	UI	32350	K
31806	U	31851	N	31905	UI	32351	K
31807	U	31852	N	31906	UI	32352	K
31808	U	31853	N	31907	UI	32353	K
31809	U	31854	N	31908	UI	32408	E6
31810	N	31855	N	31909	UI	32410	E6
31811	N	31856	N	31910	UI	32415	E6
31812	N	31857	N	31911	W	32416	E6
31813	N	31858	N	31912	W	32417	E6
31814	N	31859	N	31913	W	32418	E6
31815	N	31860	N	31914	W	32438	C2X
31816	N	31861	N	31915	W	32441	C2X
31817	N	31862	N	31916	W	32443	C2X
31818	N	31863	N	31917	W	32445	C2X
31819	N	3186,	N	31918	W	32446	C2X
31820	N	31865	N	31919	W	32448	C2X
31821	N	31866	N	31920	W	32449	C2X
31822	NI	31867	N	31921	W	32450	C2X
31823	N	31868	N	31922	W	32451	C2X
31824	N	31869	N	31923	W	32468	E4
31825	N	31870	N	31924	W	32469	E4
31826	N	31871	N	31925	W	32470	E4
31827	N	31872	N	32100	E2	32472	E4

No.	Class	No.	Class	No.	Class	No.	Class
32473	E4	32564	E4	33029	Q1	34034*	WC
32474	E4	32565	E4	33030	Q1	34035*	WC
32475	E4	32578	E4	33031	Q1	34036*	WC
32479	E4	32580	E4	33032	Q1	34037*	WC
32484	E4	32581	E4	33033	Q1	34038*	WC
32487	E4	32635	A1X	33034	Q1	34039*	WC
32491	E4	32636	A1X	33035	Q1	34040*	WC
32495	E4	32640	A1X	33036	Q1	34041*	WC
32498	E4	32646	A1X	33037	Q1	34042*	WC
32500	E4	32650	A1X	33038	Q1	34043*	WC
32503	E4	32661	A1X	33039	Q1	34044*	WC
32504	E4	32662	A1X	33040	Q1	34045*	WC
32505	E4	32670	A1X	34001*	WC	34046*	WC
32506	E4	32678	A1X	34002*	WC	34047*	WC
32509	E4	32694	E1	34003*	WC	34048*	WC
32510	E4	33001	Q1	34004*	WC	34049*	BB
32512	E4	33002	Q1	34005*	WC	34050*	BB
32515	E4	33003	Q1	34006*	WC	34051*	BB
32521	C2X	33004	Q1	34007*	WC	34052*	BB
32522	C2X	33005	Q1	34008*	WC	34053*	BB
32523	C2X	33006	Q1	34009*	WC	34054*	BB
32525	C2X	33007	Q1	34010*	WC	34055*	BB
32527	C2X	33008	Q1	34011*	WC	34056*	BB
32528	C2X	33009	Q1	34012*	WC	34057*	BB
32534	C2X	33010	Q1	34013*	WC	34058*	BB
32535	C2X	33011	Q1	34014*	WC	34059*	BB
32536	C2X	33012	Q1	34015*	WC	34060*	BB
32538	C2X	33013	Q1	34016*	WC	34061*	BB
32539	C2X	33014	Q1	34017*	WC	34062*	BB
32541	C2X	33015	Q1	34018*	WC	34063*	BB
32543	C2X	33016	Q1	34019*	WC	34064*	BB
32544	C2X	33017	Q1	34020*	WC	34065*	BB
32545	C2X	33018	Q1	34021*	WC	34066*	BB
32546	C2X	33019	Q1	34022*	WC	34067*	BB
32547	C2X	33020	Q1	34023*	WC	34068*	BB
32548	C2X	33021	Q1	34024*	WC	34069*	BB
32549	C2X	33022	Q1	34025*	WC	34070*	BB
32550	C2X	33023	Q1	34026*	WC	34071*	BB
32552	C2X	33024	Q1	34027*	WC	34072*	BB
32553	C2X	33025	Q1	34028*	WC	34073*	BB
32556	E4	33026	Q1	34029*	WC	34074*	BB
32557	E4	33027	Q1	34030*	WC	34075*	BB
32562	E4	33028	Q1	34031*	WC	34076*	BB
32563	E4			34032*	WC	34077*	BB
				34033*	WC	34078*	BB

No.	Class	No.	Class	No.	Class	No.	Class
34079*	BB	35014*	MN	34109*	BB	35016*	MN
34080*	BB	35015*	MN	34110*	BB	35017*	MN
34081*	BB	34095*	WC	35001*	MN	35018*	MN
34082*	BB	34096*	WC	35002*	MN	35019*	MN
34083*	BB	34097*	WC	35003*	MN	35020*	MN
34084*	BB	34098*	WC	35004*	MN	35021*	MN
34085*	BB	34099*	WC	35005*	MN	35022*	MN
34086*	BB	34100*	WC	35006*	MN	35023*	MN
34087*	BB	34101*	WC	35007*	MN	35024*	MN
34088*	BB	34102*	WC	35008*	MN	35025*	MN
34089*	BB	34103*	WC	35009*	MN	35026*	MN
34090*	BB	34104*	WC	35010*	MN	35027*	MN
34091*	WC	34105*	WC	35011*	MN	35028*	MN
34092*	WC	34106*	WC	35012*	MN	35029*	MN
34093*	WC	34107*	WC	35013*	MN	35030*	MN
34094*	WC	34108*	WC				

SOUTHERN REGION SERVICE LOCOMOTIVES

No.	Old No.	Class	Station
*DS 74	—	Bo-Bo Electric	Durnsford Road
*DS 75	—	Bo Electric	Waterloo & City
DS 680	{ L.B.S.C. 654 S.E.C. 751 }	A1	Lancing Carriage Works
DS 681	L.B.S.C. 659	A1X	Lancing Carriage Works
DS 1169	—	0-4-0 Diesel	Broad Clyst
DS 1173	2217	0-6-0 Diesel	Engineer's Department
DS 3152	30272	G6	Meldon Quarry

HISTORIC LOCOMOTIVES PRESERVED IN STORE					
Type	Originating Company	Pre-Grouping No.	S.R. No.	Name	Place of Preservation
4-4-0	L. & S.W.	563	563	—	Clapham
0-6-0	L.B. & S.C.	82	(380S)	Boxhill	Clapham
4-4-0	S.E. & C.	737	(1737)	—	Clapham
LOCOMOTIVES USED BY THE BLUEBELL PRESERVATION SOCIETY					
0-6-0T	L.B. & S.C.	55	(2655)	Stepney	Bluebell Line
0-6-0T	S.E. & C.	323	(1323)	Bluebell	Bluebell Line
All locomotives have been re-painted with their original numbers.					

NAMED LOCOMOTIVES

CLASS N15 "KING ARTHUR" 4-6-0

30448	Sir Tristram		30782	Sir Brian
30450	Sir Kay		30783	Sir Gillemere
30451	Sir Lamorak		30788	Sir Urre of the Mount
30453	King Arthur		30790	Sir Villiars
30457	Sir Bedivere		30793	Sir Ontzlake
30763	Sir Bors de Ganis		30794	Sir Ector de Maris
30764	Sir Gawain		30795	Sir Dinadan
30765	Sir Gareth		30796	Sir Dodinas le Savage
30768	Sir Balin		30798	Sir Hectimere
30770	Sir Prianius		30799	Sir Ironside
30771	Sir Sagramore		30800	Sir Meleaus de Lile
30772	Sir Percivale		30802	Sir Durnore
30773	Sir Lavaine		30803	Sir Harry le Fise Lake
30777	Sir Lamiel		30804	Sir Cador of Cornwall
30781	Sir Aglovale		30806	Sir Galleron

CLASS LN "LORD NELSON" 4-6-0

30850	Lord Nelson		30858	Lord Duncan
30851	Sir Francis Drake		30859	Lord Hood
30852	Sir Walter Raleigh		30860	Lord Hawke
30853	Sir Richard Grenville		30861	Lord Anson
30854	Howard of Effingham		30862	Lord Collingwood
30855	Robert Blake		30863	Lord Rodney
30856	Lord St. Vincent		30864	Sir Martin Frobisher
30857	Lord Howe		30865	Sir John Hawkins

CLASS V "SCHOOLS" 4-4-0

30900	Eton		30906	Sherborne
30901	Winchester		30907	Dulwich
30902	Wellington		30908	Westminster
30903	Charterhouse		30909	St. Paul's
30904	Lancing		30910	Merchant Taylors
30905	Tonbridge		30911	Dover

30912	Downside	30926	Repton
30913	Christ's Hospital	30927	Clifton
30914	Eastbourne	30928	Stowe
30915	Brighton	30929	Malvern
30916	Whitgift	30930	Radley
30917	Ardingly	30931	King's Wimbledon
30918	Hurstpierpoint	30932	Blundells
30919	Harrow	30933	King's Canterbury
30920	Rugby	30934	St. Lawrence
30921	Shrewsbury	30935	Sevenoaks
30922	Marlborough	30936	Cranleigh
30923	Bradfield	30937	Epsom
30924	Haileybury	30938	St. Olave's
30925	Cheltenham	30939	Leatherhead

CLASSES WC & BB 4-6-2
" WEST COUNTRY " and " BATTLE OF BRITAIN "

34001	Exeter	34029	Lundy
34002	Salisbury	34030	Watersmeet
34003	Plymouth	34031	Torrington
34004	Yeovil	34032	Camelford
34005	Barnstaple	34033	Chard
34006	Bude	34034	Honiton
34007	Wadebridge	34035	Shaftesbury
34008	Padstow	34036	Westward Ho
34009	Lyme Regis	34037	Clovelly
34010	Sidmouth	34038	Lynton
34011	Tavistock	34039	Boscastle
34012	Launceston	34040	Crewkerne
34013	Okehampton	34041	Wilton
34014	Budleigh Salterton	34042	Dorchester
34015	Exmouth	34043	Combe Martin
34016	Bodmin	34044	Woolacombe
34017	Ilfracombe	34045	Ottery St. Mary
34018	Axminster	34046	Braunton
34019	Bideford	34047	Callington
34020	Seaton	34048	Crediton
34021	Dartmoor	34049	Anti-Aircraft Command
34022	Exmoor	34050	Royal Observer Corps
34023	Blackmore Vale	34051	Winston Churchill
34024	Tamar Valley	34052	Lord Dowding
34025	Whimple	34053	Sir Keith Park
34026	Yes Tor	34054	Lord Beaverbrook
34027	Taw Valley	34055	Fighter Pilot
34028	Eddystone	34056	Croydon

34057	Biggin Hill	34085	501 Squadron
34058	Sir Frederick Pile	34086	219 Squadron
34059	Sir Archibald Sinclair	34087	145 Squadron
34060	25 Squadron	34088	213 Squadron
34061	73 Squadron	34089	602 Squadron
34062	17 Squadron	34090	Sir Eustace Missenden
34063	229 Squadron		Southern Railway
34064	Fighter Command	34091	Weymouth
34065	Hurricane	34092	City of Wells
34066	Spitfire	34093	Saunton
34067	Tangmere	34094	Mortehoe
34068	Kenley	34095	Brentor
34069	Hawkinge	34096	Trevone
34070	Manston	34097	Holsworthy
34071	601 Squadron	34098	Templecombe
34072	257 Squadron	34099	Lynmouth
34073	249 Squadron	34100	Appledore
34074	46 Squadron	34101	Hartland
34075	264 Squadron	34102	Lapford
34076	41 Squadron	34103	Calstock
34077	603 Squadron	34104	Bere Alston
34078	222 Squadron	34105	Swanage
34079	141 Squadron	34106	Lydford
34080	74 Squadron	34107	Blandford Forum
34081	92 Squadron	34108	Wincanton
34082	615 Squadron	34109	Sir Trafford
34083	605 Squadron		Leigh-Mallory
34084	253 Squadron	34110	66 Squadron

CLASS MN " MERCHANT NAVY " 4-6-2

35001	Channel Packet	35015	Rotterdam Lloyd
35002	Union Castle	35016	Elders Fyffes
35003	Royal Mail	35017	Belgian Marine
35004	Cunard White Star	35018	British India Line
35005	Canadian Pacific	35019	French Line CGT
35006	Peninsular & Oriental	35020	Bibby Line
	S.N. Co.	35021	New Zealand Line
35007	Aberdeen	35022	Holland-America Line
	Commonwealth	35023	Holland-Afrika Line
35008	Orient Line	35024	East Asiatic Company
35009	Shaw Savill	35025	Brocklebank Line
35010	Blue Star	35026	Lamport & Holt Line
35011	General Steam	35027	Port Line
	Navigation	35028	Clan Line
35012	United States Lines	35029	Ellerman Lines
35013	Blue Funnel	35030	Elder Dempster Lines
35014	Nederland Line		

ISLE OF WIGHT LOCOMOTIVES

CLASS E1 0-6-0T

4   Wroxall

CLASS O2 0-4-4T

14	Fishbourne	27	Merstone
16	Ventnor	28	Ashey
17	Seaview	29	Alverstone
18	Ningwood	30	Shorwell
20	Shanklin	31	Chale
21	Sandown	32	Bonchurch
22	Brading	33	Bembridge
24	Calbourne	35	Freshwater
25	Godshill	36	Carisbrooke
26	Whitwell		

SOUTHERN RAILWAY LOCOMOTIVE SUPERINTENDENTS AND CHIEF MECHANICAL ENGINEERS OF CONSTITUENT COMPANIES

LONDON & SOUTH WESTERN RAILWAY

J. Woods ...	... ...	1835–1841
J. V. Gooch	... ...	1841–1850
J. Beattie ...	... ...	1850–1871
W. G. Beattie	... ...	1871–1878
W. Adams ...	... ...	1878–1895
D. Drummond	... ...	1895–1912
R. W. Urie...	... ...	1912–1922

LONDON, BRIGHTON AND SOUTH COAST RAILWAY

—. Statham	... ...	? –1845
J. Gray ...	... ...	1845–1847
S. Kirtley ...	... ...	1847
J. C. Craven	... ...	1847–1869
W. Stroudley	... ...	1870–1889
R. J. Billinton	... ...	1890–1904
D. Earle Marsh	... ...	1905–1911
L. B. Billinton	... ...	1911–1922

SOUTH EASTERN RAILWAY

B. Cubitt ...	... ...	1842–1845
J. Cudworth	... ...	1845–1876
A. M. Watkin	... ...	1876
R. Mansell ...	... ...	1877–1878
J. Stirling ...	... ...	1878–1898

LONDON, CHATHAM AND DOVER RAILWAY

W. Cubitt ...	... ...	1853–1860
W. Martley	... ...	1860–1874
W. Kirtley ...	... ...	1874–1898

SOUTH EASTERN AND CHATHAM RAILWAY

H. S. Wainwright ...	...	1899–1913
R. E. L. Maunsell ...	...	1913–1922

SOUTHERN RAILWAY

R. E. L. Maunsell ...	...	1923–1937
O. V. Bulleid	... ...	1937–1949

BRITISH RAILWAYS LOCOMOTIVES
Nos. 40000-59999

The code given in bold type to the right of each Class heading, e.g. " 2P " denotes its British Railways power classification.

The numbers of locomotives in service have been checked for L.M.R. to July 16th, 1960, E. & N.E.R. to July 23rd, Sc.R. to July 2nd, S.R. to July 8th and W.R. to June 18th.

2-6-2T   **3**

Introduced 1930. Fowler L.M.S. design with parallel boiler.
*Introduced 1930. Condensing locos. for working to Moorgate, London.
Weight: { 70 tons 10 cwt.
{ 71 tons 16 cwt.*
Pressure: 200 lb. Su.
Cyls.: (O) 17½″ × 26″.
Driving Wheels: 5′ 3″.
T.E.: 21,485 lb.
Walschaerts valve gear. P.V.

40001	40016	40032*	40049
40003	40018	40033*	40050
40006	40020	40034*	40051
40007	40022*	40035*	40053
40009	40024*	40037*	40054
40010	40026*	40038*	40062
40011	40028*	40041	40063
40012	40029*	40042	40064
40015	40031*		

Total 34

2-6-2T   **3**

Introduced 1935. Stanier L.M.S. taper boiler development of Fowler design (*above*).
*Introduced 1941. Rebuilt with larger boiler.
Weight: { 71 tons 5 cwt.
{ 72 tons 10 cwt.*
Pressure: 200 lb. Su.
Cyls.: (O) 17½″ × 26″.
Driving Wheels: 5′ 3″.
T.E.: 21,485 lb.
Walschaerts valve gear. P.V.

40071	40106	40141	40177
40072	40107	40142	40178
40073	40108	40143	40179
40074	40109	40144	40180
40075	40110	40145	40181
40076	40111	40146	40182
40077	40112	40147	40183
40078	40113	40148*	40184
40079	40114	40149	40185
40080	40115	40150	40186
40081	40116	40151	40187
40082	40117	40152	40188
40083	40118	40153	40189
40085	40119	40154	40190
40086	40120	40155	40191
40087	40121	40156	40192
40088	40122	40157	40193
40089	40123	40158	40194
40090	40124	40159	40195
40091	40126	40161	40196
40092	40128	40162	40197
40093	40129	40164	40198
40094	40130	40165	40199
40095	40131	40166	40200
40097	40132	40167*	40201
40098	40133	40168	40202
40099	40134	40170	40203*
40100	40135	40171	40205
40101	40136	40173	40206
40102	40137	40174	40207
40103	40138	40175	40208
40104	40140	40176	40209
40105			

Total 129

4-4-0　　　　　　　　　　2P

Introduced 1912. Fowler rebuild of Johnson locos. with superheater and piston valves.
Weight: Loco. 53 tons 7 cwt.
Pressure: 160 lb Su.
Cyls.: 20½" × 26".
Driving Wheels: 7' 0½".
T.E.: 17,585 lb.
P.V.

40396	40452	40491	40537
40402	40453	40501	40540
40411	40454	40502	40543
40421	40487	40504	40548
40439	40489	40511	40557
40443			

Total 21

4-4-0　　　　　　　　　　2P

Introduced 1928. Post-grouping development of Midland design, with modified dimensions and reduced boiler mountings.
*Introduced 1928. Locos. built for S. & D.J.R. (taken into L.M.S. stock, 1930).
Weight: Loco. 54 tons 1 cwt.
Pressure: 180 lb. Su.
Cyls.: 19" × 26".
Driving Wheels: 6' 9".
T.E.: 17,730 lb.
P.V.

40563	40583	40612	40628
40564	40584	40613	40629
40566	40585	40614	40630
40569	40586	40615	40631
40570	40588	40618	40632
40571	40592	40619	40634*
40572	40593	40620	40635*
40574	40595	40621	40637
40575	40596	40622	40638
40577	40597	40623	40640
40578	40602	40624	40641
40579	40603	40625	40642
40580	40604	40626	40643
40581	40609	40627	40645

40646	40664	40682	40691
40647	40665	40683	40692
40648	40668	40684	40694
40650	40669	40685	40695
40651	40670	40686	40696
40657	40671	40687	40697
40659	40672	40689	40698
40661	40678	40690	40700
40663	40681		

Total 90

4-4-0 (3-Cyl. Compd.) 4P

Introduced 1924. Post-grouping development of Johnson Midland compound with modified dimensions and reduced boiler mountings.
Weight: Loco. 61 tons 14 cwt.
Pressure: 200 lb. Su.
Cyls.: $\begin{cases} \text{L.P. (2) } 21" × 26". \\ \text{H.P. (1) } 19" × 26". \end{cases}$
Driving Wheels: 6' 9".
T.E. (of L.P. cyls. at 80% boiler pressure): 22,650 lb.
P.V. (H.P. cyl. only).

40907	40936	41063	41168

Total 4

2-6-2T　　　　　　　　　　2

Introduced 1946. Ivatt L.M.S. taper boiler design.
Weight: 63 tons 5 cwt.
Pressure: 200 lb. Su.
Cyls.: $\begin{cases} \text{(O) } 16" × 24". \\ \text{(O) } 16½" × 24".* \end{cases}$
Driving Wheels: 5' 0".
T.E.: $\begin{cases} 17,410 \text{ lb.} \\ 18,510 \text{ lb.*} \end{cases}$
Walschaerts valve gear. P.V.

41200	41204	41208	41212
41201	41205	41209	41213
41202	41206	41210	41214
41203	41207	41211	41215

41216	41245	41274	41302*
41217	41246	41275	41303*
41218	41247	41276	41304*
41219	41248	41277	41305*
41220	41249	41278	41306*
41221	41250	41279	41307*
41222	41251	41280	41308*
41223	41252	41281	41309*
41224	41253	41282	41310*
41225	41254	41283	41311*
41226	41255	41284	41312*
41227	41256	41285	41313*
41228	41257	41286	41314*
41229	41258	41287	41315*
41230	41259	41288	41316*
41231	41260	41289	41317*
41232	41261	41290*	41318*
41233	41262	41291*	41319*
41234	41263	41292*	41320*
41235	41264	41293*	41321*
41236	41265	41294*	41322*
41237	41266	41295*	41323*
41238	41267	41296*	41324*
41239	41268	41297*	41325*
41240	41269	41298*	41326*
41241	41270	41299*	41327*
41242	41271	41300*	41328*
41243	41272	41301*	41329*
41244	41273		

Total 130

0-4-0T   0F

Introduced 1907. Deeley Midland design.
Weight: 32 tons 16 cwt.
Pressure: 160 lb.
Cyls.: (O) 15" × 22".
Driving Wheels: 3' 9½".
T.E.: 14,635 lb.
Walschaerts valve gear.

41528	41531	41533	41536
41529	41532	41535	41537

Total 8

0-6-0T   1F

Introduced 1878. Johnson Midland design.
*Rebuilt with Belpaire firebox.
Weight: 39 tons 11 cwt.
Pressure: { 150 lb.
          { 140 lb.*
Cyls.: 17" × 24".
Driving Wheels: 4' 7"
T.E.: { 16,080 lb.
      { 15,005 lb.*

41702*	41734*	41769*	41844*
41708*	41739*	41804*	41875*
41712*	41763*	41835	

Total 11

0-4-4T   2P

Introduced 1932. Stanier L.M.S. design. Push-and-pull fitted.
Weight: 58 tons 1 cwt.
Pressure: 160 lb.
Cyls.: 18" × 26".
Driving Wheels: 5' 7"
T.E.: 17,100 lb.

41900

Total 1

4-4-2T   3P

Introduced 1923. Midland and L.M.S. development of Whitelegg L.T. & S. " 79 " Class.
Weight: 71 tons 10 cwt.
Pressure: 170 lb.
Cyls.: (O) 19" × 26".
Driving Wheels: 6' 6".
T.E.: 17,390 lb.

41947

Total 1

0-6-2T   3F

Introduced 1903. Whitelegg L.T. & S.
" 69 " Class.
Weight: 64 tons 13 cwt.
Pressure: 170 lb.
Cyls.: 18" × 26".
Driving Wheels: 5' 3".
T.E.: 19,320 lb.

41981

Total 1

2-6-4T   4

*Introduced 1927. Fowler L.M.S.
  parallel boiler design.
†Introduced 1933. As earlier engines,
  but with side-window cab and doors.
‡Introduced 1934. Stanier taper-
  boiler 3-cylinder design for L.T. & S.
§Introduced 1935. Stanier taper-
  boiler 2-cylinder design.
¶Introduced 1945. Fairburn development of Stanier design with shorter
  wheelbase and detail alterations.

Weight:
$\begin{cases} 86 \text{ tons } 5 \text{ cwt.*†} \\ 92 \text{ tons } 5 \text{ cwt.‡} \\ 87 \text{ tons } 17 \text{ cwt.§} \\ 85 \text{ tons } 5 \text{ cwt.¶} \end{cases}$

Pressure (all types): 200 lb. Su.

Cyls.: $\begin{cases} (O) \ 19'' \times 26''.*† \\ (3) \ 16'' \times 26''.‡ \\ (O) \ 19\frac{5}{8}'' \times 26''.§¶ \end{cases}$

Driving Wheels (all types): 5' 9".

T.E.: $\begin{cases} 23,125 \text{ lb.*†} \\ 24,600 \text{ lb.‡} \\ 24,670 \text{ lb.§¶} \end{cases}$

Walschaerts valve gear. P.V.

¶FAIRBURN LOCOS.

42050	42062	42074	42086
42051	42063	42075	42087
42052	42064	42076	42088
42053	42065	42077	42089
42054	42066	42078	42090
42055	42067	42079	42091
42056	42068	42080	42092
42057	42069	42081	42093
42058	42070	42082	42094
42059	42071	42083	42095
42060	42072	42084	42096
42061	42073	42085	42097

42098	42145	42192	42239
42099	42146	42193	42240
42100	42147	42194	42241
42101	42148	42195	42242
42102	42149	42196	42243
42103	42150	42197	42244
42104	42151	42198	42245
42105	42152	42199	42246
42106	42153	42200	42247
42107	42154	42201	42248
42108	42155	42202	42249
42109	42156	42203	42250
42110	42157	42204	42251
42111	42158	42205	42252
42112	42159	42206	42253
42113	42160	42207	42254
42114	42161	42208	42255
42115	42162	42209	42256
42116	42163	42210	42257
42117	42164	42211	42258
42118	42165	42212	42259
42119	42166	42213	42260
42120	42167	42214	42261
42121	42168	42215	42262
42122	42169	42216	42263
42123	42170	42217	42264
42124	42171	42218	42265
42125	42172	42219	42266
42126	42173	42220	42267
42127	42174	42221	42268
42128	42175	42222	42269
42129	42176	42223	42270
42130	42177	42224	42271
42131	42178	42225	42272
42132	42179	42226	42273
42133	42180	42227	42274
42134	42181	42228	42275
42135	42182	42229	42276
42136	42183	42230	42277
42137	42184	42231	42278
42138	42185	42232	42279
42139	42186	42233	42280
42140	42187	42234	42281
42141	42188	42235	42282
42142	42189	42236	42283
42143	42190	42237	42284
42144	42191	42238	42285

42286	42290	42294	42297
42287	42291	42295	42298
42288	42292	42296	42299
42289	42293		

*FOWLER LOCOS.

42300	42325	42350	42373
42301	42327	42351	42374
42302	42328	42352	42375
42303	42329	42353	42376
42304	42330	42355	42377
42305	42331	42356	42378
42306	42332	42357	42379
42307	42333	42358	42380
42309	42334	42359	42381
42310	42335	42360	42382
42311	42336	42361	42383
42313	42337	42362	42384
42314	42338	42363	42385
42315	42339	42364	42386
42316	42340	42365	42387
42317	42342	42366	42388
42318	42343	42367	42389
42319	42344	42368	42390
42320	42346	42369	42391
42322	42347	42370	42392
42323	42348	42371	42393
42324	42349	42372	42394

†FOWLER LOCOS. WITH SIDE-WINDOW CAB

42395	42403	42410	42417
42396	42404	42411	42419
42397	42405	42412	42420
42398	42406	42413	42421
42399	42407	42414	42422
42400	42408	42415	42423
42401	42409	42416	42424
42402			

§STANIER 2-CYL. LOCOS.

42425	42428	42431	42434
42426	42429	42432	42435
42427	42430	42433	42436

42437	42452	42466	42480
42438	42453	42467	42481
42439	42454	42468	42482
42440	42455	42469	42483
42441	42456	42470	42484
42442	42457	42471	42485
42443	42458	42472	42486
42444	42459	42473	42487
42445	42460	42474	42488
42446	42461	42475	42489
42447	42462	42476	42491
42448	42463	42477	42492
42449	42464	42478	42493
42451	42465	42479	42494

‡STANIER 3-CYL. LOCOS.

42500	42510	42519	42528
42501	42511	42520	42529
42502	42512	42521	42530
42503	42513	42522	42531
42504	42514	42523	42532
42505	42515	42524	42533
42506	42516	42525	42534
42507	42517	42526	42535
42508	42518	42527	42536
42509			

§STANIER 2-CYL. LOCOS.

42537	42555	42573	42591
42538	42556	42574	42592
42539	42557	42575	42593
42540	42558	42576	42594
42541	42559	42577	42595
42542	42560	42578	42596
42543	42561	42579	42597
42544	42562	42580	42598
42545	42563	42581	42599
42546	42564	42582	42600
42547	42565	42583	42601
42548	42566	42584	42602
42549	42567	42585	42603
42550	42568	42586	42604
42551	42569	42587	42605
42552	42570	42588	42606
42553	42571	42589	42607
42554	42572	42590	42608

42609	42625	42641	42657
42610	42626	42642	42658
42611	42627	42643	42659
42612	42628	42644	42660
42613	42629	42645	42661
42614	42630	42646	42662
42615	42631	42647	42663
42616	42632	42648	42664
42617	42633	42649	42665
42618	42634	42650	42666
42619	42635	42651	42667
42620	42636	42652	42668
42621	42637	42653	42669
42622	42638	42654	42670
42623	42639	42655	42671
42624	42640	42656	42672

¶FAIRBURN LOCOS.

42673	42680	42687	42694
42674	42681	42688	42695
42675	42682	42689	42696
42676	42683	42690	42697
42677	42684	42691	42698
42678	42685	42692	42699
42679	42686	42693	

Total 635

2-6-0 6P5F

Introduced 1926. Hughes L.M.S. design built under Fowler's direction. Walschaerts valve gear. P.V.

*Introduced 1953. Locos. rebuilt experimentally with Lentz R.C. poppet valves in 1931; rebuilt with Reidinger rotary poppet valve gear in 1953.

Weight: Loco. 66 tons 0 cwt.
Pressure: 180 lb. Su.
Cyls.: (O) 21″ × 26″.
Driving Wheels: 5′ 6″.
T.E.: 26,580 lb.

42700	42703	42706	42709
42701	42704	42707	42710
42702	42705	42708	42711

42712	42759	42806	42853
42713	42760	42807	42854
42714	42761	42808	42855
42715	42762	42809	42856
42716	42763	42810	42857
42717	42764	42811	42858
42718	42765	42812	42859
42719	42766	42813	42860
42720	42767	42814	42861
42721	42768	42815	42862
42722	42769	42816	42863
42723	42770	42817	42864
42724	42771	42818*	42865
42725	42772	42819	42866
42726	42773	42820	42867
42727	42774	42821	42868
42728	42775	42822*	42869
42729	42776	42823	42870
42730	42777	42824*	42871
42731	42778	42825*	42872
42732	42779	42826	42873
42733	42780	42827	42874
42734	42781	42828	42875
42735	42782	42829*	42876
42736	42783	42830	42877
42737	42784	42831	42878
42738	42785	42832	42879
42739	42786	42833	42880
42740	42787	42834	42881
42741	42788	42835	42882
42742	42789	42836	42883
42743	42790	42837	42884
42744	42791	42838	42885
42745	42792	42839	42886
42746	42793	42840	42887
42747	42794	42841	42888
42748	42795	42842	42889
42749	42796	42843	42890
42750	42797	42844	42891
42751	42798	42845	42892
42752	42799	42846	42893
42753	42800	42847	42894
42754	42801	42848	42895
42755	42802	42849	42896
42756	42803	42850	42897
42757	42804	42851	42898
42758	42805	42852	42899

42900	42912	42923	42934	43008	43047	43086	43124
42901	42913	42924	42935	43009	43048	43087	43125
42902	42914	42925	42936	43010	43049	43088	43126
42903	42915	42926	42937	43011	43050	43089	43127
42904	42916	42927	42938	43012	43051	43090	43128
42905	42917	42928	42939	43013	43052	43091	43129
42906	42918	42929	42940	43014	43053	43092	43130
42907	42919	42930	42941	43015	43054	43093	43131
42903	42920	42931	42942	43016	43055	43094	43132
42909	42921	42932	42943	43017	43056	43095	43133
42910	42922	42933	42944	43018	43057	43096	43134
42911				43019	43058	43097	43135
			Total 245	43020	43059	43098	43136
				43021	43060	43099	43137
				43022	43061	43100	43138
				43023	43062	43101	43139

2-6-0   6P5F

Introduced 1933. Stanier L.M.S. taper boiler design, some with safety valves mounted on the top feed.
Weight: Loco. 69 tons 2 cwt.
Pressure: 225 lb. Su.
Cyls.: (O) 18″ × 28″.
Driving Wheels: 5′ 6″.
T.E.: 26,290 lb.
Walschaerts valve gear. P.V.

42945	42955	42965	42975
42946	42956	42966	42976
42947	42957	42967	42977
42948	42958	42968	42978
42949	42959	42969	42979
42950	42960	42970	42980
42951	42961	42971	42981
42952	42962	42972	42982
42953	42963	42973	42983
42954	42964	42974	42984

Total 40

43024	43063	43102	43140
43025	43064	43103	43141
43026	43065	43104	43142
43027	43066	43105	43143
43028	43067	43106	43144
43029	43068	43107	43145
43030	43069	43108	43146
43031	43070	43109	43147
43032	43071	43110	43148
43033	43072	43111	43149
43034	43073	43112	43150
43035	43074	43113	43151
43036	43075	43114	43152
43037	43076	43115	43153
43038	43077	43116	43154
43039	43078	43117	43155
43040	43079	43118	43156
43041	43080	43119	43157
43042	43081	43120	43158
43043	43082	43121	43159
43044	43083	43122	43160
43045	43084	43123	43161
43046	43085		

Total 162

2-6-0   4

Introduced 1947. Ivatt L.M.S. taper boiler design with double chimney. Later engines introduced with single chimney with which earlier engines are being rebuilt.
Weight: Loco. 59 tons 2 cwt.
Pressure: 225 lb. Su.
Cyls.: (O) 17½″ × 26″.
Driving Wheels: 5′ 3″.
T.E.: 24,170 lb.
Walschaerts valve gear. P.V.

43000	43002	43004	43006
43001	43003	43005	43007

0-6-0 3F

Introduced 1885. Johnson Midland locos., rebuilt from 1916 by Fowler with Belpaire firebox.

*Introduced 1885. Johnson Midland locos., rebuilt from 1920 by Fowler with Belpaire firebox.

†Introduced 1896. Locos. built for S. & D.J. (taken into L.M.S. stock 1930).

Weight: Loco. 43 tons 17 cwt.

Pressure: 175 lb.

Cyls.: 18″ × 26″.

Driving Wheels: $\begin{cases} 5'\ 3'' \\ 5'\ 3''.† \\ 4'\ 11''.* \end{cases}$

T.E.: $\begin{cases} 19,890\ lb. \\ 19,890\ lb.† \\ 21,240\ lb.* \end{cases}$

43185*	43307	43459	43615
43187*	43309	43464	43618
43189*	43321	43468	43620
43194†	43325	43474	43621
43200	43326	43482	43624
43203	43330	43484	43634
43211†	43333	43496	43637
43213	43340	43499	43639
43214	43342	43507	43644
43216†	43359	43510	43645
43225	43361	43514	43650
43234	43368	43515	43652
43235	43371	43521	43657
43240	43374	43523	43658
43242	43386	43529	43668
43243	43389	43548	43669
43245	43395	43562	43673
43250	43399	43565	43679
43254	43400	43572	43680
43257	43405	43574	43681
43261	43410	43579	43682
43263	43411	43580	43687
43266	43427	43583	43705
43267	43428	43585	43709
43268	43435	43586	43714
43277	43436	43593	43715
43282	43444	43594	43721
43284	43446	43599	43729
43295	43449	43605	43734
43306	43453	43608	43735

43737	43754	43760	43763
43751	43756	43762	43766

Total 128

0-6-0 3F

Introduced 1906. Deeley Midland design. Rebuilt by Fowler with Belpaire firebox.

Weight: Loco. 46 tons 3 cwt.

Pressure: 175 lb.

Cyls.: 18½″ × 26″.

Driving Wheels: 5′ 3″.

T.E.: 21,010 lb.

43778	43800	43812	43825
43784	43808	43814	43826
43789	43809	43822	43832
43793			

Total 13

0-6-0 4F

Introduced 1911. Fowler superheated Midland design.

Weight: Loco. 48 tons 15 cwt.

Pressure: 175 lb. Su.

Cyls.: 20″ × 26″.

Driving Wheels: 5′ 3″

T.E.: 24,555 lb.

P.V.

43840	43859	43882	43905
43844	43861	43883	43906
43345	43863	43884	43908
43846	43865	43885	43911
43848	43868	43887	43913
43849	43869	43888	43914
43850	43870	43893	43915
43853	43871	43899	43917
43854	43872	43900	43918
43855	43876	43902	43920
43856	43880	43903	43921

43922	43949	43975	44003	44081	44135	44191	44244
43923	43950	43976	44004	44082	44137	44192	44245
43924	43951	43977	44007	44083	44138	44193	44246
43925	43952	43979	44008	44085	44139	44194	44247
43928	43953	43981	44009	44086	44141	44195	44248
43929	43954	43982	44010	44087	44143	44196	44249
43931	43955	43983	44011	44088	44146	44197	44250
43932	43957	43985	44012	44089	44147	44198	44251
43933	43958	43986	44013	44090	44148	44199	44252
43935	43960	43987	44015	44091	44149	44200	44253
43937	43962	43988	44016	44092	44150	44202	44254
43938	43963	43991	44020	44094	44151	44203	44255
43940	43964	43994	44022	44096	44152	44205	44256
43942	43967	43995	44023	44097	44153	44206	44257
43944	43968	43996	44025	44098	44154	44207	44258
43945	43969	43999	44026	44099	44155	44208	44259
43947	43971	44001		44100	44156	44209	44260
43948	43972	44002		44101	44157	44210	44261
				44102	44158	44211	44262
			Total 114	44104	44159	44212	44263
				44105	44160	44213	44264
				44106	44162	44214	44265
				44107	44164	44215	44266
				44109	44165	44216	44267
				44110	44166	44218	44268
				44111	44167	44219	44269
				44112	44168	44220	44270
				44113	44169	44221	44271
				44114	44170	44222	44272
				44115	44171	44223	44273
				44117	44172	44224	44274
				44118	44174	44226	44275
				44119	44176	44228	44276
				44121	44177	44229	44277
				44122	44178	44231	44278
				44123	44179	44232	44279

0-6-0   4F

Introduced 1924. Post-grouping development of Midland design with reduced boiler mountings.
*Introduced 1922. Locos. built for S. & D.J.R. to M.R. design (taken into L.M.S. stock 1930).
Weight: Loco. 48 tons 15 cwt.
Pressure: 175 lb. Su.
Cyls.: 20″ × 26″.
Driving Wheels: 5′ 3″.
T.E.: 24,555 lb.
P.V.

				44124	44180	44233	44280
				44125	44181	44234	44281
				44126	44182	44235	44282
				44127	44183	44236	44283
				44128	44184	44237	44284
				44129	44185	44238	44286
				44130	44186	44239	44287
44027	44041	44054	44067	44131	44187	44240	44288
44028	44042	44055	44068	44132	44188	44241	44289
44030	44043	44056	44069	44133	44189	44242	44290
44033	44044	44057	44070	44134	44190	44243	44292
44034	44045	44059	44071				
44035	44046	44060	44074				
44036	44047	44061	44075				
44037	44048	44062	44076				
44038	44049	44063	44078				
44039	44051	44065	44079				
44040	44053	44066	44080				

44294	44348	44407	44463	44526	44547	44568	44587
44295	44349	44408	44464	44527	44548	44569	44588
44296	44350	44409	44465	44528	44549	44570	44589
44297	44351	44411	44466	44529	44550	44571	44590
44299	44352	44413	44467	44530	44551	44572	44591
44300	44353	44414	44468	44531	44552	44573	44592
44301	44354	44416	44469	44532	44553	44574	44593
44302	44355	44417	44470	44533	44554	44575	44594
44303	44356	44418	44472	44534	44556	44576	44595
44304	44358	44419	44474	44535	44557*	44577	44596
44305	44359	44420	44475	44536	44558*	44578	44597
44307	44362	44421	44476	44537	44559*	44579	44598
44308	44363	44422	44477	44538	44560*	44580	44599
44309	44364	44424	44478	44539	44561*	44581	44601
44310	44367	44425	44479	44540	44562	44582	44602
44311	44368	44426	44481	44541	44564	44583	44603
44312	44370	44428	44482	44542	44565	44584	44604
44314	44371	44429	44484	44543	44566	44585	44605
44315	44373	44431	44485	44544	44567	44586	44606
44318	44374	44432	44486	44545			
44319	44375	44433	44487				
44320	44376	44434	44489				
44321	44377	44435	44490				
44322	44378	44436	44491				
44323	44379	44437	44492				
44324	44380	44439	44493				
44325	44381	44440	44494				
44327	44384	44441	44497				
44328	44386	44442	44499				
44329	44387	44443	44500				
44330	44388	44444	44501				
44331	44389	44445	44504				
44332	44390	44446	44505				
44333	44392	44447	44508				
44334	44393	44448	44509				
44335	44394	44449	44512				
44336	44395	44450	44514				
44337	44396	44451	44516				
44338	44397	44452	44517				
44339	44398	44454	44518				
44340	44399	44455	44519				
44341	44400	44456	44520				
44342	44401	44457	44521				
44344	44402	44458	44522				
44345	44403	44460	44523				
44346	44404	44461	44524				
44347	44405	44462	44525				

Total 497

4-6-0   5

Introduced 1934. Stanier L.M.S. taper boiler design.

Experimental locomotives:—
1. Introduced 1947. Stephenson link motion (outside), Timken roller bearings.
2. Introduced 1948. Caprotti valve gear.
3. Introduced 1948. Caprotti valve gear, Timken roller bearings.
4. Introduced 1948. Caprotti valve gear, Timken roller bearings, double chimney.
5. Introduced 1947. Timken roller bearings.
6. Introduced 1947. Timken roller bearings, double chimney.
7. Introduced 1949. Fitted with steel firebox.
8. Introduced 1950. Skefko roller bearings.
9. Introduced 1950. Timken roller bearings on driving coupled axle only.

10. Introduced 1950. Skefko roller bearings on driving coupled axle only.

11. Introduced 1951. Caprotti valve gear, Skefko roller bearings.

Weight: Loco.
- 72 tons 2 cwt.
- 75 tons 6 cwt. (1, 5, 6, 8, 9, 10).
- 74 tons 0 cwt. (2, 3, 4, 11).
- 72 tons 2 cwt. (7).

Pressure: 225 lb. Su.
Cyls.: (O) 18½" × 28".
Driving Wheels: 6' 0".
T.E.: 25,455 lb.
Walschaerts valve gear and P.V. except where otherwise shown.

44726[7]	44756[4]	44786	44816
44727[7]	44757[4]	44787	44817
44728	44758[5]	44788	44818
44729	44759[5]	44789	44819
44730	44760[5]	44790	44820
44731	44761[5]	44791	44821
44732	44762[5]	44792	44822
44733	44763[5]	44793	44823
44734	44764[5]	44794	44824
44735	44765[6]	44795	44825
44736	44766[6]	44796	44826
44737	44767[1]	44797	44827
44738[2]	44768	44798	44828
44739[2]	44769	44799	44829
44740[2]	44770	44800	44830
44741[2]	44771	44801	44831
44742[2]	44772	44802	44832
44743[2]	44773	44803	44833
44744[2]	44774	44804	44834
44745[2]	44775	44805	44835
44746[2]	44776	44806	44836
44747[2]	44777	44807	44837
44748[3]	44778	44808	44838
44749[3]	44779	44809	44839
44750[3]	44780	44810	44840
44751[3]	44781	44811	44841
44752[3]	44782	44812	44842
44753[3]	44783	44813	44843
44754[3]	44784	44814	44844
44755[1]		44815	44845

44658	44675[10]	44692[9]	44709
44659	44676[10]	44693[9]	44710
44660	44677[10]	44694[9]	44711
44661	44678[8]	44695[9]	44712
44662	44679[8]	44696[9]	44713
44663	44680[8]	44697[9]	44714
44664	44681[8]	44698	44715
44665	44682[8]	44699	44716
44666	44683[8]	44700	44717
44667	44684[8]	44701	44718[7]
44668[10]	44685[8]	44702	44719[7]
44669[10]	44686[11]	44703	44720[7]
44670[10]	44687[11]	44704	44721[7]
44671[10]	44688[9]	44705	44722[7]
44672[10]	44689[9]	44706	44723[7]
44673[10]	44690[9]	44707	44724[7]
44674[10]	44691[9]	44708	44725[7]

44846	44893	44940	44987	45034	45074	45114	45154*
44847	44894	44941	44988	45035	45075	45115	45155
44848	44895	44942	44989	45036	45076	45116	45156*
44849	44896	44943	44990	45037	45077	45117	45157*
44850	44897	44944	44991	45038	45078	45118	45158*
44851	44898	44945	44992	45039	45079	45119	45159
44852	44899	44946	44993	45040	45080	45120	45160
44853	44900	44947	44994	45041	45081	45121	45161
44854	44901	44948	44995	45042	45082	45122	45162
44855	44902	44949	44996	45043	45083	45123	45163
44856	44903	44950	44997	45044	45084	45124	45164
44857	44904	44951	44998	45045	45085	45125	45165
44858	44905	44952	44999	45046	45086	45126	45166
44859	44906	44953	45000	45047	45087	45127	45167
44860	44907	44954	45001	45048	45088	45128	45168
44861	44908	44955	45002	45049	45089	45129	45169
44862	44909	44956	45003	45050	45090	45130	45170
44863	44910	44957	45004	45051	45091	45131	45171
44864	44911	44958	45005	45052	45092	45132	45172
44865	44912	44959	45006	45053	45093	45133	45173
44866	44913	44960	45007	45054	45094	45134	45174
44867	44914	44961	45008	45055	45095	45135	45175
44868	44915	44962	45009	45056	45096	45136	45176
44869	44916	44963	45010	45057	45097	45137	45177
44870	44917	44964	45011	45058	45098	45138	45178
44871	44918	44965	45012	45059	45099	45139	45179
44872	44919	44966	45013	45060	45100	45140	45180
44873	44920	44967	45014	45061	45101	45141	45181
44874	44921	44968	45015	45062	45102	45142	45182
44875	44922	44969	45016	45063	45103	45143	45183
44876	44923	44970	45017	45064	45104	45144	45184
44877	44924	44971	45018	45065	45105	45145	45185
44878	44925	44972	45019	45066	45106	45146	45186
44879	44926	44973	45020	45067	45107	45147	45187
44880	44927	44974	45021	45068	45108	45148	45188
44881	44928	44975	45022	45069	45109	45149	45189
44882	44929	44976	45023	45070	45110	45150	45190
44883	44930	44977	45024	45071	45111	45151	45191
44884	44931	44978	45025	45072	45112	45152	45192
44885	44932	44979	45026	45073	45113	45153	45193
44886	44933	44980	45027				
44887	44934	44981	45028				
44888	44935	44982	45029				
44889	44936	44983	45030				
44890	44937	44984	45031				
44891	44938	44985	45032				
44892	44939	44986	45033				

* NAMES :

45154	Lanarkshire Yeomanry
45156	Ayrshire Yeomanry
45157	The Glasgow Highlander
45158	Glasgow Yeomanry

45194	45241	45288	45335	45382	45412	45442	45472
45195	45242	45289	45336	45383	45413	45443	45473
45196	45243	45290	45337	45384	45414	45444	45474
45197	45244	45291	45338	45385	45415	45445	45475
45198	45245	45292	45339	45386	45416	45446	45476
45199	45246	45293	45340	45387	45417	45447	45477
45200	45247	45294	45341	45388	45418	45448	45478
45201	45248	45295	45342	45389	45419	45449	45479
45202	45249	45296	45343	45390	45420	45450	45480
45203	45250	45297	45344	45391	45421	45451	45481
45204	45251	45298	45345	45392	45422	45452	45482
45205	45252	45299	45346	45393	45423	45453	45483
45206	45253	45300	45347	45394	45424	45454	45484
45207	45254	45301	45348	45395	45425	45455	45485
45208	45255	45302	45349	45396	45426	45456	45486
45209	45256	45303	45350	45397	45427	45457	45487
45210	45257	45304	45351	45398	45428	45458	45488
45211	45258	45305	45352	45399	45429	45459	45489
45212	45259	45306	45353	45400	45430	45460	45490
45213	45260	45307	45354	45401	45431	45461	45491
45214	45261	45308	45355	45402	45432	45462	45492
45215	45262	45309	45356	45403	45433	45463	45493
45216	45263	45310	45357	45404	45434	45464	45494
45217	45264	45311	45358	45405	45435	45465	45495
45218	45265	45312	45359	45406	45436	45466	45496
45219	45266	45313	45360	45407	45437	45467	45497
45220	45267	45314	45361	45408	45438	45468	45498
45221	45268	45315	45362	45409	45439	45469	45499
45222	45269	45316	45363	45410	45440	45470	
45223	45270	45317	45364	45411	45441	45471	
45224	45271	45318	45365				
45225	45272	45319	45366				
45226	45273	45320	45367				
45227	45274	45321	45368				
45228	45275	45322	45369				
45229	45276	45323	45370				
45230	45277	45324	45371				
45231	45278	45325	45372				
45232	45279	45326	45373				
45233	45280	45327	45374				
45234	45281	45328	45375				
45235	45282	45329	45376				
45236	45283	45330	45377				
45237	45284	45331	45378				
45238	45285	45332	45379				
45239	45286	45333	45380				
45240	45287	45334	45381				

Total 842

"Patriot" Class

4-6-0   6P5F & 7P

*6P5F. Introduced 1930. Fowler 3-cyl. rebuild of L.N.W. "Claughton" Class (introduced 1912), retaining original wheels and other details.

Remainder. Introduced 1933. New locos. to Fowler design (45502–41 were officially considered as rebuilds).

†7P. Introduced 1946. Ivatt rebuild of Fowler locos. with larger taper boiler, new cylinders and double chimney.

Weight: Loco. $\begin{cases} 80 \text{ tons } 15 \text{ cwt.} \\ 80 \text{ tons } 15 \text{ cwt.*} \\ 82 \text{ tons } 0 \text{ cwt.†} \end{cases}$

Pressure: $\begin{cases} 200 \text{ lb. Su.} \\ 200 \text{ lb. Su.*} \\ 250 \text{ lb. Su.†} \end{cases}$

Cyls : $\begin{cases} (3) \ 18'' \times 26''. \\ (3) \ 18'' \times 26''.* \\ (3) \ 17'' \times 26''.† \end{cases}$

Driving Wheels: 6' 9".

T.E.: $\begin{cases} 26,520 \text{ lb.} \\ 26,520 \text{ lb.*} \\ 29,570 \text{ lb.†} \end{cases}$

Walschaerts valve gear. P.V.

45500*	Patriot
45501*	St. Dunstan's
45502	Royal Naval Division
45503	The Royal Leicestershire Regiment
45504	Royal Signals
45505	The Royal Army Ordnance Corps
45506	The Royal Pioneer Corps
45507	Royal Tank Corps
45508	
45509	The Derbyshire Yeomanry
45510	
45511	Isle of Man
45512†	Bunsen
45513	
45514†	Holyhead
45515	Caernarvon
45516	The Bedfordshire and Hertfordshire Regiment
45517	
45518	Bradshaw
45519	Lady Godiva
45520	Llandudno
45521†	Rhyl
45522†	Prestatyn
45523†	Bangor
45524	Blackpool
45525†	Colwyn Bay
45526†	Morecambe and Heysham
45527†	Southport
45528†	R.E.M.E.
45529†	Stephenson

45530†	Sir Frank Ree
45531†	Sir Frederick Harrison
45532†	Illustrious
45533	Lord Rathmore
45534†	E. Tootal Broadhurst
45535†	Sir Herbert Walker K.C.B.
45536†	Private W. Wood, V.C.
45537	Private E. Sykes, V.C.
45538	Giggleswick
45539	E. C. Trench
45540†	Sir Robert Turnbull
45541	Duke of Sutherland
45542	
45543	Home Guard
45544	
45545†	Planet
45546	Fleetwood
45547	
45548	Lytham St. Annes
45549	
45550	
45551	

Total 52

" Jubilee " Class

4-6-0   6P5F & 7P

6P5F. Introduced 1934. Stanier L.M.S. taper boiler development of the " Patriot " class.

***7P.** Introduced 1942. Rebuilt with larger boiler and double chimney.

Weight: Loco. $\begin{cases} 79 \text{ tons } 11 \text{ cwt.} \\ 82 \text{ tons } 0 \text{ cwt.*} \end{cases}$

Pressure: $\begin{cases} 225 \text{ lb. Su.} \\ 250 \text{ lb. Su.*} \end{cases}$

Cyls.: (3) 17" × 26".

Driving Wheels: 6' 9".

T.E.: $\begin{cases} 26,610 \text{ lb.} \\ 29,570 \text{ lb.*} \end{cases}$

Walschaerts valve gear. P.V.

45552	Silver Jubilee
45553	Canada
45554	Ontario
45555	Quebec

45556	Nova Scotia		45603	Solomon Islands
45557	New Brunswick		45604	Ceylon
45558	Manitoba		45605	Cyprus
45559	British Columbia		45606	Falkland Islands
45560	Prince Edward Island		45607	Fiji
45561	Saskatchewan		45608	Gibraltar
45562	Alberta		45609	Gilbert and Ellice Islands
45563	Australia		45610	Ghana
45564	New South Wales		45611	Hong Kong
45565	Victoria		45612	Jamaica
45566	Queensland		45613	Kenya
45567	South Australia		45614	Leeward Islands
45568	Western Australia		45615	Malay States
45569	Tasmania		45616	Malta G.C.
45570	New Zealand		45617	Mauritius
45571	South Africa		45618	New Hebrides
45572	Eire		45619	Nigeria
45573	Newfoundland		45620	North Borneo
45574	India		45621	Northern Rhodesia
45575	Madras		45622	Nyasaland
45576	Bombay		45623	Palestine
45577	Bengal		45624	St. Helena
45578	United Provinces		45625	Sarawak
45579	Punjab		45626	Seychelles
45580	Burma		45627	Sierra Leone
45581	Bihar and Orissa		45628	Somaliland
45582	Central Provinces		45629	Straits Settlements
45583	Assam		45630	Swaziland
45584	North West Frontier		45631	Tanganyika
45585	Hyderabad		45632	Tonga
45586	Mysore		45633	Aden
45587	Baroda		45634	Trinidad
45588	Kashmir		45635	Tobago
45589	Gwalior		45636	Uganda
45590	Travancore		45638	Zanzibar
45591	Udaipur		45639	Raleigh
45592	Indore		45640	Frobisher
45593	Kolhapur		45641	Sandwich
45594	Bhopal		45642	Boscawen
45595	Southern Rhodesia		45643	Rodney
45596	Bahamas		45644	Howe
45597	Barbados		45645	**Collingwood**
45598	Basutoland		45646	Napier
45599	Bechuanaland		45647	Sturdee
45600	Bermuda		45648	Wemyss
45601	British Guiana		45649	Hawkins
45602	British Honduras		45650	Blake

45651	Shovell
45652	Hawke
45653	Barham
45654	Hood
45655	Keith
45656	Cochrane
45657	Tyrwhitt
45658	Keyes
45659	Drake
45660	Rooke
45661	Vernon
45662	Kempenfelt
45663	Jervis
45664	Nelson
45665	Lord Rutherford Nelson
45666	Cornwallis
45667	Jellicoe
45668	Madden
45669	Fisher
45670	Howard of Effingham
45671	Prince Rupert
45672	Anson
45673	Keppel
45674	Duncan
45675	Hardy
45676	Codrington
45677	Beatty
45678	De Robeck
45679	Armada
45680	Camperdown
45681	Aboukir
45682	Trafalgar
45683	Hogue
45684	Jutland
45685	Barfleur
45686	St. Vincent
45687	Neptune
45688	Polyphemus
45689	Ajax
45690	Leander
45691	Orion
45692	Cyclops
45693	Agamemnon
45694	Bellerophon
45695	Minotaur
45696	Arethusa

45697	Achilles
45698	Mars
45699	Galatea
45700	Amethyst
45701	Conqueror
45702	Colossus
45703	Thunderer
45704	Leviathan
45705	Seahorse
45706	Express
45707	Valiant
45708	Resolution
45709	Implacable
45710	Irresistible
45711	Courageous
45712	Victory
45713	Renown
45714	Revenge
45715	Invincible
45716	Swiftsure
45717	Dauntless
45718	Dreadnought
45719	Glorious
45720	Indomitable
45721	Impregnable
45722	Defence
45723	Fearless
45724	Warspite
45725	Repulse
45726	Vindictive
45727	Inflexible
45728	Defiance
45729	Furious
45730	Ocean
45731	Perseverance
45732	Sanspareil
45733	Novelty
45734	Meteor
45735*	Comet
45736*	Phoenix
45737	Atlas
45738	Samson
45739	Ulster
45740	Munster
45741	Leinster
45742	Connaught

Total 190

"Royal Scot" Class

4-6-0   7P

Introduced 1943. Stanier rebuild of Fowler L.M.S. locos. (introduced 1927) with taper boiler, new cylinders and double chimney.

*Introduced 1935. Stanier taper boiler rebuild with simple cylinders of experimental high pressure compound loco. No. 6399 Fury. (Introduced 1929.)

Weight: Loco. $\begin{cases} 83 \text{ tons.} \\ 84 \text{ tons 1 cwt.*} \end{cases}$

Pressure: 250 lb. Su.

Cyls.: (3) 18″ × 26″.

Driving Wheels: 6′ 9″.

T.E.: 33,150 lb.

Walschaerts valve gear. P.V.

46100	Royal Scot
46101	Royal Scots Grey
46102	Black Watch
46103	Royal Scots Fusilier
46104	Scottish Borderer
46105	Cameron Highlander
46106	Gordon Highlander
46107	Argyll and Sutherland Highlander
46108	Seaforth Highlander
46109	Royal Engineer
46110	Grenadier Guardsman
46111	Royal Fusilier
46112	Sherwood Forester
46113	Cameronian
46114	Coldstream Guardsman
46115	Scots Guardsman
46116	Irish Guardsman
46117	Welsh Guardsman
46118	Royal Welch Fusilier
46119	Lancashire Fusilier
46120	Royal Inniskilling Fusilier
46121	Highland Light Infantry, City of Glasgow Regiment
46122	Royal Ulster Rifleman
46123	Royal Irish Fusilier
46124	London Scottish
46125	3rd Carabinier
46126	Royal Army Service Corps
46127	Old Contemptibles
46128	The Lovat Scouts
46129	The Scottish Horse
46130	The West Yorkshire Regiment
46131	The Royal Warwickshire Regiment
46132	The King's Regiment Liverpool
46133	The Green Howards
46134	The Cheshire Regiment
46135	The East Lancashire Regiment
46136	The Border Regiment
46137	The Prince of Wales's Volunteers (South Lancashire)
46138	The London Irish Rifleman
46139	The Welch Regiment
46140	The King's Royal Rifle Corps
46141	The North Staffordshire Regiment
46142	The York & Lancaster Regiment
46143	The South Staffordshire Regiment
46144	Honourable Artillery Company
46145	The Duke of Wellington's Regt. (West Riding)
46146	The Rifle Brigade
46147	The Northamptonshire Regiment
46148	The Manchester Regiment
46149	The Middlesex Regiment
46150	The Life Guardsman
46151	The Royal Horse Guardsman
46152	The King's Dragoon Guardsman
46153	The Royal Dragoon
46154	The Hussar

4575 Class 2-6-2T No. 4593   *[G. Wheeler*

4500 Class 2-6-2T No. 4552 (with straight-sided tanks)   *[R. C. Riley*

Vale of Rheidol 2-6-2T No. 8 *Llywelyn*   *[P. J. Sharpe*

5100 Class 2-6-2T No. 5192   *[J. Davenport]*

6100 Class 2-6-2T No. 6150   *[J. C. Haydon*

8100 Class 2-6-2T No. 8107   *[A. Smith*

9000 Class 4-4-0 No. 9015   [A. E. Davies

"City" Class 4-4-0 No. 3440 *City of Truro*   [L. Elsey

Standard Class 2 2-6-0 No. 78044   [R. A. Panting

Standard Class 9F 2-10-0 No. 92220 *Evening Star*

[*R. C. Riley*

Standard Class 7P6F 4-6-2 No. 70019 *Lightning*

[*J. Hodge*

Standard Class 4 4-6-0 No. 75008

[*G. Wheeler*

Rebuilt Class WC 4-6-2 No. 34028 *Eddystone*   [G. Wheeler

Class WC 4-6-2 No. 34035 *Shaftesbury* (with modified front end)   [P. J. Sharpe

Class WC 4-6-2 No. 34011 *Tavistock*   [K. R. Pirt

Class MN 4-6-2 No. 35022 *Holland America Line*   [*G. Wheeler*

Class V 4-4-0 No. 30919 *Harrow* (fitted with multiple jet blastpipe and chimney)
[*J. B. Bucknall*

Class V 4-4-0 No. 30935 *Sevenoaks*   [*G. Wheeler*

Class LN 4-6-0 No. 30852 *Sir Walter Raleigh* [L. Elsey

Class N15 4-6-0 No. 30457 *Sir Bedivere* [G. Wheeler

Class N15 4-6-0 No. 30788 *Sir Urre of The Mount* (later Maunsell version) [L. Elsey

Class H15 4-6-0 No. 30491 (Urie locomotive with N15 boiler) [A. *Trickett*

Class H15 4-6-0 No. 30489 (Urie locomotive)

Class H15 4-6-0 No. 30521 (Maunsell locomotive with N15 boiler) [B. E. *Morrison*

Class H16 4-6-2T No. 30519   *[L. Elsey*

Class T9 4-4-0 No. 30120   *[L. Elsey*

Class T9 4-4-0 No. 30300 (with wide cab and splashers; fitted with 6-wheeled tender)
[J. H. Aston

Class L 4-4-0 No. 31768   *[D. Marriot*

Class W 2-6-4T No. 31915   *[B. E. Morrison*

Class H 0-4-4T No. 31263   *[P. H. Groom*

Class C2X 0-6-0 No. 32539   [*K. L. Cook*

Class C 0-6-0 No. 31480   [*K. L. Cook*

Class O1 0-6-0 No. 31258   [*A. Trickett*

Class K 2-6-0 No. 32348   [J. A. Young

Class Q1 0-6-0 No. 33008   [A. R. Carpenter

Class Q 0-6-0 No. 30542   [K. R. Pirt

Class O2 0-4-4T No. 30192

[G. Wheeler

Class O415 4-4-2T No. 30583

[R. K. Evans

Class M7 0-4-4T No. 30377

[C. P. Boocock

Class Z 0-8-0T No. 30953 [*D. Penny*

Class E6 0-6-2T No. 32418 [*R. C. Riley*

Class E4 0-6-2T No. 32506 [*P. H. Groom*

Class E2 0-6-0T No. 32104   [*A. Trickett*

Class A1X 0-6-0T No. 32678   [*J. H. Aston*

Class E1 0-6-0T No. 4 *Wroxall*   [*K. L. Cook*

Class B4 0-4-0T No. 30096   [*C. P. Boocock*

Class 0298 2-4-0WT No. 30586   [*C. P. Boocock*

Class 700 0-6-0 No. 30687   [*P. J. Sharpe*

46155	The Lancer
46156	The South Wales Borderer
46157	The Royal Artilleryman
46158	The Loyal Regiment
46159	The Royal Air Force
46160	Queen Victoria's Rifleman
46161	King's Own
46162	Queen's Westminster Rifleman
46163	Civil Service Rifleman
46164	The Artists' Rifleman
46165	The Ranger (12th London Regt.)
46166	London Rifle Brigade
46167	The Hertfordshire Regiment
46168	The Girl Guide
46169	The Boy Scout
46170*	British Legion

Total 71

"Princess" Class

4-6-2   8P

*Introduced 1933. Stanier L.M.S. taper boiler design.

Remainder. Introduced 1935. Development of original design with alterations to valve gear, boiler and other details.

Weight: Loco. 104 tons 10 cwt.

Pressure: 250 lb. Su.

Cyls.: (4) $16\frac{1}{4}'' \times 28''$.

Driving Wheels: 6′ 6″.

T.E.: 40,285 lb.

Walschaerts valve gear (inside valves operated by rocking shafts on No. 46205; remainder have four sets of valve gear). P.V.

46200*	The Princess Royal
46201*	Princess Elizabeth
46203	Princess Margaret Rose
46204	Princess Louise
46205	Princess Victoria

46206	Princess Marie Louise
46207	Princess Arthur of Connaught
46208	Princess Helena Victoria
46209	Princess Beatrice
46210	Lady Patricia
46211	Queen Maud
46212	Duchess of Kent

Total 12

"Coronation" Class

4-6-2   8P

Introduced 1937. Stanier L.M.S. enlargement of "Princess Royal" class. All except Nos. 46230-4/49-55 originally streamlined. (Streamlining removed from 1946.)

*Introduced 1947. Ivatt development with roller bearings and detail alterations.

Weight: Loco. $\begin{cases} 105 \text{ tons } 5 \text{ cwt.} \\ 106 \text{ tons } 8 \text{ cwt.*} \end{cases}$

Pressure: 250 lb. Su.

Cyls.: (4) $16\frac{1}{2}'' \times 28''$.

Driving Wheels: 6′ 9″.

T.E.: 40,000 lb.

Walschaerts valve gear and rocking shafts. P.V.

46220	Coronation
46221	Queen Elizabeth
46222	Queen Mary
46223	Princess Alice
46224	Princess Alexandra
46225	Duchess of Gloucester
46226	Duchess of Norfolk
46227	Duchess of Devonshire
46228	Duchess of Rutland
46229	Duchess of Hamilton
46230	Duchess of Buccleuch
46231	Duchess of Atholl
46232	Duchess of Montrose
46233	Duchess of Sutherland
46234	Duchess of Abercorn
46235	City of Birmingham
46236	City of Bradford
46237	City of Bristol

46238	City of Carlisle		
46239	City of Chester		
46240	City of Coventry		
46241	City of Edinburgh		
46242	City of Glasgow		
46243	City of Lancaster		
46244	King George VI		
46245	City of London		
46246	City of Manchester		
46247	City of Liverpool		
46248	City of Leeds		
46249	City of Sheffield		
46250	City of Lichfield		
46251	City of Nottingham		
46252	City of Leicester		
46253	City of St. Albans		
46254	City of Stoke-on-Trent		
46255*	City of Hereford		
46256*	Sir William A. Stanier, F.R.S.		
46257*	City of Salford		

Total 38

46440	46462	46484*	46506*
46441	46463	46485*	46507*
46442	46464	46486*	46508*
46443	46465*	46487*	46509*
46444	46466*	46488*	46510*
46445	46467*	46489*	46511*
46446	46468*	46490*	46512*
46447	46469*	46491*	46513*
46448	46470*	46492*	46514*
46449	46471*	46493*	46515*
46450	46472*	46494*	46516*
46451	46473*	46495*	46517*
46452	46474*	46496*	46518*
46453	46475*	46497*	46519*
46454	46476*	46498*	46520*
46455	46477*	46499*	46521*
46456	46478*	46500*	46522*
46457	46479*	46501*	46523*
46458	46480*	46502*	46524*
46459	46481*	46503*	46525*
46460	46482*	46504*	46526*
46461	46483*	46505*	46527*

Total 128

2-6-0   2

Introduced 1946. Ivatt L.M.S. taper boiler design.

Weight: Loco. 47 tons 2 cwt.

Pressure: 200 lb. Su. .

Cyls.: $\begin{cases} \text{(O) } 16'' \times 24''. \\ \text{(O) } 16\frac{1}{2}'' \times 24''.* \end{cases}$

Driving Wheels: 5' 0".

T.E.: $\begin{cases} 17{,}410 \text{ lb.} \\ 18{,}510 \text{ lb.}* \end{cases}$

Walschaerts valve gear. P.V.

46400	46410	46420	46430
46401	46411	46421	46431
46402	46412	46422	46432
46403	46413	46423	46433
46404	46414	46424	46434
46405	46415	46425	46435
46406	46416	46426	46436
46407	46417	46427	46437
46408	46418	46428	46438
46409	46419	46429	46439

0-4-0ST   0F

Introduced 1932. Kitson design prepared to Stanier's requirements for L.M.S.

*Introduced 1953. Extended side tanks and coal space.

Weight: $\begin{cases} 33 \text{ tons 0 cwt.} \\ 34 \text{ tons 0 cwt.}* \end{cases}$

Pressure: 160 lb.

Cyls.: (O) $15\frac{1}{2}'' \times 20''$.

Driving Wheels: 3' 10".

T.E.: 14,205 lb.

47000	47003	47006*	47008*
47001	47004	47007*	47009*
47002	47005*		

Total 10

0-6-0T   2F

Introduced 1928. Fowler L.M.S. short-
wheelbase dock tanks.
Weight: 43 tons 12 cwt.
Pressure: 160 lb.
Cyls.: (O) 17″ × 22″.
Driving Wheels: 3′ 11″.
T.E.: 18,400 lb.
Walschaerts valve gear.

47160	47163	47165	47167
47161	47164	47166	47168

Total 8

0-4-0T   Sentinel

Geared Sentinel locos.

Introduced 1929. Single-speed locos.
for S. & D.J. (taken into L.M.S. stock
1930).

Weight: 27 tons 15 cwt.
Pressure: 275 lb. Su.
Cyls.: (4) 6¾″ × 9″.
Driving Wheels: 3′ 1¼″.
T.E.: 15,500 lb.
Poppet valves.

47190

Total 1

0-6-0T   3F

Introduced 1899. Johnson large Mid-
land design, rebuilt with Belpaire
firebox from 1919; fitted with
condensing apparatus for London
area.
*Introduced 1899. Non-condensing
locos.
Weight: 48 tons 15 cwt.
Pressure: 160 lb.
Cyls.: 18″ × 26″.
Driving Wheels: 4′ 7″.
T.E.: 20,835 lb.

47200	47212	47225	47241
47201*	47213	47228	47248*
47202	47217	47230*	47250*
47203	47218	47231*	47254*
47204	47221	47235*	47255*
47207	47223	47236*	47257*
47209	47224	47239*	47259*
47211			

Total 29

0-6-0T   3F

Introduced 1924. Post-grouping devel-
opment of Midland design with detail
alterations.
*Introduced 1929. Locos. built for
S. & D.J. (taken into L.M.S. stock
1930).
†Push-and-pull fitted.
Weight: 49 tons 10 cwt.
Pressure: 160 lb.
Cyls.: 18″ × 26″.
Driving Wheels: 4′ 7″
T.E.: 20,835 lb.

47261	47298	47341	47381
47262	47300	47342	47383
47263	47302	47343	47384
47264	47303	47344	47385
47265	47304	47345	47386
47266	47305	47347	47388
47267	47306	47348	47389
47268	47307	47349	47390
47269	47308	47350	47391
47270	47310*	47351	47392
47271	47311*	47353	47393
47272	47312*	47354	47395
47273	47313*	47355	47396
47275	47314*	47356	47397
47276	47316*	47357	47398
47277	47317	47358	47399
47278	47318	47359	47400
47279	47319	47360	47401
47280	47320	47361	47402
47281	47321	47362	47403
47282	47322	47365	47404
47283	47324	47366	47405
47284	47325	47367	47406
47285	47326	47368	47408
47286	47327	47369	47410
47287	47328	47371	47412
47288	47330	47372	47413
47289	47332	47373	47414
47290	47333	47375	47415
47292	47334	47376	47416
47293	47335	47377	47417
47294	47336	47378	47418
47295	47338	47379	47419
47297	47340	47380	47420

47421	47470	47521	47577	47631	47645	47658	47670
47422	47471	47522	47578	47632	47646	47659	47671
47423	47472	47523	47579	47633	47647	47660	47673
47424	47473	47524	47580	47634	47648	47661	47674
47425	47474	47526	47581	47635	47649	47662	47675
47426	47475	47529	47582	47637	47651	47664	47676
47427	47476	47530	47583	47638	47653	47665	47677
47428	47478†	47531	47584	47640	47654	47666	47678
47429	47479†	47532	47587	47641	47655†	47667	47679
47430	47480†	47533	47588	47642	47656	47668	47680
47431	47481†	47534	47589	47643	47657	47669	47681†
47432	47482	47535	47590	47644			
47433	47483	47536	47592S				
47434	47484	47537	47593			**Total 369**	
47435	47485	47539	47594				
47436	47487	47540	47596				
47437	47488	47542	47597				
47438	47490	47543	47598				
47439	47491	47544	47599				
47441	47492	47545	47601				
47442	47493	47546	47602				
47443	47494	47547	47603				
47444	47495	47548	47604				
47445	47496	47549	47605				
47446	47497	47550	47606				
47447	47499	47551	47607				
47448	47500	47552	47608				
47449	47501	47554	47609				
47450	47502	47555	47610				
47451	47503	47556	47611				
47452	47504	47557	47612				
47453	47505	47558	47614				
47454	47506	47559	47615				
47455	47507	47561	47616				
47457	47508	47562	47618				
47458	47509	47564	47619				

2-8-0   **8F**

Introduced 1935. Stanier L.M.S. taper
  boiler design.
Weight: Loco. 72 tons 2 cwt.
Pressure: 225 lb. Su.
Cyls.: (O) 18½″ × 28″.
Driving Wheels: 4′ 8½″.
T.E.: 32,440 lb.
Walschaerts valve gear. P.V.

47459	47510	47565	47620	48000	48011	48035	48057
47460	47511	47566	47621	48001	48012	48036	48060
47461	47512	47567	47622	48002	48016	48037	48061
47462	47513	47568	47623	48003	48017	48039	48062
47463	47514	47569	47624	48004	48018	48045	48063
47464	47515	47570	47625	48005	48020	48046	48064
47465	47516	47571	47626	48006	48024	48050	48065
47466	47517	47572	47627	48007	48026	48053	48067
47467	47518	47573	47628	48008	48027	48054	48069
47468	47519	47574	47629	48009	48029	48055	48070
47469	47520	47576	47630	48010	48033	48056	48073

48074	48124	48171	48218	48285	48335	48382	48429
48075	48125	48172	48219	48286	48336	48383	48430
48076	48126	48173	48220	48287	48337	48384	48431
48077	48127	48174	48221	48288	48338	48385	48432
48078	48128	48175	48222	48289	48339	48386	48433
48079	48129	48176	48223	48290	48340	48387	48434
48080	48130	48177	48224	48291	48341	48388	48435
48081	48131	48178	48225	48292	48342	48389	48436
48082	48132	48179	48246	48293	48343	48390	48437
48083	48133	48180	48247	48294	48344	48391	48438
48084	48134	48181	48248	48295	48345	48392	48439
48085	48135	48182	48249	48296	48346	48393	48440
48088	48136	48183	48250	48297	48347	48394	48441
48089	48137	48184	48251	48301	48348	48395	48442
48090	48138	48185	48252	48302	48349	48396	48443
48092	48139	48186	48253	48303	48350	48397	48444
48093	48140	48187	48254	48304	48351	48398	48445
48094	48141	48188	48255	48305	48352	48399	48446
48095	48142	48189	48256	48306	48353	48400	48447
48096	48143	48190	48257	48307	48354	48401	48448
48097	48144	48191	48258	48308	48355	48402	48449
48098	48145	48192	48259	48309	48356	48403	48450
48099	48146	48193	48260	48310	48357	48404	48451
48100	48147	48194	48261	48311	48358	48405	48452
48101	48148	48195	48262	48312	48359	48406	48453
48102	48149	48196	48263	48313	48360	48407	48454
48103	48150	48197	48264	48314	48361	48408	48455
48104	48151	48198	48265	48315	48362	48409	48456
48105	48152	48199	48266	48316	48363	48410	48457
48106	48153	48200	48267	48317	48364	48411	48458
48107	48154	48201	48268	48318	48365	48412	48459
48108	48155	48202	48269	48319	48366	48413	48460
48109	48156	48203	48270	48320	48367	48414	48461
48110	48157	48204	48271	48321	48368	48415	48462
48111	48158	48205	48272	48322	48369	48416	48463
48112	48159	48206	48273	48323	48370	48417	48464
48113	48160	48207	48274	48324	48371	48418	48465
48114	48161	48208	48275	48325	48372	48419	48466
48115	48162	48209	48276	48326	48373	48420	48467
48116	48163	48210	48277	48327	48374	48421	48468
48117	48164	48211	48278	48328	48375	48422	48469
48118	48165	48212	48279	48329	48376	48423	48470
48119	48166	48213	48280	48330	48377	48424	48471
48120	48167	48214	48281	48331	48378	48425	48472
48121	48168	48215	48282	48332	48379	48426	48473
48122	48169	48216	48283	48333	48380	48427	48474
48123	48170	48217	48284	48334	48381	48428	48475

48476	48537	48624	48671	48718	48733	48748	48762
48477	48538	48625	48672	48719	48734	48749	48763
48478	48539	48626	48673	48720	48735	48750	48764
48479	48540	48627	48674	48721	48736	48751	48765
48490	48541	48628	48675	48722	48737	48752	48766
48491	48542	48629	48676	48723	48738	48753	48767
48492	48543	48630	48677	48724	48739	48754	48768
48493	48544	48631	48678	48725	48740	48755	48769
48494	48545	48632	48679	48726	48741	48756	48770
48495	48546	48633	48680	48727	48742	48757	48771
48500	48547	48634	48681	48728	48743	48758	48772
48501	48548	48635	48682	48729	48744	48759	48773
48502	48549	48636	48683	48730	48745	48760	48774
48503	48550	48637	48684	48731	48746	48761	48775
48504	48551	48638	48685	48732	48747		

Total 666

48505	48552	48639	48686
48506	48553	48640	48687
48507	48554	48641	48688
48508	48555	48642	48689
48509	48556	48643	48690
48510	48557	48644	48691
48511	48558	48645	48692
48512	48559	48646	48693
48513	48600	48647	48694
48514	48601	48648	48695
48515	48602	48649	48696
48516	48603	48650	48697
48517	48604	48651	48698
48518	48605	48652	48699

0-8-0   7F

Introduced 1936. L.N.W. G2a Class.
Bowen-Cooke G1 superheated design
of 1912, rebuilt with G2 boiler and
Belpaire firebox.
Weight: Loco. 62 tons 0 cwt.
Pressure: 175 lb. Su.
Cyls.: $20\frac{1}{2}'' \times 24''$.
Driving Wheels: 4' $5\frac{1}{2}''$.
T.E.: 28,045 lb.
Joy valve gear.   P.V.

48519	48606	48653	48700	48895	49034	49119	49191
48520	48607	48654	48701	48898	49037	49122	49196
48521	48608	48655	48702	48915	49045	49125	49199
48522	48609	48656	48703	48927	49049	49126	49209
48523	48610	48657	48704	48930	49061	49129	49210
48524	48611	48658	48705	48932	49070	49130	49216
48525	48612	48659	48706	48942	49077	49134	49224
48526	48613	48660	48707	48950	49078	49137	49229
48527	48614	48661	48708	48951	49079	49139	49240
48528	48615	48662	48709	48953	49081	49141	49243
48529	48616	48663	48710	48964	49082	49142	49246
48530	48617	48664	48711	49002	49087	49144	49262
48531	48618	48665	48712	49007	49093	49147	49267
48532	48619	48666	48713	49008	49094	49154	49275
48533	48620	48667	48714	49020	49099	49155	49277
48534	48621	48668	48715	49021	49104	49158	49281
48535	48622	48669	48716	49023	49106	49164	49287
48536	48623	48670	48717	49025	49114	49173	49288

49293	49335	49357	49381	49505	49618	49637	49668
49310	49342	49361	49382	49508	49627		
49313	49343	49373	49391				**Total 6**
49314	49344	49375	49392				
49323	49350	49377	49394				
49328	9352 :						

Total 94

0-8-0   7F

Introduced 1921. Development of L.N.W. G2 Class. Bowen-Cooke G1 superheated design of 1912 with higher pressure boiler. Many later rebuilt with Belpaire firebox.
Weight: Loco. 62 tons 0 cwt.
Pressure: 175 lb. Su.
Cyls.: 20½″ × 24″.
Driving Wheels. 4′ 5½″.
T.E.: 28,045 lb.
Joy valve gear.   P.V.

49399	49413	49430	49443
49401	49414	49431	49444
49402	49415	49432	49446
49403	49416	49433	49447
49404	49421	49434	49448
49405	49422	49437	49449
49406	49423	49438	49451
49407	49425	49439	49452
49408	49426	49440	49453
49411	49428	49441	49454
49412			

Total 41

0-8-0   7F

Introduced 1929. Fowler L.M.S. design, developed from L.N.W. G2.
Weight: Loco. 60 tons 15 cwt.
Pressure: 200 lb. Su.
Cyls.: 19½″ × 26″.
Driving Wheels: 4′ 8½″.
T.E.: 29,745 lb.
Walschaerts valve gear.   P.V

2-4-2T   2P

Introduced 1889. Aspinall L. & Y. Class 5 with 2 tons coal capacity.
*Introduced 1898. Locos. with longer tanks and 4 tons coal capacity. Rebuilt 1910 with Belpaire firebox and extended smokebox.
Weight: { 55 tons 19 cwt.
         { 59 tons 3 cwt.*
Pressure: 180 lb.
Cyls.: 18″ × 26″.
Driving Wheels: 5′ 8″.
T.E.: 18,955 lb.
Joy valve gear.

| 50721 | 50746 | 50850* |

Total 3

0-4-0ST   0F

Introduced 1891. Aspinall L. & Y. Class 21.
Weight: 21 tons 5 cwt.
Pressure: 160 lb.
Cyls.: (O) 13″ × 18″.
Driving Wheels: 3′ 0⅜″.
T.E.: 11,335 lb.

51204	51218	51232	51244
51206	51222	51237	51246
51207	51227	51241	51253
51217	51229		

Total 14

0-6-0ST   2F

Introduced 1891. Aspinall rebuild of
L. & Y. Barton Wright Class 23 0-6-0.
Originally introduced 1877.
Weight: 43 tons 17 cwt.
Pressure: 140 lb.
Cyls.: 17½″ × 26″.
Driving Wheels: 4′ 6″.
T.E.: 17,545 lb.

See also Service locomotives.

51336	51413	51444S	51496
51371	51419	51446S	51498
51408	51429S	51486	51524
51412S	51441		

Total 18

52089	52218S	52311	52415
52093S	52225S	52312*S	52429
52119	52230	52319	52438*
52121	52240	52322	52441S
52129	52244	52341	52445*
52133	52248	52345S	52456
52154*	52252	52351	52459S
52161*	52260	52355	52461
52171	52270	52378	52464S
52179	52271	52393	52466
52182	52275	52400*	52515
52201*	52290	52411	52523
52207	52305	52413*	52526

Total 52

0-6-0T   1F

Introduced 1897. Aspinall L. & Y.
Class 24 dock tanks.
Weight: 50 tons 0 cwt.
Pressure: 140 lb.
Cyls.: (O) 17″ × 24″.
Driving Wheels: 4′ 0″.
T.E.: 15,285 lb.
Allan straight link valve gear.

51537

Total 1

2-8-0   7F

Introduced 1914. Fowler design for
S. & D.J.
(All taken into L.M.S. stock, 1930.)
Weight: Loco. 64 tons 15 cwt.
Pressure: 190 lb. Su.
Cyls.: (O) 21″ × 28″.
Driving Wheels: 4′ 8½″.
T.E.: 35,295 lb.
Walschaerts valve gear. P.V.

53801	53805	53807	53809
53803	53806	53808	53810
53804			

Total 9

0-6-0   3F

Introduced 1889. Aspinall L. & Y. Class
27. Nos. 52515–26 built superheated
with roundtop firebox and extended
smokebox, later rebuilt with satu-
rated boiler and short smokebox.
*Introduced 1911. Rebuilt with Belpaire
firebox and extended smokebox.
Weight: Loco. 42 tons 3 cwt.
Pressure: 180 lb.
Cyls.: 18″ × 26″.
Driving Wheels: 5′ 1″.
T.E.: 21,130 lb.
Joy valve gear.

4-4-0   3P

Introduced 1916. Pickersgill Caledonian
" 113 " and " 928 " classes.
Weight: Loco. 61 tons 5 cwt.
Pressure: 180 lb. Su.
Cyls.: 20″ × 26″.
Driving Wheels: 6′ 6″.
T.E.: 20,400 lb.
P.V.

54463	54465	54466	54475
54464			

Total 5

4-4-0 3P

Introduced 1920. Pickersgill Caledonian
" 72 " class.
Weight: Loco. 61 tons 5 cwt.
Pressure: 180 lb. Su.
Cyls.: 20½″ × 26″.
Driving Wheels: 6′ 6″.
T.E.: 21,435 lb.
P.V.

54478	54486	54492	54501
54480	54487	54493	54502
54482	54488	54494	54505
54483	54489	54495	54506
54485	54491	54500	54507

Total 20

0-4-4T 2P

*Introduced 1895. McIntosh Cale-
donian " 19 " class, with railed coal
bunker.
†Introduced 1897. McIntosh " 92 "
class, developed from " 29 " class
with larger tanks and highsided
coal bunker (both classes originally
fitted for condensing on Glasgow
Central Low Level lines).
Weight: $\begin{cases} 53 \text{ tons } 16 \text{ cwt.}* \\ 53 \text{ tons } 19 \text{ cwt.}† \end{cases}$
Pressure: 180 lb.
Cyls.: 18″ × 26″.
Driving Wheels: 5′ 9″.
T.E.: 18,680 lb.

55124* 55126†

Total 2

0-4-4T 2P

Introduced 1900. McIntosh Caledonian
" 439 " or " Standard Passenger "
class.
*Introduced 1915. Pickersgill locos.
with detail alterations.
Weight: $\begin{cases} 53 \text{ tons } 19 \text{ cwt.} \\ 57 \text{ tons } 12 \text{ cwt.}* \end{cases}$
Pressure: 180 lb.
Cyls.: 18″ × 26″.
Driving Wheels: 5′ 9″.
T.E.: 18,680 lb.

55165	55202	55216	55227*
55167	55203	55217	55228*
55169	55204	55219	55229*
55173	55206	55220	55230*
55185	55207	55221	55231*
55189	55208	55222	55232*
55195	55209	55223	55233*
55198	55210	55224	55234*
55199	55211	55225	55235*
55200	55214	55226	55236*
55201	55215		

Total 42

0-4-4T 2P

Introduced 1922. Pickersgill Caledonian
" 431 " class (developed from " 439 "
class) with cast-iron front buffer
beam for banking.
Weight: 57 tons 17 cwt.
Pressure: 180 lb.
Cyls.: 18¼″ × 26″.
Driving Wheels: 5′ 9″
T.E.: 19,200 lb.

55237   55238   55239   55240

Total 4

0-4-4T 2P

Introduced 1925. Post-Grouping devel-
opment of Caledonian " 439 " class.
Weight: 59 tons 12 cwt.
Pressure: 180 lb.
Cyls.: 18¼″ × 26″.
Driving Wheels: 5′ 9″.
T.E.: 19,200 lb.

55260	55263	55266	55268
55261	55264	55267	55269
55262	55265		

Total 10

0-4-0ST 0F

Introduced 1885. Drummond and
McIntosh Caledonian " Pugs."
Weight: 27 tons 7 cwt.
Pressure: 160 lb.
Cyls.: (O) 14″ × 20″.
Driving Wheels: 3′ 8″.
T.E.: 12,115 lb.

56027S	56031	56035	56039
56029	56032S		

Total 6

0-6-0T 2F

Introduced 1911. McIntosh Caledonian dock shunters, "498" class.
Weight: 47 tons 15 cwt.
Pressure: 160 lb.
Cyls.: (O) 17″ × 22″.
Driving Wheels: 4′ 0″.
T.E.: 18,015 lb.

56151	56167	56169	56172
56158	56168	56171	56173
56159			

Total 9

0-6-0T 3F

Introduced 1895. McIntosh Caledonian "29" and "782" classes (56232–9 originally condensing).
Weight: 47 tons 15 cwt.
Pressure: 160 lb.
Cyls.: 18″ × 26″.
Driving Wheels: 4′ 6″.
T.E.: 21,215 lb.

56232	56289	56324	56356
56239	56298	56325	56360
56240	56300	56326	56361
56242	56302	56335	56362
56246	56305	56336	56364
56256	56308	56337	56368
56260	56309	56338	56370
56278	56310	56341	56372
56279	56312	56343	56376
56286	56313	56347	

Total 39

0-6-0 2F

Introduced 1883. Drummond Caledonian "Standard Goods"; later additions by Lambie and McIntosh.

*Some rebuilt with L.M.S. boiler.

Weight: Loco. $\begin{cases} 41 \text{ tons } 6 \text{ cwt.} \\ 42 \text{ tons } 4 \text{ cwt.}^* \end{cases}$

Pressure: 180 lb.
Cyls.: 18″ × 26″.
Driving Wheels: 5′ 0″
T.E.: 21,480 lb.

57232	57269	57331	57383
57233	57270	57335	57384
57236	57271	57336	57385
57237	57274	57338	57386
57238	57275	57340	57389
57239	57278	57341	57392
57240	57284	57345	57398
57242	57285	57347	57404
57244	57287	57348	57411
57245	57288	57349	57416
57246	57291	57350	57417
57249	57292	57353	57418
57250	57295	57355	57426
57251	57296	57356	57429
57252	57299	57357	57431
57253	57300	57359	57432
57254	57302	57360	57434
57256	57303	57362	57436
57257	57309	57363	57441
57258	57311	57364	57445
57259	57314	57365	57446
57261	57317	57366	57447
57262	57319	57367	57451
57263	57321	57369	57461
57264	57324	57370	57463
57265	57325	57373	57470
57266	57326	57375	57472
57267	57328	57377	57473
57268	57329	57378	

Total 115

0-6-0　　　　　　　　　　3F

Introduced 1899. McIntosh Caledonian
"812" (Nos. 57550–57623) and
"652" (remainder) classes.
Weight: Loco. 45 tons 14 cwt.
Pressure: 180 lb.
Cyls.: $18\frac{1}{4}'' \times 26''$.
Driving Wheels: 5' 0".
T.E.: 22,690 lb.

57550	57577	57602	57623
57555	57579	57603	57625
57557	57580	57604	57626
57558	57581	57607	57627
57559	57583	57608	57630
57560	57585	57609	57631
57562	57586	57611	57632
57563	57587	57612	57633
57564	57590	57613	57634
57565	57591	57614	57635
57566	57592	57615	57637
57568	57593	57617	57640
57569	57594	57618	57642
57570	57596	57619	57643
57571	57597	57620	57644
57572	57600	57621	57645
57576	57601	57622	

Total 67

0-6-0　　　　　　　　　　3F

Introduced 1918. Pickersgill Caledonian
"294" class (superheated) and
"670" classes.
Weight: Loco. 50 tons 13 cwt.
Pressure: 180 lb. Su.
Cyls.: $18\frac{1}{2}'' \times 26''$.
Driving Wheels: 5' 0".
T.E.: 22,690 lb.
P.V.

57650	57661	57670	57682
57651	57663	57671	57684
57652	57665	57672	57686
57653	57666	57673	57688
57654	57667	57674	57689
57655	57668	57679	57690
57658	57669	57681	57691
57659			

Total 29

0-4-4T　　　　　　　　　　1P

Introduced 1895. Final Johnson
0-4-4T design, with higher-pitched
boiler and larger tanks, later rebuilt
with Belpaire firebox.
Push-and-pull fitted.
Weight: 53 tons 4 cwt.
Pressure: 150 lb.
Cyls.: 17" × 24".
Driving Wheels: 5' 4".
T.E.: 16,255 lb.

58086

Total 1

0-6-0　　　　　　　　　　2F

†Introduced 1917. Johnson Midland
4' 11" design of 1875 rebuilt with
Belpaire firebox.
§Introduced 1917. Johnson Midland
5' 3" design rebuilt with Belpaire
firebox.
Weight: Loco. Various—
37 tons 12 cwt. to 40 tons 3 cwt.
Pressure: 160 lb.
Cyls.: 18" × 26".
Driving Wheels: $\begin{cases} 4' \ 11''.† \\ 5' \ 3''.§ \end{cases}$
T.E.: $\begin{cases} 19,420 \ lb.† \\ 18,185 \ lb.§ \end{cases}$

58115†	58148†	58181†	58228§
58120†	58153†	58182†	58260§
58122†	58160†	58185†	58271§
58123†	58163†	58186†	58283§
58124†	58165†	58197§	58287§
58128†	58166†	58209§	58291§
58131†	58169†	58214§	58293§
58135†	58170†	58215§	58295§
58137†	58174†	58218§	58298§
58138†	58175†	58220§	58305§
58143†	58177†	58221§	

Total 43

0-6-0T   2F

Introduced 1879. Park North London
  design.
Weight: 45 tons 10 cwt.
Pressure: 160 lb.
Cyls.: (O) 17″ × 24″.
Driving Wheels: 4′ 4″.
T.E.: 18,140 lb.

58850   Total 1

PRESERVED LOCOS IN WORKING ORDER

4-4-0 (3-Cyl. Compd.) 4P

Introduced 1902. Johnson Midland
  design, rebuilt by Deeley in 1914.
  Withdrawn 1951 for preservation.
  Restored to 1914 condition and re-
  turned to service for special use 1959.
Weight: Loco. 61 tons 14 cwt.
Pressure: 200 lb.
Cyls.: { L.P. (2) 21″ × 26″.
       { H.P. (1) 19″ × 26″.
Driving Wheels: 7′ 0″.
T.E. (of L.P. cyls. at 80% boiler
  pressure): 21,840 lb.

1000

4-2-2

Introduced 1886. Neilson & Co. design
  for the Caledonian Railway incorpo-
  rating Drummond details. With-
  drawn as L.M.S. No. 14010 in 1935.
  Restored to Caledonian livery and
  returned to service for special use
  1958.
Weight: Engine and Tender: 75 tons.
Pressure: 150 lb.
Cyls.: 18″ × 26″.
Driving Wheels: 7′ 0″.
T.E.: 12,785 lb.

123

4-6-0

Introduced 1894. Jones Highland goods
  design. Withdrawn 1934 as L.M.S.
  No. 17916 for preservation. Restored
  to original condition and returned to
  service for special use 1959.
Weight: Loco. 56 tons.
Pressure: 175 lb.
Cyls.: 20″ × 26″.
Driving Wheels: 5′ 3″.
T.E.: 24,555 lb.

103

SERVICE LOCOS.

Details of Diesel Service Locomotives
are shown in ABC of British Railways
Diesels and the Diesel section of the
Combined Volume of ABC of British
Railways Locomotives.

0-4-0   Diesel

E.D.1	E.D.4	E.D.6
E.D.2	E.D.5	E.D.7
E.D.3		

0-4-0 (3′0″ gauge) Diesel

E.D.10

0-4-0 (1′ 6″ gauge) Diesel

ZM 32

0-6-0ST   2F

For details see Nos. 51336-51524.

11304   11305   11324   11368

CHIEF MECHANICAL ENGINEERS

BRITISH RAILWAYS (L.M. Region)

H. G. Ivatt ... 1948–1951

L.M.S.

George Hughes	1923–1925	Sir William Stanier ...	1932–1944
Sir Henry Fowler	1925–1931	Charles E. Fairburn ...	1944–1945
E. H. J. Lemon		H. G. Ivatt	1945–1947
(Sir Ernest Lemon)	1931–1932		

LOCOMOTIVE SUPERINTENDENTS AND C.M.E.'S—L.M.S. CONSTITUENT COMPANIES

CALEDONIAN RAILWAY

Robert Sinclair		
(First loco. engineer)*	1847–1856
Benjamin Connor	1856–1876
George Brittain	1876–1882
Dugald Drummond ...	1882–1890
Hugh Smellie	1890
J. Lambie	1890–1895
J. F. McIntosh	1895–1914
William Pickersgill ...	1914–1923

FURNESS RAILWAY

R. Mason	1890–1897
W. F. Pettigrew	1897–1918
D. J. Rutherford	1918–1923

GLASGOW AND SOUTH WESTERN RAILWAY

Patrick Stirling	1853–1866
James Stirling	1866–1878
Hugh Smellie	1878–1890
James Manson	1890–1912
Peter Drummond ...	1912–1918
R. H. Whitelegg	1918–1923

HIGHLAND RAILWAY

William Stroudley		
(First loco. engineer) ...	1866–1869
David Jones	1869–1896
Peter Drummond	1896–1911
F. G. Smith...	1912–1915
C. Cumming	1915–1923

L. & Y.R.

Sir John Hawkshaw (Consultant),*	
Hurst and Jenkins successively to 1868	
W. Hurst	1868–1876
W. Barton Wright ...	1876–1886
John A. F. Aspinall ...	1886–1899
H. A. Hoy	1899–1904
George Hughes	1904–1921

The L. & Y. amalgamated with L.N.W.R. as from January 1st, 1922.

L.N.W.R.

Francis Trevithick and J. E. McConnell, first loco. engineers, 1846, with Alexander Allan largely responsible for design at Crewe.*

John Ramsbottom... ...	1857–1871
Francis William Webb ...	1871–1903
George Whale	1903–1909
Charles John	
Bowen-Cooke	1909–1920
Capt. Hewitt Pearson	
Montague Beames ...	1920–1921
George Hughes	1922

L.T. & S.R.

Thomas Whitelegg ...	1880–1910
Robert Harben Whitelegg	1910–1912

(L.T. & S.R. absorbed by M.R., control of locos. transferred to Derby as from August, 1912.)

* Exclusive of previous service with constituent company.

LOCOMOTIVE SUPERINTENDENTS AND C.M.E.'S (continued)

MARYPORT & CARLISLE

Hugh Smellie	...	...	1870–1878
J. Campbell	...		1878–
William Coulthard	...	*	–1904
J. B. Adamson	...	...	1904–1923

MIDLAND RAILWAY

Matthew Kirtley (First loco. engineer)	...	1844–1873
Samuel Waite Johnson	...	1873–1903
Richard Mountford Deeley		1903–1909
Henry Fowler	...	1909–1923

SOMERSET AND DORSET JOINT RAILWAY

Until leased by Mid. and L. & S. W. (as from 1st November, 1875) locomotives were bought from outside builders, principally George England of Hatcham Iron Works, S.E. After the above date, Derby and its various Loco. Supts. and C.M.E.'s have acted for S. & D.J. aided by a resident Loco. Supt. stationed at Highbridge Works.

NORTH STAFFORDSHIRE RAILWAY

L. Clare	...	...	1876–1882
L. Longbottom	...	...	1882–1902
J. H. Adams		...	1902–1915
J. A. Hookham	...	...	1915–1923

W. Angus was Loco. Supt. at Stoke prior to 1876. No earlier records can be traced.

WIRRAL

Eric G. Barker	...	...	1892–1902
T. B. Hunter	...	...	1903–1923

Barker of the Wirral Railway is noteworthy for originating the 4-4-4 tank type in this country (1896).

NORTH LONDON RAILWAY

(Worked by L. & N.W. by agreement dated December, 1908.)

William Adams	...	...	1853–1873
J. C. Park	...	...	1873–1893
Henry J. Pryce	...	...	1893–1908

* Date of actual entry into office not known.

HISTORIC LOCOMOTIVES PRESERVED IN STORE

Type	Originating Company	Pre-Grouping No.	L.M.S. No.	Name	Place of Preservation
4–2–2	M.R.	118	(673)	—	Derby
2–4–0	M.R.	158A	—	—	Derby
4–4–2T	L.T. & S.	80	(2148)	Thundersley	Derby
2–2–2	L.N.W.	(49)		Columbine	York Museum
2–2–2	L.N.W.	3020	—	Cornwall	Crewe
2–4–0	L.N.W.	790	(5031)	Hardwicke	Crewe
0–4–0ST	L.N.W.	1439	—	—	Crewe
†0–4–0T	L.N.W.	—	—	Pet	Crewe
2–4–2T	L. & Y.	1008	(10621)	—	Horwich
0–4–0	F.R.	3	—	Coppernob	Horwich
0–4–2	Liverpool & Manchester	—	—	Lion	Crewe
‡4–4–0	H.R.	(2)	(14398)	Ben Alder	Boat of Garten

The unbracketed numbers are the ones at present carried by the locos.
† 18 in. gauge works shunter.
‡ Present number 54398.

NUMERICAL LIST OF ENGINES

The code given in smaller bold type at the head of each class, e.g. " 4MT ", denotes its British Railways power classification.

The numbers of locomotives in service have been checked in E. & N.E.R. to August 6th, 1960, L.M.R. to July 16th, and Sc.R. to July 2nd.

4-6-2 8P6F Class A4

Introduced 1935. Gresley streamlined design with corridor tender (except those marked †). All fitted with double blastpipe and chimney.
*Inside cylinder reduced to 17".
Weight: Loco. 102 tons 19 cwt.
Tender { 64 tons 19 cwt.
{ 60 tons 7 cwt.†
Pressure: 250 lb. Su.
Cyls.: { (3) 18½" × 26".
{ (2) 18½" × 26" (1) 17" × 26".*
Driving Wheels: 6' 8"
T.E.: { 35,455 lb.
{ 33,616 lb.*
Walschaerts valve gear and derived motion. P.V.

60001† Sir Ronald Matthews
60002† Sir Murrough Wilson
60003† Andrew K. McCosh
60004 William Whitelaw
60005† Sir Charles Newton
60006† Sir Ralph Wedgwood
60007 Sir Nigel Gresley
60008† Dwight D. Eisenhower
60009 Union of South Africa
60010 Dominion of Canada
60011 Empire of India
60012* Commonwealth of
       Australia
60013 Dominion of New
       Zealand
60014 Silver Link
60015 Quicksilver
60016† Silver King
60017 Silver Fox
60018† Sparrow Hawk
60019† Bittern
60020*† Guillemot
60021 Wild Swan

60022 Mallard
60023† Golden Eagle
60024 Kingfisher
60025 Falcon
60026† Miles Beevor
60027 Merlin
60028 Walter K. Whigham
60029 Woodcock
60030 Golden Fleece
60031 Golden Plover
60032 Gannet
60033 Seagull
60034 Lord Faringdon

Total 34

4-6-2 7P6F Class A3

Introduced 1927. Development of Gresley G.N. 180 lb. Pacific (introduced 1922, L.N.E.R. A1, later A10) with 220 lb. pressure (prototype and others rebuilt from A10). Some have G.N.-type tender with coal rails†, remainder L.N.E.R. pattern. All fitted with double blastpipe and chimney.
Weight: Loco. 96 tons 5 cwt.
Tender { 56 tons 6 cwt.†
{ 57 tons 18 cwt.
Pressure: 220 lb. Su.
Cyls.: (3) 19" × 26".
Driving Wheels: 6' 8".
T.E.: 32,910 lb.
Walschaerts valve gear and derived motion. P.V.

60035 Windsor Lad
60036 Colombo
60037 Hyperion
60038 Firdaussi

60039	Sandwich
60040	Cameronian
60041	Salmon Trout
60042	Singapore
60043	Brown Jack
60044	Melton
60045	Lemberg
60046	Diamond Jubilee
60047	Donovan
60048	Doncaster
60049	Galtee More
60050	Persimmon
60051	Blink Bonny
60052	Prince Palatine
60053	Sansovino
60054	Prince of Wales
60055	Woolwinder
60056	Centenary
60057	Ormonde
60058	Blair Athol
60059	Tracery
60060	The Tetrarch
60061	Pretty Polly
60062	Minoru
60063	Isinglass
60064	Tagalie
60065	Knight of Thistle
60066	Merry Hampton
60067	Ladas
60068	Sir Visto
60069	Sceptre
60070	Gladiateur
60071	Tranquil
60072	Sunstar
60073	St. Gatien
60074	Harvester
60075	St. Frusquin
60076	Galopin
60077	The White Knight
60078	Night Hawk
60079	Bayardo
60080	Dick Turpin
60081	Shotover
60082	Neil Gow
60083	Sir Hugo
60084	Trigo
60085	Manna

60086	Gainsborough
60087	Blenheim
60088	Book Law
60089	Felstead
60090	Grand Parade
60091	Captain Cuttle
60092	Fairway
60093	Coronach
60094	Colorado
60095	Flamingo
60096	Papyrus
60097	Humorist
60098	Spion Kop
60099	Call Boy
60100	Spearmint
60101	Cicero
60102	Sir Frederick Banbury
60103	Flying Scotsman
60105	Victor Wild
60106	Flying Fox
60107	Royal Lancer
60108	Gay Crusader
60109	Hermit
60110	Robert the Devil
60111	Enterprise
60112	St. Simon

Total 77

4-6-2   8P6F   Class A1

A1/1* Introduced 1945. Thompson rebuild of A10.
A1 Peppercorn development of A1/1 for new construction.
A1† Fitted with roller bearings.
Weight: Loco. $\begin{cases} 101 \text{ tons.*} \\ 104 \text{ tons 2 cwt.} \end{cases}$
Tender 60 tons 7 cwt.
Pressure: 250 lb. Su.
Cyls.: (3) 19″ × 26″.
Driving Wheels: 6′ 8″.
T.E.: 37,400 lb.
Walschaerts valve gear.   P.V.

60113*	Great Northern
60114	W. P. Allen
60115	Meg Merrilies
60116	Hal o' the Wynd

60117	Bois Roussel
60118	Archibald Sturrock
60119	Patrick Stirling
60120	Kittiwake
60121	Silurian
60122	Curlew
60123	H. A. Ivatt
60124	Kenilworth
60125	Scottish Union
60126	Sir Vincent Raven
60127	Wilson Worsdell
60128	Bongrace
60129	Guy Mannering
60130	Kestrel
60131	Osprey
60132	Marmion
60133	Pommern
60134	Foxhunter
60135	Madge Wildfire
60136	Alcazar
60137	Redgauntlet
60138	Boswell
60139	Sea Eagle
60140	Balmoral
60141	Abbotsford
60142	Edward Fletcher
60143	Sir Walter Scott
60144	King's Courier
60145	Saint Mungo
60146	Peregrine
60147	North Eastern
60148	Aboyeur
60149	Amadis
60150	Willbrook
60151	Midlothian
60152	Holyrood
60153†	Flamboyant
60154†	Bon Accord
60155†	Borderer
60156†	Great Central
60157†	Great Eastern
60158	Aberdonian
60159	Bonnie Dundee
60160	Auld Reekie
60161	North British
60162	Saint Johnstoun

Total 50

4-6-2 $\frac{8P7F}{(A2/1:\ 7P6F)}$ Class A2

A2/2* Introduced 1943. Thompson rebuild of Gresley Class P2 2-8-2 (introduced 1934).
Weight: Loco. 101 tons 10 cwt.
Pressure: 225 lb. Su.
Cyls.: (3) 20″ × 26″.
Driving Wheels: 6′ 2″.
T.E.: 40,320 lb.

A2/1† Introduced 1944. Development of Class A2/2, incorporating Class V2 2-6-2 boiler.
Weight: Loco. 98 tons.
Pressure: 225 lb. Su.
Cyls.: (3) 19″ × 26″.
Driving Wheels: 6′ 2″.   T.E.: 36,385 lb.

A2/3‡ Introduced 1946. Development of Class A2/2 for new construction.
Weight: Loco. 101 tons 10 cwt.
Pressure: 250 lb. Su.
Cyls.: (3) 19″ × 26″.
Driving Wheels: 6′ 2″.
T.E.: 40,430 lb.

A2§ Introduced 1947. Peppercorn development of Class A2/2 with shorter wheelbase. (No. 60539 built with double blast pipe.)

A2** Rebuilt with double blast pipe and multiple valve regulator.
Weight: Loco. 101 tons.
Pressure: 250 lb. Su.
Cyls.: (3) 19″ × 26″.
Driving Wheels: 6′ 2″.
T.E.: 40,430 lb.
Tender weight (all parts): 60 tons 7 cwt.
Walschaerts valve gear. P.V.

60500‡	Edward Thompson
60502*	Earl Marischal
60504*	Mons Meg
60506*	Wolf of Badenoch
60507†	Highland Chieftain
60508†	Duke of Rothesay
60509†	Waverley
60510†	Robert the Bruce
60511‡	Airborne
60512‡	Steady Aim
60513‡	Dante
60514‡	Chamossaire

60515‡	Sun Stream	60802
60516‡	Hycilla	60803
60517‡	Ocean Swell	60804
60518‡	Tehran	60805
60519‡	Honeyway	60806
60520‡	Owen Tudor	60807
60521‡	Watling Street	60808
60522‡	Straight Deal	60809
60523‡	Sun Castle	
60524‡	Herringbone	
60525§	A. H. Peppercorn	60810
60526**	Sugar Palm	60811
60527§	Sun Chariot	60812
60528§	Tudor Minstrel	60813
60529**	Pearl Diver	60814
60530§	Sayajirao	60815
60531§	Bahram	60816
60532**	Blue Peter	60817
60533**	Happy Knight	60818
60534§	Irish Elegance	60819
60535§	Hornet's Beauty	60820
60536§	Trimbush	60821
60537§	Bachelor's Button	60822
60538**	Velocity	60823
60539§	Bronzino	60824

60809 The Snapper, The East Yorkshire Regiment, The Duke of York's Own

Total

Class A2	15	Class A2/2	3
Class A2/1	4	Class A2/3	15

2-6-2 7P6F Class V2

Introduced 1936. Gresley design.
*Fitted with double chimney.
Weight: Loco. 93 tons 2 cwt.
      Tender 52 tons.
Pressure: 220 lb. Su.
Cyls.: (3) 18½″ × 26″.
Driving Wheels: 6′ 2″.
T.E.: 33,730 lb.
Walschaerts valve gear and derived motion. P.V.

60800 Green Arrow
60801

60825	
60826	
60827	
60828	
60829	
60830	
60831	
60832	
60833	
60834	
60835	The Green Howard Alexandra, Princess of Wales's Own Yorkshire Regiment
60836	
60837	
60838	
60839	
60840	
60841	
60842	
60843	

106

60844		60934	60942	60949	60956
60845		60935	60943	60950	60957
60846		60936	60944	60951	60958
60847	St. Peter's School York	60937	60945	60952	60959
	A.D. 627	60938	60946	60953	60960
60848		60939	60947	60954	60961
60849		60940	60948	60955	60962
60850		60941			
60851		60963*			

60964 The Durham Light Infantry

60965	60970	60975	60980
60966	60971	60976	60981
60967	60972	60977	60982
60968	60973	60978	60983
60969	60974	60979	

Total 184

60852	
60853	
60854	
60855	
60856	
60857	
60858	
60859	
60860	Durham School
60861	
60862	
60863	
60864	

4-6-0   5MT   Class B1

Introduced 1942. Thompson design.
Weight: Loco. 71 tons 3 cwt.
        Tender 52 tons.
Pressure: 225 b. Su.
Cyls.: (O) 20″ × 26″.
Driving Wheels: 6′ 2″
T E.: 26,880 lb.
Walschaerts valve gear.   P.V.

60865	
60866	
60867	
60868	
60869	
60870	
60871	
60872	King's Own Yorkshire Light Infantry
60873	Coldstreamer

61000	Springbok
61001	Eland
61002	Impala
61003	Gazelle
61004	Oryx
61005	Bongo
61006	Blackbuck
61007	Klipspringer
61008	Kudu
61009	Hartebeeste
61010	Wildebeeste
61011	Waterbuck
61012	Puku
61013	Topi
61014	Oribi
61015	Duiker
61016	Inyala
61017	Bushbuck

60874	60889	60904	60919
60875	60890	60905	60920
60876	60891	60906	60921
60877	60892	60907	60922
60878	60893	60908	60923
60879	60894	60909	60924
60880	60895	60910	60925
60881	60896	60911	60926
60882	60897	60912	60927
60883	60898	60913	60928
60884	60899	60914	60929
60885	60900	60915	60930
60886	60901	60916	60931
60887	60902	60917	60932
60888	60903	60918	60933

61018	Gnu
61019	Nilghal
61020	Gemsbok
61021	Reitbok
61022	Sassaby
61023	Hirola
61024	Addax
61025	Pallah
61026	Ourebi
61027	Madoqua
61028	Umseke
61029	Chamois
61030	Nyala
61031	Reedbuck
61032	Stembok
61033	Dibatag
61034	Chiru
61035	Pronghorn
61036	Ralph Assheton
61037	Jairou
61038	Blacktail
61039	Steinbok
61040	Roedeer

61041	61066	61090	61114
61042	61067	61091	61115
61043	61068	61092	61116
61044	61069	61093	61117
61045	61070	61094	61118
61046	61071	61095	61119
61047	61072	61096	61120
61048	61073	61097	61121
61049	61074	61098	61122
61050	61075	61099	61123
61051	61076	61100	61124
61052	61077	61101	61125
61053	61078	61102	61126
61054	61079	61103	61127
61055	61080	61104	61128
61056	61081	61105	61129
61058	61082	61106	61130
61059	61083	61107	61131
61060	61084	61108	61132
61061	61085	61109	61133
61062	61086	61110	61134
61063	61087	61111	61135
61064	61088	61112	61136
61065	61089	61113	61137

61151	61164	61177
61152	61165	61178
61153	61166	61179
61154	61167	61180
61155	61168	61181
61156	61169	61182
61157	61170	61183
61158	61171	61184
61159	61172	61185
61160	61173	61186
61161	61174	61187
61162	61175	61188
61163	61176	

61138	
61139	
61140	
61141	
61142	
61143	
61144	
61145	
61146	
61147	
61148	
61149	
61150	
61189	Sir William Gray
61190	
61191	
61192	
61193	
61194	
61195	
61196	
61197	
61198	
61199	
61200	
61201	
61202	
61203	
61204	
61205	
61206	
61207	
61208	
61209	
61210	
61211	
61212	
61213	
61214	
61215	William Henton Carver
61216	
61217	
61218	
61219	
61220	
61221	Sir Alexander Erskine-Hill

61222	61320	61335	61350	61365
61223	61321	61336	61351	61366
61224	61322	61337	61352	61367
61225	61323	61338	61353	61368
61226	61324	61339	61354	61369
61227	61325	61340	61355	61370
61228	61326	61341	61356	61371
61229	61327	61342	61357	61372
61230	61328	61343	61358	61373
61231	61329	61344	61359	61374
61232	61330	61345	61360	61375
61233	61331	61346	61361	61376
61234	61332	61347	61362	61377
61235	61333	61348	61363	61378
61236	61334	61349	61364	

61237	Geoffrey H. Kitson
61238	Leslie Runciman
61239	
61240	Harry Hinchcliffe
61241	Viscount Ridley
61242	Alexander Reith Gray
61243	Sir Harold Mitchell
61244	Strang Steel
61245	Murray of Elibank
61246	Lord Balfour of Burleigh
61247	Lord Burghley
61248	Geoffrey Gibbs
61249	FitzHerbert Wright
61250	A. Harold Bibby
61251	Oliver Bury

61379 Mayflower

61380	61388	61396	61404
61381	61389	61397	61405
61382	61390	61398	61406
61383	61391	61399	61407
61384	61392	61400	61408
61385	61393	61401	61409
61386	61394	61402	
61387	61395	61403	

Total 409

61252	61269	61286	61303
61253	61270	61287	61304
61254	61271	61288	61305
61255	61272	61289	61306
61256	61273	61290	61307
61257	61274	61291	61308
61258	61275	61292	61309
61259	61276	61293	61310
61260	61277	61294	61311
61261	61278	61295	61312
61262	61279	61296	61313
61263	61280	61297	61314
61264	61281	61298	61315
61265	61282	61299	61316
61266	61283	61300	61317
61267	61284	61301	61318
61268	61285	61302	61319

4-6-0   5MT   Class B16

B16/1 Introduced 1920. Raven N.E. design with Stephenson valve gear.

B16/2* Introduced 1937. Gresley rebuild of B16/1 with Walschaerts valve gear and derived motion for inside cylinder.

B16/3† Introduced 1944. Thompson rebuild of B16/1 with individual sets of Walschaerts valve gear for each cylinder.

Weight: Loco. $\begin{cases} 77 \text{ tons } 14 \text{ cwt.} \\ 79 \text{ tons } 4 \text{ cwt.*} \\ 78 \text{ tons } 19 \text{ cwt.†} \end{cases}$

Tender 46 tons 12 cwt.

Pressure: 180 lb. Su.
Cyls.: (3) 18½″ × 26″.
Driving Wheels: 5′ 8″.
T.E.: 30,030 lb.   P.V.

61410	61425	61445	61461†
61411	61428	61446	61462
61412	61429	61447	61453†
61413	61431	61448†	61464†
61414	61432	61449†	61466
61415	61434†	61450	61467†
61416	61435*	61451	61468†
61417†	61436	61452	61469
61418†	61437*	61453†	61471
61419	61438*	61454†	61472†
61420†	61439†	61455*	61473
61421*	61440	61457*	61475*
61422	61443	61459	61476†
61423	61444†	61460	61478
61424			

Total: Class B16/1 33

Class B16/3 17 Class B16/2 7

4-6-0   4P3F   Class B12

B12/3 Introduced 1932. Gresley rebuild of Holden G.E. design of 1911 with large boiler, round-topped firebox and long-travel valves.

Weight: Loco. 69 tons 10 cwt.
         Tender 39 tons 6 cwt.
Pressure: 180 lb. Su.
Cyls.: 20″ × 28″.
Driving Wheels: 6′ 6″.
T.E.: 21,970 lb.
P.V.

61572

Total 1

4-6-0   5P4F   Class B17

B17/6 Introduced 1943. B17/4 fitted with 100A (B1-type) boiler.

Weight: Loco. 77 tons 5 cwt.
         Tender 52 tons.
Pressure: 225 lb. Su.
Cyls.: (3) 17½″ × 26″.
Driving Wheels: 6′3′.
T.E.: 28,555 lb.
Walschaerts valve gear and derived motion. P.V.

61668   Bradford City

Total 1

2-6-0   4MT   Class K2

K2/2 Introduced 1914. Gresley G.N. design.
K2/1* Introduced 1931. Rebuilt from small-boilered K1 (introduced 1912).
†K2/2 with side-window cab.

Weight: Loco. 64 tons 8 cwt.
         Tender 43 tons 2 cwt.
Pressure: 180 lb. Su.
Cyls.: (O) 20″ × 26″.
Driving Wheels: 5′ 8″.
T.E.: 23,400 lb.
Walschaerts valve gear. P.V.

61728*	61742	61756	61761
61730	61745	61760	61763
61740	61747		

61764†   Loch Arkaig
61766
61767
61769†
61771
61773
61784†
61788†   Loch Rannoch
61792†
61794†   Loch Oich

Total

Class K2/1   1   Class K2/2 19

2-6-0 5P6F Class K3

K3/2 Introduced 1924. Development of Gresley G.N. design, built to L.N.E.R. loading gauge.

K3/3* Introduced 1929. Differ in details only, such as springs, from K3/2.

‡K3/2 fitted with G.N. tender.

(K3/1 were G.N. locos. (introduced 1920), with G.N. cabs, and K3/4, K3/5 and K3/6 were variations of K3/2 differing in weight and details These locos. have now been modified to K3/2.)

Weight: Loco.   72 tons 12 cwt.

Tender $\begin{cases} 52 \text{ tons.} \\ 43 \text{ tons } 2 \text{ cwt.‡} \end{cases}$

Pressure: 180 lb. Su.

Cyls.: (3) 18½" × 26".

Driving Wheels: 5' 8"

T.E.: 30,030 lb.

Walschaerts valve gear and derived motion. P.V.

61800	61832	61862	61897
61801	61833	61864	61899
61803	61834	61865	61901
61804	61835	61866	61902
61805	61836	61867	61903
61807	61837	61868	61904
61808	61839	61869	61905
61809	61840	61870*	61906
61810	61841‡	61871*	61907
61811	61842	61872*	61908
61812‡	61843	61873*	61910
61813	61844	61874*	61912
61814	61845	61875*	61913
61816	61846	61877*	61914
61817	61847	61880*	61915
61818	61848	61883*	61916
61819	61849	61884*	61917
61820	61850	61886*	61918
61821	61851	61887*	61919
61822	61852	61888*	61920
61824	61853	61889*	61921
61825	61854‡	61890	61922
61826	61856‡	61891	61923
61827	61857‡	61892	61924
61828	61858‡	61893	61925
61829	61859‡	61894	61926
61830	61860	61895	61927
61831	61861	61896	61929

61930	61947	61963	61976
61932	61948	61964	61977
61933	61949	61965	61978
61934	61950	61966	61979
61935	61951	61967	61980
61936	61952	61968	61981
61938	61953	61969	61982
61939	61954	61970	61984
61940	61956	61971	61985
61941	61957	61972	61986
61942	61958	61973	61987
61943	61959	61974	61989
61944	61960	61975	61990
61945	61961		
61946	61962		

Total
Class K3/2 154   Class K3/3 14

Classes
2-6-0 5P6F K1 & K4

K4* Introduced 1937. Gresley locos. for West Highland line.

Weight: Loco. 68 tons 8 cwt.
Tender 44 tons 4 cwt.

Pressure: 200 lb. Su.

Cyls.: (3) 18½" × 26".

Driving Wheels: 5' 2".

T.E.: 36,600 lb.

Walschaerts valve gear and derived motion. P.V.

K1/1† Introduced 1945. Thompson 2-cyl. loco. Rebuilt from K4.

K1 Introduced 1949. Peppercorn development of Thompson K1/1 (No. 61997) for new construction, with increased length.

Weight: Loco. 66 tons 17 cwt.
Tender 44 tons 4 cwt.

Pressure: 225 lb. Su.

Cyls.: (O) 20" × 26".

Driving Wheels: 5' 2".

T.E.: 32,080 lb.

Walschaerts valve gear. P.V.

61993*	Loch Long		
61994*	The Great Marquess		
61995*	Cameron of Lochiel		
61996*	Lord of the Isles		
61997†	MacCailin Mor		
61998*	Macleod of Macleod		

62001	62019	62037	62054
62002	62020	62038	62055
62003	62021	62039	62056
62004	62022	62040	62057
62005	62023	62041	62058
62006	62024	62042	62059
62007	62025	62043	62060
62008	62026	62044	62061
62009	62027	62045	62062
62010	62028	62046	62063
62011	62029	62047	62064
62012	62030	62048	62065
62013	62031	62049	62066
62014	62032	62050	62067
62015	62033	62051	62068
62016	62034	62052	62069
62017	62035	62053	62070
62018	62036		

Total

Class K1 70 Class K4 5
Class K1/1 1

DO NOT TRESPASS ON THE RAILWAY

4-4-0   3P   Class D34

Introduced 1913. Reid N.B. " Glen " class.
Weight: Loco. 57 tons 4 cwt.
Tender 46 tons 13 cwt.
Pressure: 165 lb. Su.
Cyls.: 20″ × 26″.
Driving Wheels: 6′ 0″.
T.E.: 20,260 lb.
P.V.

62467	Glenfinnan
62474	Glen Croe
62479	Glen Sheil
62484	Glen Lyon
62488	Glen Aladale
62495	Glen Luss
62496	Glen Loy

Total 7

4-4-0   3P1F   Class D16

D16/3 Introduced 1938. Rebuild of D16/2 with round-topped firebox, but retaining original footplating and slide valves.
Weight: Loco. 55 tons 18 cwt.
Tender 39 tons 5 cwt.
Pressure: 180 lb. Su.
Cyls.: 19″ × 26″.
Driving Wheels: 7′ 0″.
T.E.: 17,095 lb.

62613

Total 1

4-4-0   3P2F   Class D11

D11/1* Introduced 1920. Robinson G.C. " Large Director "development of D10 (introduced 1913).
D11/2 Introduced 1924. Post-grouping locos. built to Scottish loading gauge. From 1938 the class has been rebuilt with long-travel valves.

Weight: Loco. 61 tons 3 cwt.
Tender 48 tons 6 cwt.

Pressure: 180 lb. Su.

Cyls.: 20″ × 26″.

Driving Wheels: 6′ 9″.

T.E.: 19,645 lb.

P.V.

62660*	Butler-Henderson
62661*	Gerard Powys Dewhurst
62662*	Prince of Wales
62664*	Princess Mary
62666*	Zeebrugge
62667*	Somme
62668*	Jutland
62669*	Ypres
62670*	Marne
62671	Bailie MacWheeble
62672	Baron of Bradwardine
62674	Flora MacIvor
62680	Lucy Ashton
62681	Captain Craigengelt
62682	Haystoun of Bucklaw
62685	Malcolm Graeme
62686	The Fiery Cross
62687	Lord James of Douglas
62688	Ellen Douglas
62689	Maid of Lorn
62690	The Lady of the Lake
62691	Laird of Balmawhapple
62693	Roderick Dhu

Total

Class D11/1 9 Class D11/2 14

4-4-0 4P Class D49

D49/1* Introduced 1927. Gresley design with piston valves. Walschaerts valve gear and derived motion.

D49/2† Introduced 1928. Development of D49/1 with Lentz Rotary Cam poppet valves.

D49/2‡ Introduced 1949. Fitted with Reidinger R.R. Rotary valve gear.

(D49/3 comprised locos. 62720-5 as built with Lentz Oscillating Cam poppet valves. From 1938 these locos. were converted to D49/1. 62751-75 have larger valves than the earlier D49/2, and were at first classified D49/4).
[1]Fitted with G.C. tender.
[2]Fitted with N.E. tender.
[3]The remainder have L.N.E.R. tenders.

Weight: Loco. { 66 tons.*†
{ 64 tons 10 cwt.‡
Tender { 48 tons 6 cwt.[1]
{ 44 tons 2 cwt.[3]
{ 52 tons.[2]

Pressure: 180 lb. Su.
Cyls.: (3) 17″ × 26″.
Driving Wheels: 6′ 8″.
T.E.: 21,555 lb.

62710*[1]	Lincolnshire
62711*[1]	Dumbartonshire
62712*[1]	Morayshire
62716*[1]	Kincardineshire
62717*[1]	Banffshire
62718*[1]	Kinross-shire
62723*[2]	Nottinghamshire
62727†[2]	The Quorn
62729*[1]	Rutlandshire
62733*[1]	Northumberland
62734*[2]	Cumberland
62739†[3]	The Badsworth
62744‡[3]	The Holderness
62747†[3]	The Percy
62759†[3]	The Craven
62762†[3]	The Fernie
62763‡[3]	The Fitzwilliam
62765†[3]	The Goathland

Total

Class D49/1 10 Class D49/2 8

0-8-0 6F Class Q6

Introduced 1913. Raven N.E. design.
*Some locos. are fitted with tender from withdrawn B15 locos.
Weight: Loco. 65 tons 18 cwt.
Tender { 44 tons 2 cwt.
{ 44 tons.*
Pressure: 180 lb. Su.

Cyls.: (O) 20″ × 26″.
Driving Wheels: 4′ 7½″.
T.E.: 28,800 lb.
P.V.

63340	63370	63401	63431
63341	63371	63402	63432
63342	63373	63403	63433
63343	63374	63404	63434
63344	63375	63405	63435
63345	63376	63406	63436
63346	63377	63407	63437
63347	63378	63408	63438
63348	63379	63409	63439
63349	63380	63410	63440
63350	63381	63411	63441
63351	63382	63412	63442
63352	63383	63413	63443
63353	63384	63414	63444
63354	63385	63415	63445
63355	63386	63416	63446
63356	63387	63417	63447
63357	63388	63418	63448
63358	63389	63419	63449
63359	63390	63420	63450
63360	63391	63421	63451
63361	63392	63422	63452
63362	63393	63423	63453
63363	63394	63424	63454
63364	63395	63425	63455
63365	63396	63426	63456
63366	63397	63427	63457
63367	63398	63428	63458
63368	63399	63429	63459
63369	63400	63430	

Total 119

63460	63464	63468	63472
63461	63465	63469	63473
63462	63466	63470	63474
63463	63467	63471	

Total 15

Classes
2-8-0   8F (O1)   O1 & O4
7F (O4)

O4/1[1] Introduced 1911. Robinson G.C. design with small boiler, Belpaire firebox, steam and vacuum brakes and water scoop.

O4/3[3] Introduced 1917. R.O.D. locos. with steam brake only and no scoop.

O4/2[3] Introduced 1925. O4/3 with cabs and boiler mountings reduced.

O4/6[4] Introduced 1924. Rebuilt from O5 retaining higher cab (63914-20 with side windows).

O4/7[5] Introduced 1939. Rebuilt with shortened O2-type boiler, retaining G.C. smokebox.

O4/8[6] Introduced 1944. Rebuilt with 100A (B1) boiler, retaining original cylinders.

(O4/4 were rebuilds with O2 boilers, since rebuilt again; O5 was a G.C. development of O4 with larger boiler and Belpaire firebox.)

Weight: Loco. { 73 tons 4 cwt.[1]
73 tons 4 cwt.[3]
73 tons 4 cwt.[3]
74 tons 13 cwt.[4]
73 tons 4 cwt.[5]
73 tons 17 cwt.[6]
72 tons 10 cwt.[7]

Tender { 48 tons 6 cwt.
(with scoop)
47 tons 6 cwt.
(without scoop)

Pressure: 180 lb. Su.
Cyls.: (O) 21″ × 26″.
Driving Wheels: 4′ 8″.
T.E.: 31,325 lb.
P.V.

O1[7] Introduced 1944. Thompson rebuild with 100A boiler, Walschaerts valve gear and new cylinders.
Weight: Loco. 73 tons 6 cwt.
       Tender as O4.
Pressure: 225 lb. Su.
Cyls.: (O) 20″ × 26″.
Driving Wheels: 4′ 8″.
T.E.: 35,520 lb.
Walschaerts valve gear.   P.V.

0-8-0   8F   Class Q7

Introduced 1919. Raven N.E. design.
Weight: Loco. 71 tons 12 cwt.
       Tender 44 tons 2 cwt.
Pressure: 180 lb. Su.
Cyls.: (3) 18½″ × 26″.
Driving Wheels: 4′ 7½″.
T.E.: 36,965 lb.
P.V.

63570⁵	63624⁶	63684¹	63740⁷	63796⁷	63829⁶	63861⁶	63887⁷
63571⁷	63626¹	63685²	63741⁶	63798²	63832⁶	63862⁶	63890⁷
63573⁶	63628⁶	63686²	63742⁶	63799¹	63833²	63863⁷	63891⁵
63574¹	63630⁷	63687⁷	63743¹	63800⁶	63836⁶	63864⁶	63893⁶
63575⁶	63631⁶	63688⁶	63744²	63801⁶	63837⁶	63865⁷	63895⁶
63576¹	63632¹	63689⁷	63746⁷	63802⁶	63838⁷	63867⁷	63897⁶
63577¹	63633⁶	63690³	63747⁵	63803⁷	63840⁶	63868⁶	63898⁶
63578⁷	63634⁵	63691⁶	63748⁵	63805⁶	63841⁶	63869⁷	63899⁶
63579⁷	63635¹	63692¹	63750⁶	63806⁷	63842²	63870²	63900²
63584¹	63636⁶	63693¹	63752⁷	63807⁶	63843⁵	63872⁷	63901⁷
63585¹	63637²	63695²	63754⁶	63808⁷	63845²	63873⁶	63902⁴
63586¹	63639⁶	63697⁶	63755⁷	63813²	63846²	63874⁷	63904⁴
63587¹	63641⁶	63698¹	63757¹	63816⁶	63848⁶	63877⁶	63906⁴
63588⁶	63643⁶	63700¹	63758⁶	63817⁷	63850⁶	63878⁶	63907⁴
63589⁷	63644⁶	63701²	63759²	63818⁶	63852⁶	63879⁷	63908⁴
63590⁷	63645⁶	63702²	63760⁷	63819⁶	63853⁶	63880⁵	63911⁴
63591⁷	63646⁷	63703⁶	63762¹	63821²	63854⁷	63881⁶	63912⁴
63592⁷	63647⁶	63704⁶	63763⁶	63822⁶	63856⁷	63882⁶	63913⁴
63593¹	63648³	63705⁶	63764²	63823⁶	63857⁶	63883²	63914⁶
63594⁷	63649⁶	63706⁶	63765⁶	63824⁵	63858⁶	63884⁶	63915⁶
63595⁶	63650⁷	63707¹	63766²	63827⁶	63859²	63885⁶	63917⁴
63596⁷	63651⁶	63708⁵	63767²	63828⁶	63860⁶	63886⁷	63920⁴
63597¹	63652⁷	63709⁶	63768⁷				
63598¹	63653⁶	63711⁷	63770⁵	**Total**			
63599¹	63655⁶	63712⁷	63771²				
63600⁵	63656²	63713²	63772⁵	**Class O1**	**58**	**Class O4/6**	**10**
63601¹	63657⁶	63715⁶	63773⁷	**Class O4/1**	**43**	**Class O4/7**	**25**
63602¹	63658¹	63717⁶	63774²	**Class O4/2**	**2**	**Class O4/8**	**100**
63603⁵	63659²	63718⁶	63775⁵	**Class O4/3**	**38**		
63604⁶	63661⁶	63719¹	63776⁶				
63605¹	63662⁵	63720⁶	63777⁷				
63606⁶	63663⁷	63721⁶	63779²				
63607⁶	63664¹	63722¹	63780⁷				
63608¹	63665²	63724²	63781⁶				
63609¹	63666²	63725⁷	63782²				
63610⁷	63669⁵	63726⁶	63783²	**2-8-0**	**8F**	**Class O2**	
63611¹	63670⁷	63727¹	63784⁷				
63612⁶	63671¹	63728⁶	63785⁶				
63613⁶	63672⁶	63730⁶	63786⁷				
63615⁵	63674⁶	63731⁶	63787²				
63616⁵	63675⁶	63732⁶	63788⁶				
63617¹	63676⁷	63734⁶	63789⁷				
63618¹	63677¹	63735³	63791⁶				
63619⁷	63678⁷	63736¹	63792⁷				
63621¹	63679⁶	63737²	63793⁶				
63622¹	63681²	63738⁶	63794⁶				
63623¹	63683⁶	63739⁶	63795⁷				

2-8-0   **8F**   **Class O2**

O2/1* Introduced 1921. Development of experimental Gresley G.N. 3-cyl. loco. (L.N.E.R. 3921). Subsequently rebuilt with side-window cab, and reduced boiler mountings.

O2/2† Introduced 1924. Development of O2/1 with detail differences.

O2/3 Introduced 1932. Development of O2/2 with side-window cab and reduced boiler mountings.

O2/4‡ Introduced 1943. Rebuilt with 100A (B1 type) boiler and smokebox extended backwards (63924 retaining G.N. tender).

Weight: Loco. { 75 tons 16 cwt.*†
78 tons 13 cwt.
74 tons 2 cwt.‡

Tender { 43 tons 2 cwt.
(63922–46)
52 tons (63947–87).

Pressure: 180 lb. Su.
Cyls.: (3) 18½″ × 26″.
Driving Wheels: 4′ 8″.
T.E.: 36,740 lb.
Walschaerts valve gear and derived
    motion. P.V.

Total

Class O2/1 **7**	Class O2/3 **30**	
Class O2/2 **10**	Class O2/4 **18**	

63922*	63939†	63955‡	63972
63923*	63940†	63956	63973
63924‡	63941†	63957	63974
63925‡	63942†	63958	63975
63926*	63943†	63959	63976
63927*	63944†	63960	63977
63928*	63945‡	63961‡	63978
63929*	63946†	63962‡	63979
63930‡	63947	63963	63980
63931*	63948‡	63964	63981
63932‡	63949‡	63965‡	63982‡
63933‡	63950‡	63966‡	63983‡
63934†	63951	63967	63984
63935‡	63952	63968	63985
63936†	63953	63969	63986
63937†	63954	63971	63987
63938‡			

0-6-0   2P3F   **Class J6**

Introduced 1911. Gresley G.N. design.
Weight: Loco. 50 tons 10 cwt.
         Tender 43 tons 2 cwt.
Pressure: 170 lb. Su.
Cyls.: 19″ × 26″.
Driving Wheels: 5′ 2″.
T.E.: 21,875 lb.
P.V.

64170	64196	64223	64251
64171	64203	64226	64253
64173	64206	64231	64260
64174	64208	64232	64265
64177	64209	64233	64268
64182	64219	64236	64277
64185	64222	64245	64278
64191			

Total 29

HISTORIC LOCOMOTIVES PRESERVED IN STORE

Type	Originating Company	Pre-Grouping No.	L.N.E.R. No.	Name	Place of Preservation
4-2-2	G.N.R.	1	—	—	York Museum
4-4-2	G.N.R.	990	(3990)	Henry Oakley	York Museum
4-4-2	G.N.R.	251	(3251)	—	York Museum
2-2-4T	N.E.R.	66	66	Aerolite	York Museum
2-4-0	N.E.R.	910	910	—	York Museum
2-4-0	N.E.R.	1463	1463	—	York Museum
4-4-0	N.E.R.	1621	1621	—	York Museum

The unbracketed numbers are the ones at present carried by the locos.

0-6-0 2P3F Class J11

Introduced 1901. Robinson G.C. design.
Parts 1 and 4 have 3,250-gallon
tenders; Parts 2 and 5, 4,000-gallon.
Parts 1 and 2 have high boiler
mountings; Parts 4 and 5 low. All
of Parts 4 and 5 are superheated, and
some of Parts 1 and 2. There are
frequent changes between parts.

J11/3* Introduced 1942. Rebuilt with
long-travel piston valves and boiler
higher pitched.

Weight: Loco. $\begin{cases} 51 \text{ tons } 19 \text{ cwt. (Sat.)} \\ 52 \text{ tons } 2 \text{ cwt. (Su.)} \\ 53 \text{ tons } 6 \text{ cwt.} \end{cases}$

Tender $\begin{cases} 44 \text{ tons } 3 \text{ cwt. (3,250 gall.)} \\ 48 \text{ tons } 6 \text{ cwt. (4,000 gall.)} \end{cases}$

Pressure: 180 lb. SS.
Cyls.: $18\frac{1}{2}'' \times 26''$.
Driving Wheels: 5' 2".
T.E.: 21,960 lb.

64284*	64333*	64379*	64425
64288	64337	64384	64427*
64292	64341	64385	64434
64305	64346*	64386*	64435
64308	64352*	64393*	64437
64310	64354*	64394*	64439*
64311	64355	64395*	64440
64313	64359*	64402*	64441*
64314*	64362*	64404	64442*
64316*	64363	64406*	64443
64317*	64364*	64417*	64444
64318*	64371	64418*	64445
64324*	64373*	64419	64446
64325	64375*	64420*	64447
64329	64377	64423	64450*
64332*			

Total
Class J11 3 31
Class J11 (other parts) **30**

0-6-0 3F Class J35

J35/5* Introduced 1906. Reid N.B.
design with piston valves.
J35/4 Introduced 1908. Slide valves.
(Parts 1, 2 and 3 were variations of
Parts 4 and 5 before superheating.)

Weight: Loco. $\begin{cases} 51 \text{ tons.*} \\ 50 \text{ tons } 15 \text{ cwt.} \end{cases}$

Tender $\begin{cases} 38 \text{ tons } 1 \text{ cwt.*} \\ 37 \text{ tons } 15 \text{ cwt.} \end{cases}$

Pressure: 180 lb. Su.
Cyls.: $18\frac{1}{4}'' \times 26''$.
Driving Wheels: 5' 0".
T.E.: 22,080 lb.

64461*	64480	64502	64523
64462*	64482	64504	64524
64463*	64488	64505	64525
64470*	64489	64507	64527
64471*	64491	64510	64529
64472*	64493	64512	64531
64474*	64494	64514	64532
64476*	64497	64515	64533
64477*	64499	64518	64534
64478	64500	64519	64535
64479			

Total
Class J35/4 **32**   Class J35/5 **9**

0-6-0 5F Class J37

Introduced 1914. Reid N.B. design.
Superheated development of J35.
Weight: Loco. 54 tons 14 cwt.
Tender 40 tons 19 cwt.
Pressure: 180 lb. Su.
Cyls.: $19\frac{1}{2}'' \times 26''$.
Driving Wheels: 5' 0".
T.E.: 25,210 lb.
P.V.

64537	64551	64564	64578
64539	64552	64565	64579
64540	64553	64566	64580
64541	64554	64568	64581
64542	64555	64569	64582
64543	64556	64570	64583
64544	64557	64571	64585
64545	64558	64572	64586
64546	64559	64573	64587
64547	64560	64574	64588
64548	64561	64575	64589
64549	64562	64576	64590
64550	64563	64577	64591

64592	64604	64616	64628
64593	64605	64617	64629
64594	64606	64618	64630
64595	64607	64619	64631
64596	64608	64620	64632
64597	64609	64621	64633
64598	64610	64622	64634
64599	64611	64623	64635
64600	64612	64624	64636
64601	64613	64625	64637
64602	64614	64626	64638
64603	64615	64627	64639

Total 100

Weight: Loco.   54 tons 15 cwt.
          Tender 38 tons 5 cwt.
Pressure: 180 lb. Su.
Cyls.: 20″ × 28″.
Driving Wheels: 4′ 11″.
T.E.: 29,045 lb.
P.V.

64676	64681	64689	64696
64677	64682	64690	64697
64678	64685	64691	64698
64679	64686	64692	64699
64680	64687	64693	

Total 15

0-6-0   3P5F   Class J19

Introduced 1916. Hill G.E. design
  rebuilt with round-topped firebox
  from 1934.
*Rebuilt with 19″ cyls. and 180 lb.
  pressure.
Weight: Loco.   50 tons 7 cwt.
          Tender 38 tons 5 cwt.
Pressure: $\begin{cases} 170 \text{ lb. Su.} \\ 180 \text{ lb. Su.}* \end{cases}$
Cyls.: $\begin{cases} 20″ × 26″. \\ 19″ × 26″.* \end{cases}$
Driving Wheels: 4′ 11″.
T.E.: $\begin{cases} 27,430 \text{ lb.} \\ 26,215 \text{ lb.}* \end{cases}$

64643	64653	64663	64669
64646	64655	64664*	64671*
64650	64657	64666	64673
64652	64660	64667	64674

Total 16

0-6-0   5F   Class J20

J20/1 Introduced 1943. Hill G.E.
  design with Belpaire firebox (introduced 1920) rebuilt with B12/1-type
  boiler with round-topped firebox.

0-6-0   4P5F   Class J39

Introduced 1926. Gresley design.
J39/1   Standard 3,500-gallon tender.
J39/2*   Standard 4,200-gallon tender.
J39/3†   Various N.E. tenders (3,940-
  gallon on 64843-5, 4,125-gallon on
  64855-9).
Weight: Loco.   57 tons 17 cwt.
          Tender $\begin{cases} 44 \text{ tons 4 cwt.} \\ 52 \text{ tons 13 cwt.}* \end{cases}$
                  and others.
Pressure: 180 lb. Su.
Cyls.: 20″ × 26″.
Driving Wheels: 5′ 2″.
T.E.: 25,665 lb.
P.V.

64700†	64720	64745	64778
64701	64723	64746	64779
64703	64725	64747	64783
64704	64726	64748	64784*
64705	64727	64749	64786*
64706	64729	64754	64790*
64707	64730	64756	64791*
64708	64732	64757	64792*
64709	64733	64758	64794*
64710	64736	64760	64795*
64711	64738	64764	64796
64713	64739	64765	64798
64716	64740	64767	64801
64717	64742	64770	64804
64718	64743	64772	64806
64719	64744	64775	64808

64809	64852	64889*	64931*
64810	64853	64892*	64932*
64811	64854	64895*	64933
64812	64855†	64896*	64934
64813	64856†	64897*	64935
64814	64857†	64899*	64936
64815	64858†	64901*	64938
64816	64859†	64903*	64939
64817	64860	64904*	64940
64818	64861	64906*	64941
64819	64862	64907*	64942
64820*	64863	64908*	64943
64821*	64864	64909*	64944
64822*	64865	64910*	64945*
64823	64866	64911*	64946*
64825	64867	64914*	64947*
64831	64868	64915*	64949*
64833	64869	64916*	64950*
64835	64870	64917*	64955*
64836	64871	64918*	64961*
64837	64872*	64919*	64963*
64839*	64874*	64920*	64964*
64840*	64875*	64921*	64969*
64842*	64877*	64922*	64970*
64843†	64878*	64923*	64971†
64844†	64879*	64924*	64974*
64845†	64880*	64925*	64975†
64846	64882*	64926†	64978†
64847	64884*	64927*	64979†
64848	64885*	64928*	64982*
64849	64886*	64929*	64986†
64850	64888*	64930*	64987†
64851			

Total

Class J39/1 106 **Class J39/3 18**
Class J39/2 69

0-6-0   **2F**   **Class J21**

Introduced 1886. T. W. Worsdell N.E. design. Majority built as 2-cyl. compounds and later rebuilt as simple locos., subsequently rebuilt with superheater and piston valves, superheater later removed.

Weight: Loco. 42 tons 9 cwt.
         Tender 36 tons 19 cwt.
Pressure: 160 lb. SS.
Cyls.: 19″ × 24″.
Driving Wheels: 5′ 1¼″.
T.E.: 19,240 lb.

65033   65070   65099

Total 3

0-6-0   **2F**   **Class J10**

J10/4* Introduced 1896. Pollitt development of J10/2 with larger bearings and larger tender.
J10/6 Introduced 1901. Robinson locos. with larger bearings and small tender.
Weight: Loco.   41 tons 6 cwt.
         Tender { 37 tons 6 cwt.
                 43 tons.*
Pressure: 160 lb.
Cyls.: 18″ × 26″.
Driving Wheels: 5′ 1″.
T.E.: 18,780 lb.

65157* 65198

Total

Class J10/4 1   **Class J10/6 1**

0-6-0   **2F**   **Class J36**

Introduced 1388. Holmes N.B. design.
Weight: Loco. 41 tons 19 cwt.
         Tender 33 tons 9 cwt.
Pressure: 165 lb.
Cyls.: 18½″ × 26″.
Driving Wheels: 5′ 0″.
T.E.: 19,690 lb.

65210
65211
65214
65216 Byng
65217 French
65218

65222	Somme
65224	Mons
65227	
65228	
65230	
65232	
65233	Plumer
65234	
65235	Gough
65237	
65239	
65241	
65243	Maude
65246	
65249	
65251	
65253	Joffre

65257	65260	65265	65267
65258	65261	65266	
65268	Allenby		
65273	65282	65295	65305
65275	65285	65296	65306
65276	65287	65297	65307
65277	65288	65300	65309
65280	65290	65303	65310
65281	65293	65304	
65311	Haig		
65312	65319	65329	65338
65313	65320	65330	65341
65315	65321	65331	65344
65316	65323	65334	65345
65317	65325	65335	65346
65318	65327		

Total 77

65361	65446	65460	65469
65389	65450	65462	65476
65420	65453	65464	65478
65440	65457	65465	65479
65445	65458		

Total 18

0-6-0   2P4F   Class J17

Introduced 1901. J. Holden G.E. design. Many rebuilt from round-top firebox J16, introduced 1900.
*Fitted with small tender.
Weight: Loco.   45 tons 8 cwt.
      Tender $\begin{cases} 38 \text{ tons } 5 \text{ cwt.} \\ 30 \text{ tons } 12 \text{ cwt.*} \end{cases}$
Pressure: 180 lb. Su.
Cyls.: 19" × 26".
Driving Wheels: 4' 11".
T.E.: 24,340 lb.

65503*	65528*	65560	65581
65506*	65532	65564	65582
65507*	65539	65567	65583
65511*	65541	65576	65586
65513*	65549	65577	65588
65520	65554	65578	65589
65521	65556		

Total 26

0-6-0   3F   Class J25

Introduced 1898. W. Worsdell N.E. design.
*Original design, saturated, with slide valves.
†Rebuilt with superheater and piston valves.
Weight: Loco. $\begin{cases} 39 \text{ tons } 11 \text{ cwt.*} \\ 41 \text{ tons } 14 \text{ cwt.†} \end{cases}$
      Tender 36 tons 19 cwt.
Pressure: 160 lb. SS.
Cyls.: 18½" × 26".
Driving Wheels: 4' 7¼".
T.E.: 21,905 lb.

0-6-0   1P2F   Class J15

Introduced 1883. Worsdell G.E. design, modified by J. Holden.
Weight: Loco.   37 tons 2 cwt.
      Tender 30 tons 13 cwt.
Pressure: 160 lb.
Cyls.: 17½" × 24".
Driving Wheels: 4' 11".
T.E.: 16,940 lb.

Class 4 (Fowler) 2-6-4T No. 42389

[J. B. Bucknall

Class 4 (Fowler) 2-6-4T No. 42417 (fitted with side window cab)

[B. K. B. Green

Standard Class 4 2-6-4T No. 80015

[W. M. J. Jackson

Class 2P (ex-Midland) 4-4-0 No. 40502 [R. J. Buckley

Class 2P (ex-L.M.S.) 4-4-0 No. 40614 [K. R. Pirt

Class 4P 4-4-0 No. 40907 [F. W. Day

Class 6P5F (Stanier) 2-6-0 No. 42956   [*J. E. Wilkinson*

Class 6P5F (Hughes-Fowler) 2-6-0 No. 42890   [*P. H. Groom*

Class 6P5F (Hughes-Fowler) 2-6-0 No. 42822 (with Reidinger rotary poppet valve gear)   [*J. Davenport*

Standard Class 5 4-6-0 No. 73009   *[J. Robertson*

Class 6P5F 4-6-0 No. 45509 *The Derbyshire Yeomanry*   *[J. E. Wilkinson*

Class 6P5F 4-6-0 No. 45600 *Bermuda*   *[G. Wheeler*

Class 7P 4-6-0 No. 45525 *Colwyn Bay* [J. B. Bucknall

Class 7P 4-6-0 No. 46126 *The Royal Army Service Corps* [J. B. Bucknall

Class 7P 4-6-0 No. 46106 *Gordon Highlander* (fitted with B.R.-type smoke deflectors)
[J. B. Bucknall

Class 8P 4-6-2 No. 46252 *City of Leicester*   [J. B. Bucknall

Class 8P 4-6-2 No. 46257 *City of Salford* (with detail differences)   [J. B. Bucknall

Class 8P 4-6-2 No. 46212 *Duchess of Kent*   [J. Smith

Class 7F (Fowler) 0-8-0 No. 49618   *[J. E. Wilkinson*

Class 7F 0-8-0 No. 49452   *[J. B. Bucknall*

Class 7F 0-8-0 No. 49454 (with tender cab)   *[F. W. Day*

Class 8F 2-8-0 No. 48419   [P. H. Groom

Class 8F 2-8-0 No. 48045 (with Fowler type tender)   [A. W. Martin

Class 7F 2-8-0 No. 53807   [R. J. Blenkinsop

Class 3P 4-4-2T No. 41947   [*J. B. Bucknall*

Class 1P 0-4-4T No. 58086   [*R. C. Riley*

Class 2F 0-6-0 No. 58305 (with 5′ 3″ driving wheels)   [*K. R. Pirt*

Right: Class 3F 0-6-0T
No. 47221

[P. J. Sharpe

Centre: Class IF 0-6-0T
No. 41835 (the last
Midland engine in ser-
vice to retain the round
top firebox and Midland
dome and safety valve
casing)

[P. J. Lynch

Bottom: Class IF 0-6-0T
No. 41844

[J. Cupit

Sentinel 0-4-0T No. 47190   [R. M. Casserley

Class 0F 0-4-0ST No. 51244

Class 0F 0-4-0T No. 41537   [Ivo Peters

Class 2P 0-4-4T No. 55124 (McIntosh "19" class)　　　　　　　　　　[K. R. Pirt

Class 2P 0-4-4T No. 55204 (McIntosh "439" class)　　　　　　　　[D. A. Anderson

Class 2P 0-4-4T No. 55269 (post-grouping development of "439" class)　　[K. R. Pirt

Class 3P 4-4-0 No. 54478   [*W. S. Sellar*

Standard Class 2 2-6-2T No. 84023   [*P. H. Groom*

Standard Class 3 2-6-2T No. 82016   [*B. A. Haresnape*

Standard Class 8P 4-6-2 No. 71000 *Duke of Gloucester* [*P. Ransome-Wallis*

Standard Class 7P6F 4-6-2 No. 70048 *The Territorial Army 1908-1938* [*J. E. Wilkinson*

Standard Class 6P5F 4-6-2 No. 72007 *Clan Mackintosh* [*J. E. Wilkinson*

Class A4 4-6-2 No. 60007 *Sir Nigel Gresley* [*K. R. Pirt*

Class A3 4-6-2 No. 60060 *The Tetrarch* [*K. R. Pirt*

Class A3 4-6-2 No. 60061 *Pretty Polly* (fitted with small-type smoke deflectors)
[*P. Ransome-Wallis*

Class A1 4-6-2 No. 60127 *Wilson Worsdell* [*J. R. Paterson*

Class A2 4-6-2 No. 60533 *Happy Knight* (fitted with double chimney and multiple-valve regulator) [*K. R. Pirt*

Class A2 4 6-2 No. 60534 *Irish Elegance* [*G. Wheeler*

65645†	65693*	65713*	65726*
65663*	65695*	65714*	65727*
65670*	65712*	65720*	65728*
65691*			

Total 13

0-6-0   5F   Class J26

Introduced 1904. W. Worsdell N.E. design.

Weight: Loco. 46 tons 16 cwt.
        Tender 36 tons 19 cwt.

Pressure: 180 lb.

Cyls.: 18¼″ × 26″.

Driving Wheels: 4′ 7¼″.

T.E.: 24,640 lb.

65731	65751	65762	65776
65735	65753	65763	65777
65736	65755	65768	65778
65741	65756	65769	65779
65743	65757	65772	
65745	65760	65773	
65747	65761	65774	

Total 25

0-6-0   5F   Class J27

Introduced 1906. W. Worsdell N.E. design developed from J26.
*Introduced 1921. Raven locos. Superheated, with piston valves.
†Introduced 1943. Piston valves, but superheater removed.

Weight: Loco. { 47 tons Sat.
              { 49 tons 10 cwt. Su.
        Tender 36 tons 19 cwt.

Pressure: 180 lb. SS.

Cyls.: 18½″ × 26″.

Driving Wheels: 4′ 7¼″.

T.E.: 24,640 lb.

65782	65813	65844	65871*
65786	65814	65845	65872†
65787	65815	65846	65873†
65788	65817	65849	65874†
65789	65818	65850	65875†
65790	65819	65851	65876†
65791	65820	65852	65877†
65792	65821	65853	65878†
65794	65822	65854	65879†
65795	65823	65855	65880*
65796	65825	65857	65881*
65797	65828	65858	65882†
65799	65830	65859	65883*
65800	65831	65860†	65884†
65801	65832	65861†	65885†
65802	65833	65862†	65887*
65804	65834	65863†	65888†
65805	65835	65864†	65889†
65807	65837	65865†	65890*
65808	65838	65867†	65891†
65809	65839	65868†	65892†
65810	65841	65869†	65893*
65811	65842	65870†	65894*
65812			

Total 93

0-6-0   6F   Class J38

Introduced 1926. Gresley design. Predecessor of J39, with 4′ 8″ wheels, boiler 6″ longer than J39 and smokebox 6″ shorter.
*Rebuilt with J39 boiler.

Weight: Loco. 58 tons 19 cwt.
        Tender 44 tons 4 cwt.

Pressure: 180 lb. Su.

Cyls.: 20″ × 26″.

Driving Wheels: 4′ 8″.

T.E.: 28,415 lb.

P.V.

65900	65905	65910	65915
65901	65906*	65911	65916
65902	65907	65912	65917*
65903*	65908*	65913	65918*
65904	65909	65914	65919

65920	65924	65928	65932
65921	65925	65929	65933
65922	65926*	65930	65934
65923	65927*	65931	

Total 35

4-4-2T　2P　Class C16

Introduced 1915. Reid N.B. design, superheated development of C15.
Weight: 72 tons 10 cwt.
Pressure: 165 lb. Su.
Cyls.: 19″ × 26″.
Driving Wheels: 5′ 9″.
T.E.: 19,080 lb.
P.V.

67485　67489　67494

Total 3

Classes
2-6-2T　V1 (3MT)　V1 & V3
##　　　　V3 (4MT)

V1 Introduced 1930. Gresley design.
V3* Introduced 1939. Development of V1 with higher pressure (locos. numbered below 67682 rebuilt from V1).

Weight: { 84 tons.
{ 86 tons 16 cwt.*
Pressure: { 180 lb. Su.
{ 200 lb. Su.*

Cyls.: (3) 16″ × 26″.

Driving Wheels: 5′ 8″.

T.E.: { 22,465 lb.
{ 24,960 lb.*

Walschaerts valve gear and derived motion. P.V.

67600*	67607*	67614*	67621*
67601	67608	67615*	67622
67602	67609*	67616	67623*
67603	67610	67617*	67624*
67604*	67611*	67618*	67625*
67605*	67612*	67619*	67626*
67606*	67613*	67620*	67627*

67628*	67644*	67660*	67676
67629	67645*	67661*	67677*
67630	67646*	67662*	67678*
67631	67647*	67663*	67679*
67632*	67648*	67664	67680
67633*	67649	67665	67681*
67634*	67650*	67666	67682*
67635	67651*	67667*	67683*
67636*	67652*	67668*	67684*
67637	67653*	67669*	67685*
67638*	67654*	67670*	67686*
67639	67655	67671	67687*
67640	67656*	67672*	67688*
67641	67657*	67673	67689*
67642*	67658*	67674*	67690*
67643*	67659	67675*	67691*

Total
Class V1 25　　　Class V3 67

2-6-4T　4MT　Class L1

Introduced 1945. Thompson design.
*Introduced 1954. Cylinder diameter reduced.

Weight: 89 tons 9 cwt.

Pressure: 225 lb.

Cyls.: { (O) 20″ × 26″.
{ (O) 18¾″ × 26″.*

Driving Wheels: 5′ 2″.

T.E.: { 32,080 lb.
{ 28,180 lb.*

Walschaerts valve gear. P.V.

67701	67711	67721	67731
67702	67712	67722	67732
67703	67713	67723	67733
67704	67714	67724	67734
67705	67715	67725	67735
67706	67716	67726	67736
67707	67717	67727	67737
67708	67718	67728	67738
67709	67719	67729	67739
67710	67720	67730	67740

67741	67756	67771*	67786
67742	67757	67772*	67787
67743	67758	67773	67788
67744	67759	67774	67789
67745	67760	67775	67790
67746	67761	67776*	67791
67747	67762	67777	67792
67748	67763	67778	67793
67749	67764	67779*	67794
67750	67765	67780	67795
67751	67766	67781	67796
67752	67767	67782	67797
67753	67768	67783	67798
67754	67769	67784	67799
67755	67770*	67785	67800

Total 100

0-6-0ST 4F Class J94

Introduced 1943. Riddles M.o.S. design.
  (Bought from M.o.S., 1946.)
Weight: 48 tons 5 cwt.
Pressure: 170 lb.
Cyls.: 18″ × 26″.
Driving Wheels: 4′ 3″.
T.E.: 23,870 lb.

68006	68025	68044	68063
68007	68026	68045	68064
68008	68027	68046	68065
68009	68028	68047	68066
68010	68029	68048	68067
68011	68030	68049	68068
68012	68031	68050	68069
68013	68032	68051	68070
68014	68033	68052	68071
68015	68034	68053	68072
68016	68035	68054	68073
68017	68036	68055	68074
68018	68037	68056	68075
68019	68038	68057	68076
68020	68039	68058	68077
68021	68040	68059	68078
68022	68041	68060	68079
68023	68042	68061	68080
68024	68043	68062	

Total 75

0-4-0ST 0F Class Y9

Introduced 1882. Holmes N.B. design.
*Locos. running permanently attached
  to wooden tender.
Weight: Loco. 27 tons 16 cwt.
          Tender 6 tons.*
Pressure: 130 lb.
Cyls.: (O) 14″ × 20″.
Driving Wheels: 3′ 8″.
T.E.: 9,845 lb.

68095	68104	68114*	68119*
68101	68110	68117*	68123

Total 8

0-6-0T Unclass. Class J71

Introduced 1886. T. W. Worsdell N.E.
  design.
*Altered cylinder dimensions.
Weight: 37 tons 12 cwt.
Pressure: 140 lb.
Driving Wheels 4′ 7¼″.
Cyls.: $\begin{cases} 16″ \times 22″. \\ 16\frac{3}{4}″ \times 22″.* \end{cases}$
T.E.: $\begin{cases} 12,130 \text{ lb.} \\ 13,300 \text{ lb.}* \end{cases}$

68233	68254	68272	68278
68235	68269	68275	68316*

Total 8

0-6-0T 0F Class J88

Introduced 1904. Reid N.B. design
with short wheelbase.
Weight: 38 tons 14 cwt.
Pressure: 130 lb.
Cyls.: (O) 15″ × 22″.
Driving Wheels: 3′ 9″.
T.E.: 12,155 lb.

68325	68338	68345	68350
68332	68342	68346	68353
68335	68343	68349	68354
68336	68344		

Total 14

DEPARTMENTAL LOCOMOTIVES

(Former running no. in brackets)

0-6-0ST 3F Class J52/2

2 (68858)   9 (68840)

0-4-0T Un-class. Class Y3

Introduced 1927.
Sentinel Wagon Works design.
  Two-speed Geared Sentinel locos.
Sprocket gear ratio 15: 19.
Weight: 20 tons 16 cwt.
Pressure: 275 lb. Su.
Cyls.: 6¾" × 9".
Driving Wheels: 2' 6".
T.E.: {Low Gear: 15,960 lb.
      {High Gear: 5,960 lb.
Poppet valves.

7 (68166)   41 (68177)
21 (68162)   42 (68178)
40 (68173)   57 (68160)

Total 6

0-6-0T 2F Class J66

Introduced 1886. J. Holden G.E.
  design.
Weight: 40 tons 6 cwt.
Pressure: 160 lb.
Cyls.: 16½" × 22".
Driving Wheels: 4' 0".
T.E.: 16,970 lb.

32 (68370)

Total 1

0-6-0T 2F Class J69

44(68498)   45(68543)

0-4-0T Un-class. Class Y1/1

Sentinel Wagon Works design.
Single-speed Geared Sentinel
locomotives. The parts of this
class differ in details, including size
of boiler and fuel capacity.

Y1/1* Introduced 1925.
Y1/2† Introduced 1927.
Sprocket gear ratio 11: 25.
Weight: {20 tons 17 cwt.*
        {19 tons 16 cwt.†
Pressure: 275 lb. Su.
Cyls.: 6¾" × 9".
Driving Wheels: 2' 6".
T.E.: 7,260 lb.*†
Poppet valves.

39*(68131)   54†(68153)
Total
Class Y1/1 1 Class Y1/2 1

0-4-0T Dock Tank Class Y4

Introduced 1913. Hill G.E. design.
Weight: 38 tons 1 cwt.
Pressure: 180 lb.
Cyls.: (O) 17" × 20".
Driving Wheels: 3' 10".
T.E.: 19,225 lb.
Walschaerts valve gear.

33 (68129)

Total 1

0-4-0 Diesel Mechanical

52 (11104)

0-4-0 Diesel Mechanical

56   81   85

0-6-0 Diesel Mechanical

91   92

Bo-Bo EB1 Electric

100 (26510)

NOTE. (For details of Departmental diesel and electric locomotives, see ABC British Railways Diesels or Electrics
and Diesel and Electric Section of combined volume.)

0-6-0T   3F   Class J73

Introduced 1891. W. Worsdell N.E. design.
Weight: 46 tons 15 cwt.
Pressure: 160 lb.
Cyls.: 19" × 24".
Driving Wheels: 4' 7½".
T.E.: 21,320 lb.

68361

Total 1

0-6-0T   2F   Class J77

Introduced 1899. W. Worsdell N.E. rebuild of Fletcher 0-4-4T originally built 1874–84.
Some engines of this class have square-cornered and some round-cornered cab roofs.
Weight: 43 tons.
Pressure: 160 lb.
Cyls.: 17" × 22".
Driving Wheels: 4' 1¼".
T.E.: 17,560 lb.

68408   68410

Total 2

0-6-0T   2F   Class J83

Introduced 1900. Holmes N.B. design.
Weight: 45 tons 5 cwt.
Pressure: 150 lb.
Cyls.: 17" × 26".
Driving Wheels: 4' 6".
T.E.: 17,745 b.

68442	68448	68458	68472
68443	68453	68459	68477
68445	68454	68470	68479
68447	68456	68471	68481

Total 16

0-6-0T   2F   Class J69

J69/1† Introduced 1902. Development of Holden J67 with 180 lb. pressure, larger tanks and larger firebox (some rebuilt from J67).

J69/2§ Introduced 1950. J67/1 rebuilt with 180 lb. boiler and larger firebox.
Weight: 40 tons 9 cwt.
Pressure: 180 lb.
Cyls.: 16½" × 22".
Driving Wheels: 4' 0".
T.E.: 19,090 lb.
(See also E.R. Departmental Locos.)

68497†	68538†	68563†	68609†
68499†	68542†	68565†	68612†
68500†	68545†	68566†	68613†
68501†	68549†	68570†	68619†
68502†	68550†	68573†	68621†
68508†	68552†	68575†	68623†
68513§	68554†	68577†	68626†
68522§	68556†	68578†	68633†
68526†	68558†	68600†	68635†
68530†	68560†		

Total

Class J69/2   2   Class J69/1   38

0-6-0T   2F   Class J68

Introduced 1912. Hill G.E. development of J69 with side-window cab.
Weight: 42 tons 9 cwt.
Pressure: 180 lb.
Cyls.: 16½" × 22".
Driving Wheels: 4' 0".
T.E.: 19,090 lb.

68642	68646	68649	68660
68644	68647	68650	68663

Total 8

141

0-6-0T   2F   Class J72

Introduced 1898. W. Worsdell N.E.
design.
*Altered cylinder dimensions.
Weight: 38 tons 12 cwt.
Pressure: 140 lb.
Cyls.: $\begin{cases} 17'' \times 24''. \\ 18'' \times 24''.* \end{cases}$
Driving Wheels: 4' 1¼".
T.E.: $\begin{cases} 16,760 \text{ lb.} \\ 18,790 \text{ lb.}* \end{cases}$

68672	68690	68711	68733
68673	68691	68713	68734
68674	68692	68715	68736
68675	68693	68716	68737
68676	68695	68717	68738
68677	68696	68719	68740
68678	68698	68720	68742
68680	68701	68721	68743
68681	68702	68723	68744
68683	68703	68724	68745
68684	68704	68726	68747
68685*	68705	68728	68749
68686	68706	68729	68750
68687	68707	68730	68753
68688	68708	68732	68754
68689	68709		

(Class continued with No. 69001)

0-6-0ST   3F   Class J52

J52/2 Introduced 1897. Ivatt G.N.
saddletank with domed boiler.
Weight: 51 tons 14 cwt.
Pressure: 170 lb.
Cyls.: 18" × 26".
Driving Wheels: 4' 8".
T.E.: 21,735 lb.

(See also E.R. Departmental Locos.)

68869   68875

Total 4

0-6-0T   4F   Class J50

J50/2* Introduced 1922. Gresley G.N.
design (68900–19 rebuilt from smaller
J51, built 1915–22).

J50/3† Introduced 1926. Post-grouping
development with detail differences.

J50/1‡ Introduced 1929. Rebuilt from
smaller J51, built 1913–14.

J50/4§ Introduced 1937. Development
of J50/3 with larger bunker.
Weight: $\begin{cases} 57 \text{ tons.}* \\ 56 \text{ tons 6 cwt.}‡ \\ 58 \text{ tons 3 cwt.}†§ \end{cases}$
Pressure: 175 lb.
Cyls.: 18½" × 26".
Driving Wheels: 4' 8".
T.E.: 23,635 lb.

68890‡	68917*	68939*	68965†
68891‡	68918*	68941†	68966†
68892‡	68920*	68943†	68968†
68894‡	68921*	68944†	68970†
68896‡	68922*	68945†	68971†
68897‡	68923*	68946†	68972†
68899‡	68924*	68947†	68975†
68900*	68925*	68948†	68976†
68901*	68926*	68950†	68977†
68902*	68927*	68951†	68979§
68903*	68928*	68952†	68981§
68904*	68929*	68954†	68982§
68905*	68930*	68956†	68983§
68907*	68931*	68957†	68984§
68908*	68932*	68959†	68986§
68910*	68933*	68960†	68987§
68911*	68934*	68961†	68988§
68913*	68935*	68962†	68989§
68914*	68936*	68963†	68990§
68915*	68937*	68964†	68991§
68916*			

Total

Class J50/1   7   Class J50/3 28

Class J50/2 35   Class J50/4 11

0-6-0T 2F Class J72

(Continued from 68754)

69001	69008	69015	69022
69002	69009	69016	69023
69003	69010	69017	69024
69004	69011	69018	69025
69005	69012	69019	69026
69006	69013	69020	69027
69007	69014	69021	69028

Total 90

0-6-2T 3F Class N10

Introduced 1902. W. Worsdell N.E. design.
Weight: 57 tons 14 cwt.
Pressure: 160 lb.
Cyls.: $18\frac{1}{4}'' \times 26''$.
Driving Wheels: $4' 7\frac{1}{4}''$.
T.E.: 21,905 lb.

69097	69101	69105	69109

Total 4

0-6-2T 3MT Class N15

N15/2* Introduced 1910. Reid N.B. design developed from N14. Cowlairs Incline banking locos.

N15/1 Introduced 1910. Development of N15/2 with smaller bunker for normal duties.

Weight: $\begin{cases} 62 \text{ tons } 1 \text{ cwt.*} \\ 60 \text{ tons } 18 \text{ cwt.} \end{cases}$
Pressure: 175 lb.
Cyls.: $18'' \times 26''$.
Driving Wheels: $4' 6''$.
T.E.: 23,205 lb.

69126*	69132	69135	69138
69128*	69133	69136	69141
69131*	69134	69137	69143

69150	69178	69191	69212
69155	69179	69194	69216
69156	69180	69196	69218
69159	69181	69199	69219
69161	69183	69204	69221
69163	69184	69209	69223
69173	69188	69211	69224
69177	69190		

Total

Class N15/1 39 Class N15/2 3

0-6-2T 2MT Class N5

N5/2. Introduced 1891. Parker M.S. & L. design developed from N4.
Weight: 62 tons 7 cwt.
Pressure: 160 lb.
Cyls.: $18'' \times 26''$
Driving Wheels: $5' 1''$.
T.E.: 18,780 lb.

69258	69274	69296	69309
69263	69286	69307	69370
69266	69293		

Total 10

0-6-2T 3P2F Class N2

N2/2* Introduced 1925. Post-grouping development of Gresley G.N. N2/1, introduced 1920, which class is now included in N2/2. Built with condensing apparatus and small chimney.

N2/2† Condensing apparatus removed.

N2/3‡ Introduced 1925. Locos. built non-condensing, originally fitted with large chimney. Some now with small chimney.

N2/4§ Introduced 1928. Development of N2/2, slightly heavier. Built with condensing apparatus and small chimney.

(The small chimneys are to suit the Metropolitan loading gauge, for working to Moorgate. Condensing apparatus has been removed from or added to certain locos. transferred from or to the London area.)

Weight: $\begin{cases} \text{70 tons 5 cwt.*†} \\ \text{70 tons 8 cwt.‡} \\ \text{71 tons 9 cwt.§} \end{cases}$

Pressure: 170 lb. Su.
Cyls.: 19″ × 26″.
Driving Wheels: 5′ 8″
T.E.: 19,945 lb.
P.V.

69498*	69520*	69546*	69579§
69504*	69521*	69549*	69580§
69505†	69523*	69560†	69581§
69506*	69529*	69561†	69582§
69509†	69530*	69564‡	69583§
69511†	69531*	69568§	69585§
69512*	69533*	69571§	69586§
69513*	69535*	69572§	69592§
69516†	69538*	69574§	69593§
69518†	69543*	69575§	69596‡

Total

Class N2/2 24   Class N2/4 14

Class N2/3 2

N7/5⁴ Introduced 1943. Post-grouping development of G.E. design N7/1, rebuilt with round-topped firebox, retaining short-travel valves.

Weight: $\begin{cases} \text{64 tons.}^{1\,2\,4} \\ \text{61 tons 16 cwt.}^{3} \end{cases}$

Pressure: 180 lb. Su.
Cyls.: 18″ × 24″.
Driving Wheels: 4′ 10″.
T.E.: 20,515 lb.
Walschaerts valve gear.   P.V.

69611[3]	69654[4]	69687[2]	69712[1]
69614[3]	69656[4]	69688[2]	69713[1]
69615[3]	69658[4]	69690[2]	69714[1]
69618[3]	69663[4]	69691[2]	69715[1]
69620[3]	69664[4]	69692[2]	69718[1]
69621[3]	69668[4]	69693[2]	69719[1]
69629[4]	69670[4]	69694[2]	69720[1]
69630[4]	69671[4]	69696[2]	69721[1]
69631[4]	69673[2]	69697[2]	69722[1]
69632[4]	69674[2]	69698[2]	69723[1]
69636[4]	69675[2]	69699[2]	69724[1]
69640[4]	69677[2]	69700[2]	69725[1]
69642[4]	69678[2]	69701[2]	69726[1]
69645[4]	69679[2]	69702[1]	69727[1]
69646[4]	69680[2]	69704[1]	69728[1]
69647[4]	69681[2]	69706[1]	69729[1]
69648[4]	69682[2]	69707[1]	69730[1]
69651[4]	69684[2]	69708[1]	69732[1]
69652[4]	69685[2]	69709[1]	69733[1]
69653[4]	69686[2]	69710[1]	

Total

Class N7/3 51   Class N7/4   6

Class N7/5 22

0-6-2T   3MT   Class N7

N7/3¹ Introduced 1927. Doncaster-built version of N7/2 (see below) but with round-topped firebox.

N7/3² Introduced 1943. N7/2 post-grouping development of Hill G.E. design (N7) with long-travel valves rebuilt with round-topped firebox.

N7/4³ Introduced 1940. Pre-grouping G.E. design (N7), rebuilt with round-topped firebox, retaining short-travel valves.

4-6-2T   3MT   Class A5

A5/1 Introduced 1911. Robinson G.C. design.
Weight: 85 tons 18 cwt.
Pressure: 180 lb. Su.
Cyls.: 20″ × 26″.
Driving Wheels: 5′ 7″.
T.E.: 23,750 lb.
P.V.

69808	69814	69820

Total 3

4-8-0T   5F   Class T1

Introduced 1909. W. Worsdell N.E.
design.
Weight: 85 tons 8 cwt.
Pressure: 175 lb.
Cyls.: (3) 18" × 26".
Driving Wheels: 4' 7¼".
T.E.: 34,080 lb.
P.V.

69921

Total 1

PRESERVED LOCOS IN WORKING ORDER

4-4-0

Introduced 1920. Heywood G. N. of S.
superheated, development of Pickersgill 1899 design. Withdrawn 1958 as
B.R. No 62277 and restored to original condition, being returned to service for special use in 1959. (L.N.E.R.
Class D40)

Weight: Loco.   48 tons 13 cwt.
         Tender 37 tons 8 cwt.
Pressure: 165 lb. Su.
Cyls.: 18" × 26".
Driving Wheels: 6' 1".
T.E.: 16,185 lb.

49 Gordon Highlander

4-4-0

Introduced 1913. Reid N.B. "Glen"
class. Withdrawn 1959 as B.R. No.
62469 and restored to original livery.
Returned to service for special use
1959. (L.N.E.R. Class D34)

Weight: Loco.   57 tons 4 cwt.
         Tender 46 tons 13 cwt.
Pressure: 165 lb. Su.
Cyls.: 20" × 26".
Driving Wheels: 6' 0".
T.E.: 20,260 lb.
P.V.

256 Glen Douglas

EASTERN REGION DIESEL LOCOMOTIVE CLASSIFICATION

Horse-power	Description			Loco. Nos.		Code
153	Hunslet/Gardner	...	...	D2950–2	...	D1/1
153	Barclay/Gardner	...	...	D2953–6	...	D1/2
165	Ruston & Hornsby	...	...	D2957–8	...	D1/3
200	N.B. Loco. Co./Paxman	...		D2700–7	...	D2/1
204	B.R./Gardner	...	...	D2000–2142	...	D2/2
204	Drewry/Gardner (3' 3" wheel)	...		D2200–14/42–86	...	D2/3
204	Drewry/Gardner (3' 6" wheel)	...		D2215–41	...	D2/4
204	Barclay/Gardner (4-speed)		...	D2400–9	...	D2/5

Horse-power	Description	Loco. Nos.	Code
204	Barclay/Gardner (5-speed) ...	D2410–44	D2/6
204	Hudswell-Clarke/Gardner...	D2500–9	D2/7
204	Hunslet/Gardner ...	D2550–D2618 ...	D2/8
225	N.B. Loco. Co./M.A.N. ...	D2708–79	D2/9
330	N.B. Loco. Co./M.A.N. ...	D2900–10	D3/1
350	B.R./English Electric ...	D3000–16/27–36/67 –3438/54–72, 3503– 3611/52–3899	} D3/2
350	B.R./Crossley	D3117–26	D3/3
350	B.R./Blackstone/G.E.C. ...	D3137–51, 3439–53 /73–3502, 3612–51	} D3/4
350	B.R./Blackstone/B.T.H. ...	D3152–66	D3/5
350	L.M.S./English Electric (4' 0½" wheel)	12000–1	D3/6
350	L.M.S./English Electric (4' 3" wheel)	12003–32	D3/7
350	B.R./English Electric	12033–12138 ...	D3/8
350	L.N.E./English Electric ...	15000–3	D3/9
350	G.W./English Electric (4' 1" wheel)	15100	D3/10
350	G.W./English Electric (4' 0½" wheel)	15101–6	D3/11
350	S.R./English Electric	15201–3	D3/12
350	S.R./English Electric	15211–36	D3/13
360	L.N.E./Petter	15004	D3/14
800	B.T.H./Paxman	D8200–36 ...	D8/1
800	N.B. Loco. Co./Paxman ...	D8400–9 ...	D8/2
1,000	N.B. Loco. Co./M.A.N./G.E.C.	D6101–6/8/9 ...	D10/1
1,000	N.B. Loco. Co./M.A.N./Voith ...	D6300–57 ...	D10/2
1,000	English Electric	D8000–49 ...	D10/3
1,100	English Electric/Napier	D5900–9 ...	D11/1
1,100	N.B. Loco. Co./M.A.N./G.E.C. ,	D6100/7/10–57 ...	D11/2
1,160	B.R./Sulzer	D5000–D5150 ...	D11/3
1,160	Birmingham/Sulzer... ...	D5300–46 ...	D11/4
1,200	Metro. Vickers/Crossley ...	D5700–19 ...	D12/1
1,250	Brush/Mirlees	D5500–19 ...	D12/2
1,365	Brush/Mirlees	D5520–5679 ...	D13/1
1,550	Birmingham/Sulzer... ...	D6500–76 ...	D15/1
1,600	L.M.S./English Electric ...	10000–1 ...	D16/1
1,600	S.R./English Electric ...	10201–2 ...	D16/2
1,750	English Electric	D6700–41 ...	D17/1
2,000	English Electric	D200–324 ...	D20/1
2,000	N.B. Loco. Co./M.A.N./Voith ...	D600–4 ...	D20/2
2,000	S.R./English Electric	10203 ...	D20/3
2,200	Maybach/Mekydro	D800–32 ...	D22/1
2,200	N.B. Loco. Co./	D833–65 ...	D22/2
2,200	B.R./	D866–70 ...	D22/3
2,300	B.R./Sulzer	D1–D124 ...	D23/1
2,500	B.R./Sulzer	D125–47 ...	D25/1
3,300	English Electric/Napier Deltic ...	D9000–21 ...	D33/1

ROUTE AVAILABILITY OF LOCOMOTIVES

CLASSES OF LOCOMOTIVES

R.A. No.	Ex-L.N.E.R. including Electric Locomotives	Ex-L.M.S.	B.R. including Diesel Locomotives
1	J15, J71, Y1, Y3	2MT (2-6-2T)	DJI2, DJI3, DJI4, DJI5, DYI, DY2, DY5, DYII
2	J72, J77, Y9	2MT (2-6-0)	—
3	J10, J21, J25, J36, J66, J68, J69, J88. N10	2F (0-6-0), 1F (0-6-0T), 3MT (2-6-2T P.B.), 3MT (2-6-2T T.B.)	2MT (2-6-0), 2MT (2-6-2T)
4	B12/3, J17, J26, J55, J83, N5, N14, EM2 (Co-Co)	3F (0-6-0 L. & Y.), 3F (0-6-0 Mid.), 4MT (2-6-0), 1P (0-4-4T), 2P (0-4-4T), 4MT (2-6-4T 2-cyl. T.B.)	3MT (2-6-0), 4MT (2-6-0), 3MT (2-6-2T), DE1 (800 h.p. N.B.).
5	B1, B17, D16/3, J6, J11, J19 J20, J27 , K2, A5, J52, J73, J94, N7, EB1 (Bo-Bo)	2P (4-4-0), 4F (0-6-0), 7F (0-8-0 Std.), 3F (0-6-0T), 4MT (2-6-4T P.B.), 3F (0-6-2T)	DE2 (1,000 h.p. N.B.), DE2 (1,100 h.p. E.E.), 4MT (2-6-4T), DEJI, DEJ2, DEJ3, DEJ4, DEJ5, DEJ6
6	C16, D11, D34, J35, J39, K1, K4, N15 O1, O2, O4, WD8, Q6, J50, N2, V1, Y4.	8F (2-8-0 Std.), 7F (0-8-0 L.N.W.), 3P (4-4-2T)	DE1 (1,000 h.p. E.E.), DE2 (1,160 h.p. B.R.), DE2 (1 250 h.p. Brush), DE2 (1,365 h.p. Brush)
7	Q7, L1, V3	5MT (4-6-0), 4P (4-4-0), 6P/5F (2-6-0 P.B.), 6P/5F (2-6-0 T.B.), 4MT (2-6-4T 3-cyl.)	4MT (4-6-0), 5MT (4-6-0), DE2 (1,160 h.p. B.C.W.), DE4 (2,000 h.p. E.E.), DE4 (2,000 h.p. N.B.)
8	B16/1, B16/2, B16/3, D49, J37, J38, K3, T1	6P (4-6-0 " Jubilee "), 6P (4-6-0 " Patriot ")	6MT (4-6-2), 7MT (4-6-2)
9	A1, A2, A3, A4, V2, EM1 (Bo-Bo)	7P (4-6-0 Converted " Jubilee "), 7P (4-6-0 Converted " Patriot "), 7P (4-6-0 " Scot ")	9F (2-10-0)

BRITISH RAILWAYS
EASTERN & NORTH EASTERN REGIONS

CHIEF MECHANICAL ENGINEER
A. H. Peppercorn ... 1948–1949
(*post abolished*)

LOCOMOTIVE SUPERINTENDENTS AND CHIEF MECHANICAL ENGINEERS OF THE L.N.E.R.

Sir Nigel Gresley	1923–1941	E. Thompson ... ... 1941 - 1946
A. H. Peppercorn ...	... 1946–1947	

GREAT NORTHERN RAILWAY

A. Sturrock	...	...	1850–1866
P. Stirling	...	...	1866–1895
H. A. Ivatt	...	...	1896–1911
H. N. Gresley	...	...	1911–1922

NORTH EASTERN RAILWAY

E. Fletcher	...	...	1854–1883
A. McDonnell*	...	...	1883–1884
T. W. Worsdell	...	...	1885–1890
W. Worsdell	...	...	1890–1910
Sir Vincent Raven	...	1910–1922

GREAT EASTERN RAILWAY

R. Sinclair	...	...	1862–1866
S. W. Johnson	...	...	1866–1873
W. Adams	...	...	1873–1878
M. Bromley	...	...	1878–1881
T. W. Worsdell	...	...	1881–1885
J. Holden	...	...	1885–1907
S. D. Holden	...	...	1908–1912
A. J. Hill	...	...	1912–1922

LANCASHIRE, DERBYSHIRE AND EAST COAST RAILWAY

R. A. Thom	...	...	1902–1907

MANCHESTER, SHEFFIELD AND LINCOLNSHIRE RAILWAY

Richard Peacock	...	...	–1854
W. G. Craig	...	...	1854–1859

GREAT CENTRAL RAILWAY

Charles Sacré	...	...	1859–1886
T. Parker	...	...	1886–1893
H. Pollitt	...	...	1893–1897

GREAT CENTRAL RAILWAY

H. Pollitt	...	...	1897–1900
J. G. Robinson	...	...	1900–1922

HULL AND BARNSLEY RAILWAY

M. Stirling	...	...	1885–1922

MIDLAND AND GREAT NORTHERN JOINT RAILWAY

W. Marriott	...	...	1884–1924

NORTH BRITISH RAILWAY

T. Wheatley†	...	...	1867–1874
D. Drummond	...	...	1875–1882
M. Holmes	...	...	1882–1903
W. P. Reid	...	...	1903–1919
W. Chalmers	...	...	1919–1922

GREAT NORTH OF SCOTLAND RAILWAY

D. K. Clark	...	...	1853–1855
J. F. Ruthven	...	...	1855–1857
W. Cowan	...	...	1857–1883
J. Manson	...	...	1883–1890
J. Johnson	...	...	1890–1894
W. Pickersgill	...	...	1894–1914
T. E. Heywood	...	...	1914–1922

* Between McDonnell and T. W. Worsdell there was an interval during which the office was covered by a Locomotive Committee.

† Previous to whom the records are indeterminate.

BRITISH RAILWAYS STANDARD LOCOMOTIVES

Chief Mechanical Engineer
J. F. HARRISON

4-6-2   **7P6F**

Introduced 1951. Designed at Derby.
Weight: Loco. 94 tons 0 cwt.
Pressure: 250 lb. Su.
Cyls.: (O) 20″ × 28″.
Driving Wheels: 6′ 2″. T.E.: 32,150 lb.
Walschaerts valve gear. P V.

70000	Britannia
70001	Lord Hurcomb
70002	Geoffrey Chaucer
70003	John Bunyan
70004	William Shakespeare
70005	John Milton
70006	Robert Burns
70007	Coeur-de-Lion
70008	Black Prince
70009	Alfred the Great
70010	Owen Glendower
70011	Hotspur
70012	John of Gaunt
70013	Oliver Cromwell
70014	Iron Duke
70015	Apollo
70016	Ariel
70017	Arrow
70018	Flying Dutchman
70019	Lightning
70020	Mercury
70021	Morning Star
70022	Tornado
70023	Venus
70024	Vulcan
70025	Western Star
70026	Polar Star
70027	Rising Star
70028	Royal Star
70029	Shooting Star
70030	William Wordsworth
70031	Byron
70032	Tennyson
70033	Charles Dickens
70034	Thomas Hardy
70035	Rudyard Kipling
70036	Boadicea
70037	Hereward the Wake
70038	Robin Hood
70039	Sir Christopher Wren
70040	Clive of India
70041	Sir John Moore
70042	Lord Roberts
70043	Lord Kitchener
70044	Earl Haig
70045	Lord Rowallan
70046	Anzac
70047	
70048	The Territorial Army 1908-1958
70049	Solway Firth
70050	Firth of Clyde
70051	Firth of Forth
70052	Firth of Tay
70053	Moray Firth
70054	Dornoch Firth

Total 55

4-6-2   **8P**

Introduced 1954. Designed at Derby.
Weight: Loco. 101 tons 5 cwt.
Pressure: 250 lb. Su.
Cyls: (3) 18″ × 28″.
Driving Wheels: 6′ 2″. T.E.: 39,080 lb.
Caprotti valve gear.

71000	Duke of Gloucester

Total 1

4-6-2   **6P5F**

Introduced 1952. Designed at Derby.
Weight: Loco. 86 tons 19 cwt.
Pressure: 225 lb. Su.
Cyls.: (O) 19¼″ × 28″.
Driving Wheels: 6′ 2″. T.E.: 27,520 lb.
Walschaerts valve gear. P.V. ′

72000	Clan Buchanan
72001	Clan Cameron
72002	Clan Campbell

72003	Clan Fraser	
72004	Clan Macdonald	
72005	Clan Macgregor	
72006	Clan Mackenzie	
72007	Clan Mackintosh	
72008	Clan Macleod	
72009	Clan Stewart	**Total 10**

4-6-0   5

Introduced 1951. Designed at Doncaster.
*Introduced 1956. Fitted with Caprotti valve gear.
Weight: Loco. 76 tons 4 cwt.
Pressure: 225 lb. Su.
Cyls.: (O) 19″ × 28″.
Driving Wheels: 6′ 2″. T.E.: 26,120 lb.
Walschaerts valve gear. P.V.

73000	73020	73040	73060
73001	73021	73041	73061
73002	73022	73042	73062
73003	73023	73043	73063
73004	73024	73044	73064
73005	73025	73045	73065
73006	73026	73046	73066
73007	73027	73047	73067
73008	73028	73048	73068
73009	73029	73049	73069
73010	73030	73050	73070
73011	73031	73051	73071
73012	73032	73052	73072
73013	73033	73053	73073
73014	73034	73054	73074
73015	73035	73055	73075
73016	73036	73056	73076
73017	73037	73057	73077
73018	73038	73058	73078
73019	73039	73059	73079

73080	Merlin
73081	Excalibur
73082	Camelot
73083	Pendragon
73084	Tintagel
73085	Melisande
73086	The Green Knight
73087	Linette
73088	Joyous Gard
73089	Maid of Astolat

73090	73095	73100	73105
73091	73096	73101	73106
73092	73097	73102	73107
73093	73098	73103	73108
73094	73099	73104	73109

73110	The Red Knight
73111	King Uther
73112	Morgan le Fay
73113	Lyonnesse
73114	Etarre
73115	King Pellinore
73116	Iseult
73117	Vivien
73118	King Leodegrance
73119	Elaine

73120	73133*	73146*	73159
73121	73134*	73147*	73160
73122	73135*	73148*	73161
73123	73136*	73149*	73162
73124	73137*	73150*	73163
73125*	73138*	73151*	73164
73126*	73139*	73152*	73165
73127*	73140*	73153*	73166
73128*	73141*	73154*	73167
73129*	73142*	73155	73168
73130*	73143*	73156	73169
73131*	73144*	73157	73170
73132*	73145*	73158	73171

Total 172

4-6-0   4

Introduced 1951. Designed at Brighton.
*Introduced 1957. Fitted with double chimney.
Weight: Loco. 69 tons 0 cwt.
Pressure: 225 lb. Su.
Cyls.: (O) 18″ × 28″.
Driving Wheels: 5′ 8″. T.E.: 25,100 lb.
Walschaerts valve gear. P.V.

75000	75008	75016	75024
75001	75009	75017	75025
75002	75010	75018	75026
75003	75011	75019	75027
75004	75012	75020	75028
75005	75013	75021	75029*
75006	75014	75022	75030
75007	75015	75023	75031

75032	75044	75056	75068
75033	75045	75057	75069
75034	75046	75058	75070
75035	75047	75059	75071
75036	75048	75060	75072
75037	75049	75061	75073
75038	75050	75062	75074
75039	75051	75063	75075
75040	75052	75064	75076
75041	75053	75065	75077
75042	75054	75066	75078
75043	75055	75067	75079

Total 80

2-6-0   4

Introduced 1953. Designed at Doncaster.
Weight: Loco. 59 tons 2 cwt.
Pressure: 225 lb. Su.
Cyls.: (O) 17½″ × 26″.
Driving Wheels: 5′ 3″. T.E.: 24,170 lb.
Walschaerts valve gear. P.V.

76000	76026	76052	76078
76001	76027	76053	76079
76002	76028	76054	76080
76003	76029	76055	76081
76004	76030	76056	76082
76005	76031	76057	76083
76006	76032	76058	76084
76007	76033	76059	76085
76008	76034	76060	76086
76009	76035	76061	76087
76010	76036	76062	76088
76011	76037	76063	76089
76012	76038	76064	76090
76013	76039	76065	76091
76014	76040	76066	76092
76015	76041	76067	76093
76016	76042	76068	76094
76017	76043	76069	76095
76018	76044	76070	76096
76019	76045	76071	76097
76020	76046	76072	76098
76021	76047	76073	76099
76022	76048	76074	76100
76023	76049	76075	76101
76024	76050	76076	76102
76025	76051	76077	76103

76104	76107	76110	76113
76105	76108	76111	76114
76106	76109	76112	

Total 115

2-6-0   3

Introduced 1954. Designed at Swindon.
Weight: Loco. 57 tons 9 cwt.
Pressure: 200 lb. Su.
Cyls.: (O) 17½″ × 26″.
Driving Wheels: 5′ 3″. T.E.: 21,490 lb.
Walschaerts valve gear. P.V.

77000	77005	77010	77015
77001	77006	77011	77016
77002	77007	77012	77017
77003	77008	77013	77018
77004	77009	77014	77019

Total 20

2-6-0   2

Introduced 1953. Designed at Derby.
Weight: Loco. 49 tons 5 cwt.
Pressure: 200 lb. Su.
Cyls.: (O) 16½″ × 24″.
Driving Wheels: 5′ 0″. T.E.: 18,515 lb.
Walschaerts valve gear. P.V.

78000	78017	78033	78049
78001	78018	78034	78050
78002	78019	78035	78051
78003	78020	78036	78052
78004	78021	78037	78053
78005	78022	78038	78054
78006	78023	78039	78055
78007	78024	78040	78056
78008	78025	78041	78057
78009	78026	78042	78058
78010	78027	78043	78059
78011	78028	78044	78060
78012	78029	78045	78061
78013	78030	78046	78062
78014	78031	78047	78063
78015	78032	78048	78064
78016			

Total 65

2-6-4T   4

Introduced 1951. Designed at Brighton.
Weight: 88 tons 10 cwt.
Pressure: 225 lb. Su.
Cyls.: (O) 18″ × 28″.
Driving Wheels: 5′ 8″. T.E.: 25,100 lb.
Walschaerts valve gear.   P.V.

80000	80039	80078	80117
80001	80040	80079	80118
80002	80041	80080	80119
80003	80042	80081	80120
80004	80043	80082	80121
80005	80044	80083	80122
80006	80045	80084	80123
80007	80046	80085	80124
80008	80047	80086	80125
80009	80048	80087	80126
80010	80049	80088	80127
80011	80050	80089	80128
80012	80051	80090	80129
80013	80052	80091	80130
80014	80053	80092	80131
80015	80054	80093	80132
80016	80055	80094	80133
80017	80056	80095	80134
80018	80057	80096	80135
80019	80058	80097	80136
80020	80059	80098	80137
80021	80060	80099	80138
80022	80061	80100	80139
80023	80062	80101	80140
80024	80063	80102	80141
80025	80064	80103	80142
80026	80065	80104	80143
80027	80066	80105	80144
80028	80067	80106	80145
80029	80068	80107	80146
80030	80069	80108	80147
80031	80070	80109	80148
80032	80071	80110	80149
80033	80072	80111	80150
80034	80073	80112	80151
80035	80074	80113	80152
80036	80075	80114	80153
80037	80076	80115	80154
80038	80077	80116	

Total 155

2-6-2T   3

Introduced 1952. Designed at Swindon.
Weight: 73 tons 10 cwt.
Pressure: 200 lb. Su.
Cyls.: (O) 17½″ × 26″.
Driving Wheels: 5′ 3″. T.E.: 21,490 lb.
Walschaerts valve gear.   P.V.

82000	82012	82024	82036
82001	82013	82025	82037
82002	82014	82026	82038
82003	82015	82027	82039
82004	82016	82028	82040
82005	82017	82029	82041
82006	82018	82030	82042
82007	82019	82031	82043
82008	82020	82032	82044
82009	82021	82033	
82010	82022	82034	
82011	82023	82035	

Total 45

2-6-2T   2

Introduced 1953. Designed at Derby.
Weight: 63 tons 5 cwt.
Pressure: 200 lb. Su.
Cyls.: (O) 16½″ × 24″.
Driving Wheels: 5′ 0″. T.E.: 18,515 lb.
Walschaerts valve gear.   P.V.

84000	84008	84016	84023
84001	84009	84017	84024
84002	84010	84018	84025
84003	84011	84019	84026
84004	84012	84020	84027
84005	84013	84021	84028
84006	84014	84022	84029
84007	84015		

Total 30

2-8-0   8F   WD

Ministry of Supply " Austerity " 2-8-0
    locomotives purchased by British
    Railways, 1948.
Introduced 1943. Riddles M.o.S. design.
Weight: Loco.   70 tons 5 cwt.
         Tender 55 tons 10 cwt.
Pressure: 225 lb. Su.
Cyls.: (O) 19″ × 28″.
Driving Wheels: 4′ 8½″. T.E.: 34,215 lb.
Walschaerts valve gear.   P.V.

90000	90047	90096	90143	90190	90238	90285	90332
90001	90048	90097	90144	90192	90239	90286	90333
90002	90049	90098	90145	90193	90240	90287	90334
90003	90050	90099	90146	90194	90241	90288	90335
90004	90051	90100	90147	90195	90242	90289	90336
90005	90052	90101	90148	90196	90243	90290	90337
90006	90053	90102	90149	90197	90244	90291	90338
90007	90054	90103	90150	90198	90245	90292	90339
90008	90055	90104	90151	90199	90246	90293	90340
90009	90056	90105	90152	90200	90247	90294	90341
90010	90057	90106	90153	90201	90248	90295	90342
90011	90058	90107	90154	90202	90249	90296	90343
90012	90059	90108	90155	90203	90250	90297	90344
90013	90060	90109	90156	90204	90251	90298	90345
90014	90061	90110	90157	90205	90252	90299	90346
90015	90063	90111	90158	90206	90253	90300	90347
90016	90064	90112	90159	90207	90254	90301	90348
90017	90065	90113	90160	90208	90255	90302	90349
90018	90066	90114	90161	90209	90256	90303	90350
90019	90067	90115	90162	90210	90257	90304	90351
90020	90068	90116	90163	90211	90258	90305	90352
90021	90069	90117	90164	90212	90259	90306	90353
90022	90070	90118	90165	90213	90260	90307	90354
90023	90071	90119	90166	90214	90261	90308	90355
90024	90072	90120	90167	90215	90262	90309	90356
90025	90073	90121	90168	90216	90263	90310	90357
90026	90074	90122	90169	90217	90264	90311	90358
90027	90075	90123	90170	90218	90265	90312	90359
90028	90076	90124	90171	90219	90266	90313	90360
90029	90077	90125	90172	90220	90267	90314	90361
90030	90078	90126	90173	90221	90268	90315	90362
90031	90079	90127	90174	90222	90269	90316	90363
90032	90080	90128	90175	90223	90270	90317	90364
90033	90081	90129	90176	90224	90271	90318	90365
90034	90082	90130	90177	90225	90272	90319	90366
90035	90084	90131	90178	90226	90273	90320	90367
90036	90085	90132	90179	90227	90274	90321	90368
90037	90086	90133	90180	90228	90275	90322	90369
90038	90087	90134	90181	90229	90276	90323	90370
90039	90088	90135	90182	90230	90277	90324	90371
90040	90089	90136	90183	90231	90278	90325	90372
90041	90090	90137	90184	90232	90279	90326	90373
90042	90091	90138	90185	90233	90280	90327	90374
90043	90092	90139	90186	90234	90281	90328	90375
90044	90093	90140	90187	90235	90282	90329	90376
90045	90094	90141	90188	90236	90283	90330	90377
90046	90095	90142	90189	90237	90284	90331	90378

90379	90426	90473	90520	90567	90610	90653	90696
90380	90427	90474	90521	90568	90611	90654	90697
90381	90428	90475	90522	90569	90612	90655	90698
90382	90429	90476	90523	90570	90613	90656	90699
90383	90430	90477	90524	90571	90614	90657	90700
90384	90431	90478	90525	90572	90615	90658	90701
90385	90432	90479	90526	90573	90616	90659	90702
90386	90433	90480	90527	90574	90617	90660	90703
90387	90434	90481	90528	90575	90618	90661	90704
90388	90435	90482	90529	90576	90619	90662	90705
90389	90436	90483	90530	90577	90620	90663	90706
90390	90437	90484	90531	90578	90621	90664	90707
90391	90438	90485	90532	90579	90622	90665	90708
90392	90439	90486	90533	90580	90623	90666	90709
90393	90440	90487	90534	90581	90624	90667	90710
90394	90441	90488	90535	90582	90625	90668	90711
90395	90442	90489	90536	90583	90626	90669	90712
90396	90443	90490	90537	90584	90627	90670	90713
90397	90444	90491	90538	90585	90628	90671	90714
90398	90445	90492	90539	90586	90629	90672	90715
90399	90446	90493	90540	90587	90630	90673	90716
90400	90447	90494	90541	90588	90631	90674	90717
90401	90448	90495	90542	90589	90632	90675	90718
90402	90449	90496	90543	90590	90633	90676	90719
90403	90450	90497	90544	90591	90634	90677	90720
90404	90451	90498	90545	90592	90635	90678	90721
90405	90452	90499	90546	90593	90636	90679	90722
90406	90453	90500	90547	90594	90637	90680	90723
90407	90454	90501	90548	90595	90638	90681	90724
90408	90455	90502	90549	90596	90639	90682	90725
90409	90456	90503	90550	90597	90640	90683	90726
90410	90457	90504	90551	90598	90641	90684	90727
90411	90458	90505	90552	90599	90642	90685	90728
90412	90459	90506	90553	90600	90643	90686	90729
90413	90460	90507	90554	90601	90644	90687	90730
90414	90461	90508	90555	90602	90645	90688	90731
90415	90462	90509	90556	90603	90646	90689	90732
90416	90463	90510	90557	90604	90647	90690	Vulcan
90417	90464	90511	90558	90605	90648	90691	
90418	90465	90512	90559	90606	90649	90692	
90419	90466	90513	90560	90607	90650	90693	
90420	90467	90514	90561	90608	90651	90694	
90421	90468	90515	90562	90609	90652	90695	
90422	90469	90516	90563				
90423	90470	90517	90564				**Total 730**
90424	90471	90518	90565				
90425	90472	90519	90566				

2-10-0 WD

Ministry of Supply " Austerity " 2-10-0 locomotives purchased by British Railways, 1948.
Introduced 1943. Riddles M.o.S. design.
Weight: Loco. 78 tons 6 cwt.
　　　　　Tender 55 tons 10 cwt.
Pressure: 225 lb. Su.
Cyls.: (O) 19″ × 28″.
Driving Wheels: 4′ 8½″. T.E.: 34,215 lb.
Walschaerts valve gear. P.V.

90750	90757	90763	90769
90751	90758	90764	90770
90752	90759	90765	90771
90753	90760	90766	90772
90754	90761	90767	90773
90755	90762	90768	90774
90756			**Total 25**

2-10-0 9F

Introduced 1954. Designed at Brighton.
*Introduced 1955. Fitted with Crosti boiler, some engines later having Crosti pre-heater sealed off for orthodox working.
†Introduced 1957. Fitted with double chimney.
‡Introduced 1958. Fitted with Mechanical Stoker and double chimney.
Weight: Loco. {86 tons 14 cwt.
　　　　　　{90 tons 4 cwt.*
Pressure: 250 lb. Su.
Cyls.: (O) 20″ × 28″.
Driving Wheels: 5′ 0″. T.E.: 39,670 lb.
Walschaerts valve gear. P.V.

92000†	92018	92036	92054	92072	92117	92162	92207†
92001	92019	92037	92055	92073	92118	92163	92208†
92002	92020*	92038	92056	92074	92119	92164	92209†
92003	92021*	92039	92057	92075	92120	92165‡	92210†
92004	92022*	92040	92058	92076	92121	92166‡	92211†
92005	92023*	92041	92059	92077	92122	92167‡	92212†
92006	92024*	92042	92060	92078	92123	92168	92213†
92007	92025*	92043	92061	92079†	92124	92169	92214†
92008	92026*	92044	92062	92080	92125	92170	92215†
92009	92027*	92045	92063	92081	92126	92171	92216†
92010	92028*	92046	92064	92082	92127	92172	92217†
92011	92029*	92047	92065	92083	92128	92173	92218†
92012	92030	92048	92066	92084	92129	92174	92219†
92013	92031	92049	92067	92085	92130	92175	92220†§
92014	92032	92050	92068	92086	92131	92176	92221†
92015	92033	92051	92069	92087	92132	92177	92222†
92016	92034	92052	92070	92088	92133	92178†	92223†
92017	92035	92053	92071	92089	92134	92179	92224†
				92090	92135	92180	92225†
				92091	92136	92181	92226†
				92092	92137	92182	92227†
				92093	92138	92183†	92228†
				92094	92139	92184†	92229†
				92095	92140	92185†	92230†
				92096	92141	92186†	92231†
				92097	92142	92187†	92232†
				92098	92143	92188†	92233†
				92099	92144	92189†	92234†
				92100	92145	92190†	92235†
				92101	92146	92191†	92236†
				92102	92147	92192†	92237†
				92103	92148	92193†	92238†
				92104	92149	92194†	92239†
				92105	92150	92195†	92240†
				92106	92151	92196†	92241†
				92107	92152	92197†	92242†
				92108	92153	92198†	92243†
				92109	92154	92199†	92244†
				92110	92155	92200†	92245†
				92111	92156	92201†	92246†
				92112	92157	92202†	92247†
				92113	92158	92203†	92248†
				92114	92159	92204†	92249†
				92115	92160	92205†	92250†
				92116	92161	92206†	**Total 251**

§ 92220 named *Evening Star.*

BRITISH RAILWAYS DIESEL

LOCOMOTIVE CLASSES

The lists of numbers include all locomotives on order at the time of going to press. For details of delivery, see the Locomotive Stock change list each month in Trains Illustrated.

ICo-CoI   " 4 "

"PEAK" CLASS

Introduced: 1959.

Locomotive manufacturer: B.R.

Total b.h.p.: $\begin{cases} 2,300. \\ 2,500*† \end{cases}$

Engine: Sulzer 12LDA28 twin bank pressure charged, 12-cyl. type of 2,300 b.h.p. (2.500 b.h.p.†) at 750 r.p.m.

Transmission: **Electric.** Six Crompton Parkinson 305 h.p. axle-hung nose-suspended traction motors.

  Electric: Six Brush traction motors.†

Weight: 138 tons 2 cwt.

Driving Wheels: 3′ 9″.

Maximum tractive effort: 70,000 lb.

DI	Scafell Pike
D2*	Helvellyn
D3	Skiddaw
D4	Great Gable
D5	Cross Fell
D6	Whernside
D7	Ingleborough
D8	Penyghent
D9	Snowdon
D10	Tryfan

DII*	DI5*	DI9*	D23*
DI2*	DI6*	D20*	D24*
DI3*	DI7*	D2I*	D25*
DI4*	DI8*	D22*	D26*

D27*	D58*	D89*	DI20*
D28*	D59*	D90*	DI2I*
D29*	D60*	D9I*	DI22*
D30*	D6I*	D92*	DI23*
D3I*	D62*	D93*	DI24*
D32*	D63*	D94*	DI25*
D33*	D64*	D95*	DI26*
D34*	D65*	D96*	DI27*
D35*	D66*	D97*	DI28*
D36*	D67*	D98*	DI29*
D37*	D68*	D99*	DI30*
D38*	D69*	DI00*	DI3I*
D39*	D70*	DI0I*	DI32*
D40*	D7I*	DI02*	DI33*
D4I*	D72*	DI03*	DI34*
D42*	D73*	DI04*	DI35*
D43*	D74*	DI05*	DI36*
D44*	D75*	DI06*	DI37*
D45*	D76*	DI07*	DI38*
D46*	D77*	DI08*	DI39*
D47*	D78*	DI09*	DI40*
D48*	D79*	DII0*	DI4I*
D49*	D80*	DIII*	DI42*
D50*	D8I*	DII2*	DI43*
D5I*	D82*	DII3*	DI44*
D52*	D83*	DII4*	DI45*
D53*	D84*	DII5*	DI46*
D54*	D85*	DII6*	DI47*
D55*	D86*	DII7*	DI48†
D56*	D87*	DII8*	DI49†
D57*	D88*	DII9*	DI50†

D151†	D164†	D177†	D190†
D152†	D165†	D178†	D191†
D153†	D166†	D179†	D192†
D154†	D167†	D180†	D193†
D155†	D168†	D181†	D194†
D156†	D169†	D182†	D195†
D157†	D170†	D183†	D196†
D158†	D171†	D184†	D197†
D159†	D172†	D185†	D198†
D160†	D173†	D186†	D199†
D161†	D174†	D187†	
D162†	D175†	D188†	
D163†	D176†	D189†	

ICo-CoI   " 4 "

Introduced: 1958.
Locomotive manufacturer: English Electric.
Total b.h.p.: 2,000.
Engine: English Electric 16SVT. Mk. II of 2,000 b.h.p. at 850 r.p.m.
Transmission: **Electric.** Six English Electric nose-suspended traction motors.
Weight: 133 tons.
Driving Wheels: 3′ 9″
Maximum tractive effort: 52,000 lb.
Classified **D20**/**1** by the E. & N.E.R.

D200	D218	D236	D254
D201	D219	D237	D255
D202	D220	D238	D256
D203	D221	D239	D257
D204	D222	D240	D258
D205	D223	D241	D259
D206	D224	D242	D260
D207	D225	D243	D261
D208	D226	D244	D262
D209	D227	D245	D263
D210*	D228	D246	D264
D211	D229	D247	D265
D212	D230	D248	D266
D213	D231	D249	D267
D214	D232	D250	D268
D215	D233	D251	D269
D216	D234	D252	D270
D217	D235	D253	D271

D272	D304	D336	D368
D273	D305	D337	D369
D274	D306	D338	D370
D275	D307	D339	D371
D276	D308	D340	D372
D277	D309	D341	D373
D278	D310	D342	D374
D279	D311	D343	D375
D280	D312	D344	D376
D281	D313	D345	D377
D282	D314	D346	D378
D283	D315	D347	D379
D284	D316	D348	D380
D285	D317	D349	D381
D286	D318	D350	D382
D287	D319	D351	D383
D288	D320	D352	D384
D289	D321	D353	D385
D290	D322	D354	D386
D291	D323	D355	D387
D292	D324	D356	D388
D293	D325	D357	D389
D294	D326	D358	D390
D295	D327	D359	D391
D296	D328	D360	D392
D297	D329	D361	D393
D298	D330	D362	D394
D299	D331	D363	D395
D300	D332	D364	D396
D301	D333	D365	D397
D302	D334	D366	D398
D303	D335	D367	D399

* Named " Empress of Britain. "

AIA-AIA   " 4 "

" WARSHIP " CLASS

Introduced: 1958.
Locomotive manufacturer: North British Locomotive Co.
Total b.h.p.: 2,000.
Engines: Two N.B.L./M.A.N. type L12V 18/21S 12-cyl. of 1,000 b.h.p.
Transmission: **Hydraulic.** Two Hardy Spicer cardan shafts to Voith-North British type L306r hydraulic transmissions each containing three torque converters.

Weight: 117 tons 8 cwt.
Driving Wheels: 3′ 7″.
Maximum tractive effort: 50,000 lb.

D600	Active
D601	Ark Royal
D602	Bulldog
D603	Conquest
D604	Cossack

B-B   " 4 "

" WARSHIP " CLASS

Introduced: 1958.
Locomotive manufacturer: Swindon Works, B.R.
Total b.h.p.: 2,000*
2,200.
2,400†
Engines: Two-Bristol-Siddeley-Maybach MD 650 V-type of 1,152 b.h.p. at 1,530 r.p.m. (*1,056 b.h.p. at 1.400 r.p.m.)
†Two Paxman 12-cyl. high-speed 12YJXL of 1,200 b.h.p. at 1,500 r.p.m.
Transmission: **Hydraulic.** Two Mekydro type K104 hydraulic transmissions containing permanently filled single torque converter and four-speed automatic gearbox.
Weight: 78 tons.
Driving Wheels: 3′ 3½″.
Maximum tractive effort: 52,400 lb.

D800*	Sir Brian Robertson
D801*	Vanguard
D802*	Formidable
D803	Albion
D804	Avenger
D805	Benbow
D806	Cambrian
D807	Caradoc
D808	Centaur
D809	Champion
D810	Cockade
D811	Daring
D812	Royal Naval Reserve 1859-1959
D813	Diadem
D814	Dragon
D815	Druid

D816	Eclipse
D817	Foxhound
D818	Glory
D819	Goliath
D820	Grenville
D821	Greyhound
D822	Hercules
D823	Hermes
D824	Highflyer
D825	Intrepid
D826	Jupiter
D827	Kelly
D828	Magnificent
D829	Magpie
D830	Majestic
D831	Monarch
D832†	Onslaught

B-B   " 4 "

" WARSHIP " CLASS

Introduced: 1960.
Locomotive manufacturer: North British Locomotive Co.
Total b.h.p.: 2,200.
Engines:
Transmission: **Hydraulic.**
Weight:
Driving Wheels:
Maximum tractive effort:

D833	Panther
D834	Pathfinder
D835	Pegasus
D836	Powerful
D837	Ramillies
D838	Rapid
D839	Relentless
D840	Resistance
D841	Roebuck
D842	Royal Oak
D843	Sharpshooter
D844	Spartan
D845	Sprightly
D846	Steadfast
D847	Strongbow
D848	Sultan
D849	Superb

D850	Swift
D851	Temeraire
D852	Tenacious
D853	Thruster
D854	Tiger
D855	Triumph
D856	Trojan
D857	Undaunted
D858	Valorous
D859	Vanquisher
D860	Victorious
D861	Vigilant
D862	Viking
D863	Warrior
D864	Zealous
D865	Zenith

B-B   "4"

D866-70 for particulars see Nos. D800-32.

D866
D867
D868
D869
D870

C-C   "4"

To be introduced:
Locomotive manufacturer: B.R.
Total b.h.p.: 2,700.
Engines: Maybach M.D. 655.
Transmission: **Hydraulic** Voith.
Weight:
Driving Wheels:
Maximum tractive effort:

D1000	D1007	D1014	D1021
D1001	D1008	D1015	D1022
D1002	D1009	D1016	D1023
D1003	D1010	D1017	D1024
D1004	D1011	D1018	D1025
D1005	D1012	D1019	D1026
D1006	D1013	D1020	D1027

D1028	D1040	D1052	D1064
D1029	D1041	D1053	D1065
D1030	D1042	D1054	D1066
D1031	D1043	D1055	D1067
D1032	D1044	D1056	D1068
D1033	D1045	D1057	D1069
D1034	D1046	D1058	D1070
D1035	D1047	D1059	D1071
D1036	D1048	D1060	D1072
D1037	D1049	D1061	D1073
D1038	D1050	D1062	
D1039	D1051	D1063	

ICo-Col   "4"

"PEAK" CLASS

D1500-12 for particulars see Nos. D1-199.

D1500†	D1504†	D1508†	D1512†
D1501†	D1505†	D1509†	
D1502†	D1506†	D1510†	
D1503†	D1507†	D1511†	

0-6-0   Shunter

Introduced: 1957.
Locomotive manufacturer: B.R.
Total b.h.p.: 204
Engine: Gardner type 8L3 of 204 b.h.p. at 1,200 r.p.m.
Transmission: **Mechanical.** Vulcan-Sinclair type 23 fluid coupling. Wilson-Drewry C.A.5 type five-speed epicyclic gearbox. Type RF 11 spiral bevel reverse and final drive unit.
Weight: 30 tons 16 cwt.
Driving Wheels: 3' 7".
Maximum tractive effort: 15,650 lb.
Classified **D2/2** by the E. & N.E.R.

(Original numbers in brackets)

D2000 (11187)	D2005 (11192)
D2001 (11188)	D2006 (11193)
D2002 (11189)	D2007 (11194)
D2003 (11190)	D2008 (11195)
D2004 (11191)	D2009 (11196)

D2010 (11197)	D2017 (11204)
D2011 (11198)	D2018 (11205)
D2012 (11199)	D2019 (11206)
D2013 (11200)	D2020 (11207)
D2014 (11201)	D2021 (11208)
D2015 (11202)	D2022 (11209)
D2016 (11203)	

D2023	D2061	D2099	D2137
D2024	D2062	D2100	D2138
D2025	D2063	D2101	D2139
D2026	D2064	D2102	D2140
D2027	D2065	D2103	D2141
D2028	D2066	D2104	D2142
D2029	D2067	D2105	D2143
D2030	D2068	D2106	D2144
D2031	D2069	D2107	D2145
D2032	D2070	D2108	D2146
D2033	D2071	D2109	D2147
D2034	D2072	D2110	D2148
D2035	D2073	D2111	D2149
D2036	D2074	D2112	D2150
D2037	D2075	D2113	D2151
D2038	D2076	D2114	D2152
D2039	D2077	D2115	D2153
D2040	D2078	D2116	D2154
D2041	D2079	D2117	D2155
D2042	D2080	D2118	D2156
D2043	D2081	D2119	D2157
D2044	D2082	D2120	D2158
D2045	D2083	D2121	D2159
D2046	D2084	D2122	D2160
D2047	D2085	D2123	D2161
D2048	D2086	D2124	D2162
D2049	D2087	D2125	D2163
D2050	D2088	D2126	D2164
D2051	D2089	D2127	D2165
D2052	D2090	D2128	D2166
D2053	D2091	D2129	D2167
D2054	D2092	D2130	D2168
D2055	D2093	D2131	D2169
D2056	D2094	D2132	D2170
D2057	D2095	D2133	D2171
D2058	D2096	D2134	D2172
D2059	D2097	D2135	D2173
D2060	D2098	D2136	D2174

0-6-0 Shunter

Introduced: 1952.
Locomotive manufacturer: Drewry.
Total b.h.p.: 204.
Engine: Gardner type 8L3 of 204 b.h.p. at 1,200 r.p.m.
Transmission: **Mechanical.** Vulcan-Sinclair type 23 fluid coupling. Wilson-Drewry C.A.5 type five-speed epicyclic gearbox. Type RF 11 spiral bevel reverse and final drive unit.
Weight: 29 tons 15 cwt.
Driving Wheels: 3′ 3″.
Maximum tractive effort: 16,850 lb.
Classified **D2/3** by the E. & N.E.R.

(Original numbers in brackets)

D2200 (11100)	D2208 (11109)
D2201 (11101)	D2209 (11110)
D2202 (11102)	D2210 (11111)
D2203 (11103)	D2211 (11112)
D2204 (11105)	D2212 (11113)
D2205 (11106)	D2213 (11114)
D2206 (11107)	D2214 (11115)
D2207 (11108)	

0-6-0 Shunter

Introduced: 1955.
Locomotive manufacturer: Drewry.
Total b.h.p.: 204.
Engine: Gardner type 8L3 of 204 b.h.p. at 1,200 r.p.m.
Transmission: **Mechanical.** Vulcan-Sinclair type 23 fluid coupling. Wilson-Drewry C.A.5 type five-speed epicyclic gearbox. Type RF 11 spiral bevel reverse and final drive unit.
Weight: 29 tons 15 cwt.
Driving Wheels: 3′ 6″.
Maximum tractive effort: 15,650 lb.
Classified **D2/4** by the E. & N.E.R.

(Original numbers in brackets)

D2215 (11121)	D2223 (11129)
D2216 (11122)	D2224 (11130)
D2217 (11123)	D2225 (11131)
D2218 (11124)	D2226 (11132)
D2219 (11125)	D2227 (11133)
D2220 (11126)	D2228 (11134)
D2221 (11127)	D2229 (11135)
D2222 (11128)	D2230 (11149)

D2231 (11150)	D2237 (11156)
D2232 (11151)	D2238 (11157)
D2233 (11152)	D2239 (11158)
D2234 (11153)	D2240 (11159)
D2235 (11154)	D2241 (11160)
D2236 (11155)	

Maximum tractive effort: 15,340 lb.
Classified **D2/5** by the E. & N.E.R.

(Original numbers in brackets)

D2400 (11177)	D2405 (11182)
D2401 (11178)	D2406 (11183)
D2402 (11179)	D2407 (11184)
D2403 (11180)	D2408 (11185)
D2404 (11181)	D2409 (11186)

0-6-0   Shunter
D2242-D2295, FOR PARTICULARS SEE D2200-D2214.

(Original numbers in brackets)

D2242 (11212)	D2251 (11221)
D2243 (11213)	D2252 (11222)
D2244 (11214)	D2253 (11223)
D2245 (11215)	D2254 (11224)
D2246 (11216)	D2255 (11225)
D2247 (11217)	D2256 (11226)
D2248 (11218)	D2257 (11227)
D2249 (11219)	D2258 (11228)
D2250 (11220)	D2259 (11229)

D2260	D2269	D2278	D2287
D2261	D2270	D2279	D2288
D2262	D2271	D2280	D2289
D2263	D2272	D2281	D2290
D2264	D2273	D2282	D2291
D2265	D2274	D2283	D2292
D2266	D2275	D2284	D2293
D2267	D2276	D2285	D2294
D2268	D2277	D2286	D2295

0-4-0   Shunter
Introduced: 1958.
Locomotive manufacturer: Barclay.
Total b.h.p.: 204.
Engine: Gardner type 8L3 of 204 b.h.p. at 1,200 r.p.m.
Transmission: **Mechanical.** Vulcan-Sinclair type 23 fluid coupling. Wilson-Drewry C.A.5 type five-speed epicyclic gearbox. Wiseman type 15. R.L.G.B. reverse and final drive unit.
Weight: 35 tons.
Driving Wheels: 3′ 7″.
Maximum tractive effort: 20,000 lb.
Classified **D2/6** by the E. & N.E.R.

D2410	D2419	D2428	D2437
D2411	D2420	D2429	D2438
D2412	D2421	D2430	D2439
D2413	D2422	D2431	D2440
D2414	D2423	D2432	D2441
D2415	D2424	D2433	D2442
D2416	D2425	D2434	D2443
D2417	D2426	D2435	D2444
D2418	D2427	D2436	

0-6-0   Shunter
Introduced: 1956.
Locomotive manufacturer: Barclay.
Total b.h.p.: 204.
Engine: Gardner type 8L3 or 204 b.h.p. at 1,200 r.p.m.
Transmission: **Mechanical.** Vulcan-Sinclair type 23 fluid coupling. Wilson C.A.4 type four-speed epicyclic gearbox. Wiseman type 15 RLGB reverse and final drive unit.
Weight: 32 tons 0 cwt.
Driving Wheels: 3′ 6″.

0-6-0   Shunter
Introduced: 1956.
Locomotive manufacturer. Hudswell-Clarke.
Total b.h.p.: 204
Engine: Gardner type 8L3 of 204 b.h.p. at 1,200 r.p.m.
Transmission: **Mechanical.** S.C.R.5 type, size 23 scoop control fluid coupling. Three-speed " SSS Power-flow " double synchro-type gearbox and final drive.

Weight: 36 tons 7 cwt.
Driving Wheels: 3′ 6″.
Maximum tractive effort: 16,100 lb.
Classified **D2/7** by the E. & N.E.R.

(Original numbers in brackets)

D2500 (11116)	D2505 (11144)
D2501 (11117)	D2506 (11145)
D2502 (11118)	D2507 (11146)
D2503 (11119)	D2508 (11147)
D2504 (11120)	D2509 (11148)

0-6-0   Shunter

Introduced: 1955.
Locomotive manufacturer: Hunslet.
Total b.h.p.: 204.
Engine: Gardner type 8L3 of 204 b.h.p. at 1,200 r.p.m.
Transmission: **Mechanical.** Hunslet patent friction clutch. Hunslet four-speed gearbox incorporating reverse and final drive gears.
Weight: 30 tons 0 cwt.
Driving Wheels: 3′ 4″.
Maximum tractive effort: 14,500 lb.
Classified **D2/8** by E. & N.E.R.

(Original numbers in brackets)

D2550 (11136)	D2562 (11165)
D2551 (11137)	D2563 (11166)
D2552 (11138)	D2564 (11167)
D2553 (11139)	D2565 (11168)
D2554 (11140)	D2566 (11169)
D2555 (11141)	D2567 (11170)
D2556 (11142)	D2568 (11171)
D2557 (11143)	D2569 (11172)
D2558 (11161)	D2570 (11173)
D2559 (11162)	D2571 (11174)
D2560 (11163)	D2572 (11175)
D2561 (11164)	D2573 (11176)

D2574	D2583	D2592	D2601
D2575	D2584	D2593	D2602
D2576	D2585	D2594	D2603
D2577	D2586	D2595	D2604
D2578	D2587	D2596	D2605
D2579	D2588	D2597	D2606
D2580	D2589	D2598	D2607
D2581	D2590	D2599	D2608
D2582	D2591	D2600	D2609

D2610	D2613	D2615	D2617
D2611	D2614	D2616	D2618
D2612			

0-4-0   Shunter

Introduced: 1953.
Locomotive manufacturer: North British Locomotive Co.
Total b.h.p.: 200.
Engine: Paxman type 6RPH of 200 b.h.p. at 1,000 r.p.m.
Transmission: **Hydraulic.** Voith-North British hydraulic torque converter type L33YU. North British bevel gears and reversing dog clutch coupled through reduction gearing to jackshaft.
Weight: 32 tons.
Driving Wheels: 3′ 6″.
Maximum tractive effort: 21,500 lb.
Classified **D2/1** by the E. & N.E.R.

(Original numbers in brackets)

D2700 (11700)	D2704 (11704)
D2701 (11701)	D2705 (11705)
D2702 (11702)	D2706 (11706)
D2703 (11703)	D2707 (11707)

0-4-0   Shunter

Introduced: 1957.
Locomotive manufacturer: North British Locomotive Co.
Total b.h.p.: 225.
Engine: North British type M.A.N. W6V 17.5/22A of 225 b.h.p. at 1,100 r.p.m. (12 hr. rating).
Transmission: **Hydraulic.** Voith-North British hydraulic torque converter type LCCYU. North British bevel gears and reversing dog clutch coupled through reduction gearing to jackshaft.
Weight: 30 tons.
Driving Wheels: 3′ 6″.
Maximum tractive effort: 20,080 lb.
Classified **D2/9** by the E. & N.E.R.

(Original numbers in brackets)

D2708 (11708)	D2714 (11714)
D2709 (11709)	D2715 (11715)
D2710 (11710)	D2716 (11716)
D2711 (11711)	D2717 (11717)
D2712 (11712)	D2718 (11718)
D2713 (11713)	D2719 (11719)

D2720	D2735	D2750	D2765
D2721	D2736	D2751	D2766
D2722	D2737	D2752	D2767
D2723	D2738	D2753	D2768
D2724	D2739	D2754	D2769
D2725	D2740	D2755	D2770
D2726	D2741	D2756	D2771
D2727	D2742	D2757	D2772
D2728	D2743	D2758	D2773
D2729	D2744	D2759	D2774
D2730	D2745	D2760	D2775
D2731	D2746	D2761	D2776
D2732	D2747	D2762	D2777
D2733	D2748	D2763	D2778
D2734	D2749	D2764	D2779

0-4-0   Shunter

Introduced: 1958.
Locomotive manufacturer: North British Locomotive Co.
Total b.h.p.: 330.
Engine: North British/M.A.N. type W6V 17.5/22 AS, super-charged.
Transmission: **Hydraulic.** Voith-North British hydraulic torque converter type L24V. North British spiral bevel gears, reversing and reduction gears to jackshaft.
Weight: 36 tons.
Driving Wheels: 3′ 9″.
Maximum tractive effort: 24,100 lb.
Classified **D3/1** by the E. & N.E.R.

D2900	D2906	D2912	D2918
D2901	D2907	D2913	D2919
D2902	D2908	D2914	D2920
D2903	D2909	D2915	
D2904	D2910	D2916	
D2905	D2911	D2917	

0-4-0   Shunter

Introduced: 1955.
Locomotive manufacturer: Hunslet.
Total b.h.p.: 153.
Engine: Gardner type 6L3 of 153 b.h.p. at 1,200 r.p.m.

Transmission.: **Mechanical.** Hunslet patent friction clutch and four-speed gearbox incorporating reverse and final drive gears.
Weight: 22 tons 9 cwt.
Driving Wheels: 3′ 4″.
Maximum tractive effort: 10,800 lb.
Classified **D1/1** by E. & N.E.R.

(Original numbers in brackets)

D2950 (11500)	D2952 (11502)
D2951 (11501)	

0-4-0   Shunter

Introduced: 1956.
Locomotive manufacturer: Barclay.
Total b.h.p.: 153.
Engine: Gardner type 6L3 of 153 b.h.p. at 1,200 r.p.m.
Transmission: **Mechanical.** Vulcan-Sinclair rigid type hydraulic coupling. Wilson S.E. 4 type four-speed epicyclic gearbox. Wiseman type 15 RLGB reverse and final drive unit.
Weight: 25 tons.
Driving Wheels: 3′ 2″.
Maximum tractive effort: 12,750 lb.
Classified **D1/2** by E. & N.E.R.

(Original numbers in brackets)

D2953 (11503)	D2955 (11505)
D2954 (11504)	D2956 (11506)

0-4-0   Shunter

Introduced: 1956.
Locomotive manufacturer: Ruston & Hornsby.
Total b.h.p.: 165.
Engine: Ruston type 6VPHL of 165 b.h.p. at 1,250 r.p.m. (1 hr. rating).
Transmission: **Mechanical.** Oil pressure-operated S.L.M. type friction clutches incorporated in Ruston constant mesh type gearbox. Reverse gear and final drive unit incorporating bevel gears and dog clutches and reduction gear to final drive.
Weight: 28 tons.
Driving Wheels: 3′ 4″.
Maximum tractive effort: 14,350 lb.
Classified **D1/3** by the E. & N.E.R.

(Original numbers in brackets)

D2957 (11507)	D2958 (11508)

0-6-0 Shunter

Engines D3000-D3336 were originally numbered 13000-13336 and are being renumbered as they are overhauled.

Introduced: 1953.
Locomotive manufacturer: British Railways.
Total b.h.p.: 400.
Engine: English Electric 6-cyl. type 6KT of 400 b.h.p. at 630 r.p.m.
Transmission: **Electric.** Two English Electric nose-suspended traction motors. Double reduction gear drive.
Weight: 49 tons 0 cwt.
Driving Wheels: 4' 6".
Maximum tractive effort: 35,000 lb.
Classified **D3/2** by the E. & N.E.R.
Note: Nos. D3000-91 and D3102-3116 fitted for vacuum brake operation.

D3000	D3030	D3060	D3090
D3001	D3031	D3061	D3091
D3002	D3032	D3062	D3092
D3003	D3033	D3063	D3093
D3004	D3034	D3064	D3094
D3005	D3035	D3065	D3095
D3006	D3036	D3066	D3096
D3007	D3037	D3067	D3097
D3008	D3038	D3068	D3098
D3009	D3039	D3069	D3099
D3010	D3040	D3070	D3100
D3011	D3041	D3071	D3101
D3012	D3042	D3072	D3102
D3013	D3043	D3073	D3103
D3014	D3044	D3074	D3104
D3015	D3045	D3075	D3105
D3016	D3046	D3076	D3106
D3017	D3047	D3077	D3107
D3018	D3048	D3078	D3108
D3019	D3049	D3079	D3109
D3020	D3050	D3080	D3110
D3021	D3051	D3081	D3111
D3022	D3052	D3082	D3112
D3023	D3053	D3083	D3113
D3024	D3054	D3084	D3114
D3025	D3055	D3085	D3115
D3026	D3056	D3086	D3116
D3027	D3057	D3087	
D3028	D3058	D3088	
D3029	D3059	D3089	

0-6-0 Shunter

Introduced: 1955.
Locomotive manufacturer: British Railways.
Total b.h.p.: 350.
Engine: Crossley 6-cyl. type ESNT 6 of 350 b.h.p. at 825 r.p.m. (continuous rating).
Transmission: **Electric.** Two Crompton Parkinson nose-suspended traction motors. Double reduction gear drive.
Weight: 47 tons 10 cwt.
Driving Wheels: 4' 6".
Maximum tractive effort: 35,000 lb.
Classified **D3/3** by the E. & N.E.R.

D3117	D3120	D3123	D3126
D3118	D3121	D3124	
D3119	D3122	D3125	

0-6-0 Shunter

Introduced: 1953.
Locomotive manufacturer: British Railways.
Total b.h.p.: 400.
Engine: English Electric 6-cyl. type 6KT of 400 b.h.p. at 680 r.p.m.
Transmission: **Electric.** Two English Electric nose-suspended traction motors. Double reduction gear drive.
Weight: 48 tons 0 cwt.
Driving Wheels: 4' 6".
Maximum tractive effort: 35,000 lb.
Fitted for vacuum brake operation
Classified **D3/2** by the E. & N.E.R.

D3127	D3130	D3133	D3136
D3128	D3131	D3134	
D3129	D3132	D3135	

0-6-0 Shunter

Introduced: 1955.
Locomotive manufacturer: British Railways.
Total b.h.p.: 370.
Engine: Blackstone 6-cyl. type ER6T of 370 b.h.p. at 750 r.p.m.
Transmission: **Electric.** Two G.E.C. nose-suspended traction motors. Double reduction gear drive.

Weight: 47 tons 10 cwts.
Driving Wheels: 4' 6".
Maximum tractive effort: 35,000 lb.
Fitted for vacuum brake operation.
Classified **D3**/4 by the E. & N.E.R.

D3137	D3141	D3145	D3149
D3138	D3142	D3146	D3150
D3139	D3143	D3147	D3151
D3140	D3144	D3148	

0-6-0   Shunter

Introduced: 1955.
Locomotive manufacturer: British Railways.
Total b.h.p.: 370.
Engine: Blackstone 6-cyl. type ER6T of 370 b.h.p. at 750 r.p.m.

Transmission: **Electric.** Two B.T.H. nose-suspended traction motors. Double reduction gear drive.
Weight: 47 tons 0 cwt.
Driving Wheels: 4' 6".
Maximum tractive effort: 35,000 lb.
Classified **D3**/5 by the E. & N.E.R.

D3152	D3156	D3160	D3164
D3153	D3157	D3161	D3165
D3154	D3158	D3162	D3166
D3155	D3159	D3163	

D3167-D3438. FOR PARTICULARS SEE Nos. D3127-D3136.

D3167	D3182	D3197	D3212
D3168	D3183	D3198	D3213
D3169	D3184	D3199	D3214
D3170	D3185	D3200	D3215
D3171	D3186	D3201	D3216
D3172	D3187	D3202	D3217
D3173	D3188	D3203	D3218
D3174	D3189	D3204	D3219
D3175	D3190	D3205	D3220
D3176	D3191	D3206	D3221
D3177	D3192	D3207	D3222
D3178	D3193	D3208	D3223
D3179	D3194	D3209	D3224
D3180	D3195	D3210	D3225
D3181	D3196	D3211	D3226

D3227	D3272	D3317	D3362
D3228	D3273	D3318	D3363
D3229	D3274	D3319	D3364
D3230	D3275	D3320	D3365
D3231	D3276	D3321	D3366
D3232	D3277	D3322	D3367
D3233	D3278	D3323	D3368
D3234	D3279	D3324	D3369
D3235	D3280	D3325	D3370
D3236	D3281	D3326	D3371
D3237	D3282	D3327	D3372
D3238	D3283	D3328	D3373
D3239	D3284	D3329	D3374
D3240	D3285	D3330	D3375
D3241	D3286	D3331	D3376
D3242	D3287	D3332	D3377
D3243	D3288	D3333	D3378
D3244	D3289	D3334	D3379
D2345	D3290	D3335	D3380
D3246	D3291	D3336	D3381
D3247	D3292	D3337	D3382
D3248	D3293	D3338	D3383
D3249	D3294	D3339	D3384
D3250	D3295	D3340	D3385
D3251	D3296	D3341	D3386
D3252	D3297	D3342	D3387
D3253	D3298	D3343	D3388
D3254	D3299	D3344	D3389
D3255	D3300	D3345	D3390
D3256	D3301	D3346	D3391
D3257	D3302	D3347	D3392
D3258	D3303	D3348	D3393
D3259	D3304	D3349	D3394
D3260	D3305	D3350	D3395
D3261	D3306	D3351	D3396
D3262	D3307	D3352	D3397
D3263	D3308	D3353	D3398
D3264	D3309	D3354	D3399
D3265	D3310	D3355	D3400
D3266	D3311	D3356	D3401
D3267	D3312	D3357	D3402
D3268	D3313	D3358	D3403
D3269	D3314	D3359	D3404
D3270	D3315	D3360	D3405
D3271	D3316	D3361	D3406

D3407	D3415	D3423	D3431
D3408	D3416	D3424	D3432
D3409	D3417	D3425	D3433
D3410	D3418	D3426	D3434
D3411	D3419	D3427	D3435
D3412	D3420	D3428	D3436
D3413	D3421	D3429	D3437
D3414	D3422	D3430	D3438

D3439-D3453. FOR PARTICULARS SEE D3137-D3151.

D3439	D3443	D3447	D3451
D3440	D3444	D3448	D3452
D3441	D3445	D3449	D3453
D3442	D3446	D3450	

D3454-D3472. FOR PARTICULARS SEE D3127-D3136.

D3454	D3459	D3464	D3469
D3455	D3460	D3465	D3470
D3456	D3461	D3466	D3471
D3457	D3462	D3467	D3472
D3458	D3463	D3468	

D3473-D3502. FOR PARTICULARS SEE D3137-D3151.

D3473	D3481	D3489	D3497
D3474	D3482	D3490	D3498
D3475	D3483	D3491	D3499
D3476	D3484	D3492	D3500
D3477	D3485	D3493	D3501
D3478	D3486	D3494	D3502
D3479	D3487	D3495	
D3480	D3488	D3496	

D3503-D3611. FOR PARTICULARS SEE D3127-D3136.

D3503	D3506	D3509	D3512
D3504	D3507	D3510	D3513
D3505	D3508	D3511	D3514

D3515	D3540	D3565	D3590
D3516	D3541	D3566	D3591
D3517	D3542	D3567	D3592
D3518	D3543	D3568	D3593
D3519	D3544	D3569	D3594
D3520	D3545	D3570	D3595
D3521	D3546	D3571	D3596
D3522	D3547	D3572	D3597
D3523	D3548	D3573	D3598
D3524	D3549	D3574	D3599
D3525	D3550	D3575	D3600
D3526	D3551	D3576	D3601
D3527	D3552	D3577	D3602
D3528	D3553	D3578	D3603
D3529	D3554	D3579	D3604
D3530	D3555	D3580	D3605
D3531	D3556	D3581	D3606
D3532	D3557	D3582	D3607
D3533	D3558	D3583	D3608
D3534	D3559	D3584	D3609
D3535	D3560	D3585	D3610
D3536	D3561	D3586	D3611
D3537	D3562	D3587	
D3538	D3563	D3588	
D3539	D3564	D3589	

D3612-D3651. FOR PARTICULARS SEE D3137-D3151.

D3612	D3622	D3632	D3642
D3613	D3623	D3633	D3643
D3614	D3624	D3634	D3644
D3615	D3625	D3635	D3645
D3616	D3626	D3636	D3646
D3617	D3627	D3637	D3647
D3618	D3628	D3638	D3648
D3619	D3629	D3639	D3649
D3620	D3630	D3640	D3650
D3621	D3631	D3641	D3651

D3652-D4094. FOR PARTICULARS SEE D3127-D3136.

D3652	D3655	D3658	D3661
D3653	D3656	D3659	D3662
D3654	D3657	D3660	D3663

D3664	D3709	D3754	D3799	D3844	D3889	D3934	D3979
D3665	D3710	D3755	D3800	D3845	D3890	D3935	D3980
D3666	D3711	D3756	D3801	D3846	D3891	D3936	D3981
D3667	D3712	D3757	D3802	D3847	D3892	D3937	D3982
D3668	D3713	D3758	D3803	D3848	D3893	D3938	D3983
D3669	D3714	D3759	D3804	D3849	D3894	D3939	D3984
D3670	D3715	D3760	D3805	D3850	D3895	D3940	D3985
D3671	D3716	D3761	D3806	D3851	D3896	D3941	D3986
D3672	D3717	D3762	D3807	D3852	D3897	D3942	D3987
D3673	D3718	D3763	D3808	D3853	D3898	D3943	D3988
D3674	D3719	D3764	D3809	D3854	D3899	D3944	D3989
D3675	D3720	D3765	D3810	D3855	D3900	D3945	D3990
D3676	D3721	D3766	D3811	D3856	D3901	D3946	D3991
D3677	D3722	D3767	D3812	D3857	D3902	D3947	D3992
D3678	D3723	D3768	D3813	D3858	D3903	D3948	D3993
D3679	D3724	D3769	D3814	D3859	D3904	D3949	D3994
D3680	D3725	D3770	D3815	D3860	D3905	D3950	D3995
D3681	D3726	D3771	D3816	D3861	D3906	D3951	D3996
D3682	D3727	D3772	D3817	D3862	D3907	D9352	D3997
D3683	D3728	D3773	D3818	D3863	D3908	D3953	D3998
D3684	D3729	D3774	D3819	D3864	D3909	D3954	D3999
D3685	D3730	D3775	D3820	D3865	D3910	D3955	D4000
D3686	D3731	D3776	D3821	D3866	D3911	D3956	D4001
D3687	D3732	D3777	D3822	D3867	D3912	D3957	D4002
D3688	D3733	D3778	D3823	D3868	D3913	D3958	D4003
D3689	D3734	D3779	D3824	D3869	D3914	D3959	D4004
D3690	D3735	D3780	D3825	D3870	D3915	D3960	D4005
D3691	D3736	D3781	D3826	D3871	D3916	D3961	D4006
D3692	D3737	D3782	D3827	D3872	D3917	D3962	D4007
D3693	D3738	D3783	D3828	D3873	D3918	D3963	D4008
D3694	D3739	D3784	D3829	D3874	D3919	D3964	D4009
D3695	D3740	D3785	D3830	D3875	D3920	D3965	D4010
D3696	D3741	D3786	D3831	D3876	D3921	D3966	D4011
D3697	D3742	D3787	D3832	D3877	D3922	D3967	D4012
D3698	D3743	D3788	D3833	D3878	D3923	D3968	D4013
D3699	D3744	D3789	D3834	D3879	D3924	D3969	D4014
D3700	D3745	D3790	D3835	D3880	D3925	D3970	D4015
D3701	D3746	D3791	D3836	D3881	D3926	D3971	D4016
D3702	D3747	D3792	D3837	D3882	D3927	D3972	D4017
D3703	D3748	D3793	D3838	D3883	D3928	D3973	D4018
D3704	D3749	D3794	D3839	D3884	D3929	D3974	D4019
D3705	D3750	D3795	D3840	D3885	D3930	D3975	D4020
D3706	D3751	D3796	D3841	D3886	D3931	D3976	D4021
D3707	D3752	D3797	D3842	D3887	D3932	D3977	D4022
D3708	D3753	D3798	D3843	D3888	D3933	D3978	D4023

D4024	D4042	D4060	D4078
D4025	D4043	D4061	D4079
D4026	D4044	D4062	D4080
D4027	D4045	D4063	D4081
D4028	D4046	D4064	D4082
D4029	D4047	D4065	D4083
D4030	D4048	D4066	D4084
D4031	D4049	D4067	D4085
D4032	D4050	D4068	D4086
D4033	D4051	D4069	D4087
D4034	D4052	D4070	D4088
D4035	D4053	D4071	D4089
D4036	D4054	D4072	D4090
D4037	D4055	D4073	D4091
D4038	D4056	D4074	D4092
D4039	D4057	D4075	D4093
D4040	D4058	D4076	D4094
D4041	D4059	D4077	

D5048	D5080	D5112*	D5144*
D5049	D5081	D5113*	D5145*
D5050	D5082	D5114*	D5146*
D5051	D5083	D5115*	D5147*
D5052	D5084	D5116*	D5148*
D5053	D5085	D5117*	D5149*
D5054	D5086	D5118*	D5150*
D5055	D5087	D5119*	D5151†
D5056	D5088	D5120*	D5152†
D5057	D5089	D5121*	D5153†
D5058	D5090	D5122*	D5154†
D5059	D5091	D5123*	D5155†
D5060	D5092	D5124*	D5156†
D5061	D5093	D5125*	D5157†
D5062	D5094*	D5126*	D5158†
D5063	D5095*	D5127*	D5159†
D5064	D5096*	D5128*	D5160†
D5065	D5097*	D5129*	D5161†
D5066	D5098*	D5130*	D5162†
D5067	D5099*	D5131*	D5163†
D5068	D5100*	D5132*	D5164†
D5069	D5101*	D5133*	D5165†
D5070	D5102*	D5134*	D5166†
D5071	D5103*	D5135*	D5167†
D5072	D5104*	D5136*	D5168†
D5073	D5105*	D5137*	D5169†
D5074	D5106*	D5138*	D5170†
D5075	D5107*	D5139*	D5171†
D5076	D5108*	D5140*	D5172†
D5077	D5109*	D5141*	D5173†
D5078	D5110*	D5142*	D5174†
D5079	D5111*	D5143*	D5175†

Bo-Bo   " 2 "

Introduced: 1958.
Locomotive manufacturer: B.R.
Total b.h.p.: { 1,160.
{ 1,250†.
Engine: Sulzer 6-cyl. type 6LDA28 of 1,160 b.h.p. at 750 r.p.m.
†Sulzer 6-cyl. type 6LDA28-B of 1,250 b.h.p. at 750 r.p.m.
Transmission: Electric. Four B.T.H. axle-hung, nose-suspended traction motors of 213 h.p. (continuous rating).
Weight: { 75 tons.
{ 72 tons 17 cwt.*
{ 72 tons 17 cwt.†
Driving Wheels: 3' 9".
Maximum tractive effort: 40,000 lb.
Classified D11/3 by the E. & N.E.R.

D5000	D5012	D5024	D5036
D5001	D5013	D5025	D5037
D5002	D5014	D5026	D5038
D5003	D5015	D5027	D5039
D5004	D5016	D5028	D5040
D5005	D5017	D5029	D5041
D5006	D5018	D5030	D5042
D5007	D5019	D5031	D5043
D5008	D5020	D5032	D5044
D5009	D5021	D5033	D5045
D5010	D5022	D5034	D5046
D5011	D5023	D5035	D5047

Bo-Bo   " 2 "

Introduced: 1958.
Locomotive manufacturer: Birmingham R.C. & W. Co.
Total b.h.p.: { 1,160.
{ 1,250†.
Engine: Sulzer 6-cyl. type 6LDA28 of 1,160 b.h.p. at 750 r.p.m.
†Sulzer 6-cyl. type 6LDA28-B of 1,250 b.h.p. at 750 r.p.m.
Transmission: Electric. Four Crompton Parkinson axle-hung, nose-suspended traction motors.
†Electric. Four G.E.C. axle-hung, nose-suspended traction.
Weight: { 77 tons 10 cwt.*.
{ 74 tons.

Class B1 4-6-0 No. 61178
[J. Robertson

Class B17/6 4-6-0 No. 61668 *Bradford City*
[B. K. B. Green

Class D49/1 4-4-0 No. 62733 *Northumberland*
[J. R. Paterson

Class K4 2-6-0 No. 61994 *The Great Marquess* [*P. H. Groom*

Class K3 2-6-0 No. 61865 [*P. H. Groom*

Class V2 2-6-2 No. 60857 [*J. B. Bucknall*

Class D16/3 4-4-0 No. 62613   [*T. E. K. Chambers*

Class B12/3 4-6-0 No. 61572   [*T. E. K. Chambers*

Class B16/1 4-6-0 No. 61413   [*D. A. Anderson*

Class D30/2 4-4-0 No. 62426 *Cuddie Headrigg* (since withdrawn) [*A.W. Martin*

Class D34 4-4-0 No. 62496 *Glen Loy*   [*J. R. Paterson*

Class D11/1 4-4-0 No. 62660 *Butler Henderson*   [*K. R. Pirt*

Class O4/8 2-8-0 No. 63679   [A. H. Wells

Class O1 2-8-0 No. 63890   [R. E. Vincent

Class O2/1 2-8-0 No. 63927   [K. R. Pirt

Class Q6 0-8-0 No. 63367

[*W. S. Sellar*

Class J38 0-6-0 No. 65922

[*W. S. Sellar*

Class J38 0-6-0 No. 64906 (rebuilt with J39 boiler)

[*K. R. Pirt*

Class J17 0-6-0 No. 65528   [R. C. Riley

Class J11 0-6-0 No. 64377   [T. Booth

Class J10/4 0-6-0 No. 65157   [B. E. Morrison

Class J6 0-6-0 No. 64222

[*K. R. Pirt*

Class J36 0-6-0 No. 65338

[*D. A. Anderson*

Class J37 0-6-0 No. 64582

[*J. L. Swanson*

Class J83 0-6-0T No. 68481   [*R. J. Buckley*

Class J83 0-6-0T No. 68349   [*K. R. Pirt*

Class J72 0-6-0T No. 68736 (repainted in N.E.R. livery)   [*F. Ingham*

Class A5 4-6-2T No. 69820   [J. Davenport]

Class T1 4-8-0T No. 69921   [R. K. Evans]

Class C16 4-4-2T No. 67494   [W. S. Sellar]

Class N5 0-6-2T No. 69286   *[J. Davenport*

Class N2/2 0-6-2T No. 69561   *[G. Wheeler*

Class N2/2 0-6-2T No. 69533 (fitted with condensing apparatus)   *[B. E. Morrison*

Class N15/2 0-6-2T No. 69131   [*D. A. Anderson*

Ex-G.N.S.R. 4-4-0 No. 49 *Gordon Highlander*   [*K. R. Pirt*

Ex-N.B.R. 4-4-0 No. 256 *Glen Douglas*   [*K. R. Pirt*

Derby/Sulzer Type 4 2,300 b.h.p. diesel-electric 1Co-Co1 No. D3 *Skiddaw*   [*P. J. Sharpe*

English Electric Type 4 2,000 b.h.p. diesel-electric 1Co-Co1 No. D228   [*R. J. Buckley*

Prototype English Electric 3,300 b.h.p. "Deltic" diesel-electric Co-Co   [*P. N. Townend*

Swindon/Maybach Type 4 2,200 b.h.p. diesel-hydraulic B-B No. D817
Foxhound   [J. A. Coiley

North British Type 4 2,000 b.h.p. diesel-hydraulic A1A-A1A No. D600
Active   [N.B.L.

Brown-Boveri 2,500 b.h.p. gas turbine A1A-A1A No. 18000   [R. J. Buckley

Hunslet 204 b.h.p. 0-6-0 diesel-mechanical shunter No. D2556 [*P. J. Sharpe*

North British 200 b.h.p. 0-4-0 diesel-hydraulic shunter No. D2702
[*J. B. Bucknall*

North British 330 b.h.p. 0-4-0 diesel-hydraulic shunter No. D2900   [*R. A. Panting*

North British Type 2 1,100 b.h.p. diesel-hydraulic B-B No. D6302   [*P. J. Sharpe*

North British Type 2 1,100 b.h.p. diesel-electric Bo-Bo No. D6107   [*B. A. Haresnape*

English Electric Type 2 1,100 b.h.p. diesel-electric Bo-Bo No. D5907   [*A. E. Baker*

Driving Wheels: 3' 7".
Maximum tractive effort: 42,000 lb.
Classified **D11/4** by the E. & N.E.R.

D5300*	D5329	D5358†	D5387†
D5301*	D5330	D5359†	D5388†
D5302*	D5331	D5360†	D5389†
D5303*	D5332	D5361†	D5390†
D5304*	D5333	D5362†	D5391†
D5305*	D5334	D5363†	D5392†
D5306*	D5335	D5364†	D5393†
D5307*	D5336	D5365†	D5394†
D5308*	D5337	D5366†	D5395†
D5309*	D5338	D5367†	D5396†
D5310*	D5339	D5368†	D5397†
D5311*	D5340	D5369†	D5398†
D5312*	D5341	D5370†	D5399†
D5313*	D5342	D5371†	D5400†
D5314*	D5343	D5372†	D5401†
D5315*	D5344	D5373†	D5402†
D5316*	D5345	D5374†	D5403†
D5317*	D5346	D5375†	D5404†
D5318*	D5347†	D5376†	D5405†
D5319*	D5348†	D5377†	D5406†
D5320	D5349†	D5378†	D5407†
D5321	D5350†	D5379†	D5408†
D5322	D5351†	D5380†	D5409†
D5323	D5352†	D5381†	D5410†
D5324	D5353†	D5382†	D5411†
D5325	D5354†	D5383†	D5412†
D5326	D5355†	D5384†	D5413†
D5327	D5356†	D5385†	D5414†
D5328	D5357†	D5386†	D5415†

AIA-AIA   "2"

Introduced: 1957.
Locomotive manufacturer: Brush Traction Ltd.

Total b.h.p.: { 1,250* / 1,365. / 1,600† }

Engine: Mirrlees, Bickerton & Day 12-cyl. JVS12T of 1,250*, 1,365 or 1,600† b.h.p. at 850*, 900 or 950† r.p.m.
Transmission: **Electric.** Four Brush 250 h.p. traction motors, single reduction gear drive.
Weight: 104 tons.
Driving Wheels: 3' 7".
Maximum tractive effort: 42,000 lb.
Classified (**D12/2***) **D13/1** by the E. & N.E.R.

D5500*	D5545†	D5590	D5635
D5501*	D5546	D5591	D5636
D5502*	D5547	D5592	D5637
D5503*	D5548	D5593	D5638
D5504*	D5549	D5594	D5639
D5505*	D5550	D5595	D5640
D5506*	D5551	D5596	D5641
D5507*	D5552	D5597	D5642
D5508*	D5553	D5598	D5643
D5509*	D5554	D5599	D5644
D5510*	D5555	D5600	D5645
D5511*	D5556	D5601	D5646
D5512*	D5557	D5602	D5647
D5513*	D5558	D5603	D5648
D5514*	D5559	D5604	D5649
D5515*	D5560	D5605	D5650
D5516*	D5561	D5606	D5651
D5517*	D5562	D5607	D5652
D5518*	D5563	D5608	D5653
D5519*	D5564	D5609	D5654
D5520	D5565	D5610	D5655
D5521	D5566	D5611	D5656
D5522	D5567	D5612	D5657
D5523	D5568	D5613	D5658
D5524	D5569	D5614	D5659
D5525	D5570	D5615	D5660
D5526	D5571	D5616	D5661
D5527	D5572	D5617	D5662
D5528	D5573	D5618	D5663
D5529	D5574	D5619	D5664
D5530	D5575	D5620	D5665
D5531	D5576	D5621	D5666
D5532	D5577	D5622	D5667
D5533	D5578	D5623	D5668
D5534	D5579	D5624	D5669
D5535	D5580	D5625	D5670
D5536	D5581	D5626	D5671
D5537	D5582	D5627	D5672
D5538	D5583	D5628	D5673
D5539	D5584	D5629	D5674
D5540	D5585	D5630	D5675
D5541	D5586	D5631	D5676
D5542	D5587	D5632	D5677
D5543	D5588	D5633	D5678
D5544	D5589	D5634	D5679

D5680	D5685	D5690	D5695
D5681	D5686	D5691	D5696
D5682	D5687	D5692	D5697
D5683	D5688	D5693	D5698
D5684	D5689	D5694	D5699

Co-Bo   "2"

Introduced: 1958.
Locomotive manufacturer: Metropolitan Vickers.
Total b.h.p.: 1,200.
Engine: Crossley 8-cyl. HST Vee 8 of 1,200 b.h.p. at 625 r.p.m. (continuous).
Transmission: **Electric.** Five Metropolitan-Vickers 180 h.p. axle-hung nose-suspended traction motors.
Weight: 97 tons.
Driving Wheels: 3′ 3½″.
Maximum tractive effort: 50,000 lb.

D5700	D5705	D5710	D5715
D5701	D5706	D5711	D5716
D5702	D5707	D5712	D5717
D5703	D5708	D5713	D5718
D5704	D5709	D5714	D5719

AIA-AIA   "2"

D5800-25 for particulars see Nos. D5500-5679.

D5800	D5807	D5814	D5821
D5801	D5808	D5815	D5822
D5802	D5809	D5816	D5823
D5803	D5810	D5817	D5824
D5804	D5811	D5818	D5825
D5805	D5812	D5819	
D5806	D5813	D5820	

Bo-Bo   "2"

Introduced: 1959.
Locomotive manufacturer: English Electric.
Total b.h.p.: 1,100.
Engine: Napier " Deltic " T9-29 **9** cyl., two-stroke pressure charged type of 1,100 b.h.p. at 1,600 r.p.m.

Transmission: **Electric.** Four English Electric axle-hung nose-suspended traction motors.
Weight: 73 tons 17 cwt.
Driving Wheels: 3′ 7″.
Maximum tractive effort.: 47,000 lb.
Classified **D11/1** by the E. & N.E.R.

D5900	D5903	D5906	D5909
D5901	D5904	D5907	
D5902	D5905	D5908	

Bo-Bo   "2"

Introduced: 1959.
Locomotive manufacturer: North British Locomotive Co.
Total b.h.p.: $\begin{cases} 1,000* \\ 1,100. \end{cases}$
Engine: N.B.L./M.A.N. 12-cyl. pressure charged L12V/18/21S of (1,000*) 1,100 b.h.p.
Transmission: **Electric.** Four G.E.C. nose-suspended traction motors.
Weight: 72 tons 10 cwt.
Driving Wheels: 3′ 7″.
Maximum tractive effort: 45,000 lb.
Classified **(D10/1*) D11/2** by the E .& N.E.R.

D6100	D6115	D6130	D6145
D6101*	D6116	D6131	D6146
D6102*	D6117	D6132	D6147
D6103*	D6118	D6133	D6148
D6104*	D6119	D6134	D6149
D6105*	D6120	D6135	D6150
D6106*	D6121	D6136	D6151
D6107	D6122	D6137	D6152
D6108*	D6123	D6138	D6153
D6109*	D6124	D6139	D6154
D6110	D6125	D6140	D6155
D6111	D6126	D6141	D6156
D6112	D6127	D6142	D6157
D6113	D6128	D6143	
D6114	D6129	D6144	

B-B   "2"

Introduced: 1959.
Locomotive manufacturer: North British Locomotive Co.
Total b.h.p.: $\begin{cases} 1.000.* \\ 1,100. \end{cases}$
Engine: N. B. L. / M. A. N. 12-cyl. L12V18/21M of 1,000 b.h.p.* or 1,100 b.h.p.

Transmission: **Hydraulic.** Voith—N.B.L. L.T.306r hydraulic transmission and cardan shafts to primary gear-boxes on the inner axles and secondary gear-boxes on the outer axles.
Weight: { 68 tons.* / 65 tons. }
Driving Wheels: 3' 7".
Maximum tractive effort: 40,000 lbs.

D6300*	D6315	D6330	D6345
D6301*	D6316	D6331	D6346
D6302*	D6317	D6332	D6347
D6303*	D6318	D6333	D6348
D6304*	D6319	D6334	D6349
D6305*	D6320	D6335	D6350
D6306	D6321	D6336	D6351
D6307	D6322	D6337	D6352
D6308	D6323	D6338	D6353
D6309	D6324	D6339	D6354
D6310	D6325	D6340	D6355
D6311	D6326	D6341	D6356
D6312	D6327	D6342	D6357
D6313	D6328	D6343	
D6314	D6329	D6344	

Bo-Bo "3"

Introduced: 1960.
Locomotive manufacturer: Birmingham R.C. & W. Co.
Total b.h.p.: 1,550.
Engines: Sulzer 8LDA28 pressure-charged 8-cyl cf 1,550 b.h.p. at 750 r.p.m. (continuous).
Transmission: **Electric.** Four Crompton Parkinson 305 h.p. axle-hung nose-suspended traction motors.
Weight: 73 tons 8 cwt.
Driving Wheels: 3' 7".
Maximum tractive effort: 45,000 lb.

D6500	D6511	D6522	D6533
D6501	D6512	D6523	D6534
D6502	D6513	D6524	D6535
D6503	D6514	D6525	D6536
D6504	D6515	D6526	D6537
D6505	D6516	D6527	D6538
D6506	D6517	D6528	D6539
D6507	D6518	D6529	D6540
D6508	D6519	D6530	D6541
D6509	D6520	D6531	D6542
D6510	D6521	D6532	D6543

D6544	D6558	D6572	D6586
D6545	D6559	D6573	D6587
D6546	D6560	D6574	D6588
D6547	D6561	D6575	D6589
D6548	D6562	D6576	D6590
D6549	D6563	D6577	D6591
D6550	D6564	D6578	D6592
D6551	D6565	D6579	D6593
D6552	D6566	D6580	D6594
D6553	D6567	D6581	D6595
D6554	D6568	D6582	D6596
D6555	D6569	D6583	D6597
D6556	D6570	D6584	
D6557	D6571	D6585	

Co-Co "3"

To be introduced:
Locomotive manufacturer: English Electric.
Total b.h.p.: 1,750.
Engine:
Transmission: **Electric.**
Weight:
Driving Wheels:
Maximum tractive effort:

D6700	D6720	D6740	D6760
D6701	D6721	D6741	D6761
D6702	D6722	D6742	D6762
D6703	D6723	D6743	D6763
D6704	D6724	D6744	D6764
D6705	D6725	D6745	D6765
D6706	D6726	D6746	D6766
D6707	D6727	D6747	D6767
D6708	D6728	D6748	D6768
D6709	D6729	D6749	D6769
D6710	D6730	D6750	D6770
D6711	D6731	D6751	D6771
D6712	D6732	D6752	D6772
D6713	D6733	D6753	D6773
D6714	D6734	D6754	D6774
D6715	D6735	D6755	D6775
D6716	D6736	D6756	D6776
D6717	D6737	D6757	D6777
D6718	D6738	D6758	D6778
D6719	D6739	D6759	

B-B   "3"

To be introduced:
Locomotive manufacturer: Beyer-Peacock (Hymek).
Total b.h.p.: 1,700.
Engine: Bristol-Siddeley-Maybach type MD870 of 1,700 b.h.p.
Transmission: **Hydraulic.** Stone-Maybach "Mekydro" type 6184U.
Weight: 74 tons.
Driving Wheels: 3' 9"
Maximum tractive effort: 49,700 lb.

D7000	D7024	D7048	D7072
D7001	D7025	D7049	D7073
D7002	D7026	D7050	D7074
D7003	D7027	D7051	D7075
D7004	D7028	D7052	D7076
D7005	D7029	D7053	D7077
D7006	D7030	D7054	D7078
D7007	D7031	D7055	D7079
D7008	D7032	D7056	D7080
D7009	D7033	D7057	D7081
D7010	D7034	D7058	D7082
D7011	D7035	D7059	D7083
D7012	D7036	D7060	D7084
D7013	D7037	D7061	D7085
D7014	D7038	D7062	D7086
D7015	D7039	D7063	D7087
D7016	D7040	D7064	D7088
D7017	D7041	D7065	D7089
D7018	D7042	D7066	D7090
D7019	D7043	D7067	D7091
D7020	D7044	D7068	D7092
D7021	D7045	D7069	D7093
D7022	D7046	D7070	D7094
D7023	D7047	D7071	

Driving Wheels: 3' 7".
Maximum tractive effort: 42,000 lb.
Classified **D10/3** by the E. & N.E.R.

D8000	D8032	D8064	D8096
D8001	D8033	D8065	D8097
D8002	D8034	D8066	D8098
D8003	D8035	D8067	D8099
D8004	D8036	D8068	D8100
D8005	D8037	D8069	D8101
D8006	D8038	D8070	D8102
D8007	D8039	D8071	D8103
D8008	D8040	D8072	D8104
D8009	D8041	D8073	D8105
D8010	D8042	D8074	D8106
D8011	D8043	D8075	D8107
D8012	D8044	D8076	D8108
D8013	D8045	D8077	D8109
D8014	D8046	D8078	D8110
D8015	D8047	D8079	D8111
D8016	D8048	D8080	D8112
D8017	D8049	D8081	D8113
D8018	D8050	D8082	D8114
D8019	D8051	D8083	D8115
D8020	D8052	D8084	D8116
D8021	D8053	D8085	D8117
D8022	D8054	D8086	D8118
D8023	D8055	D8087	D8119
D8024	D8056	D8088	D8120
D8025	D8057	D8089	D8121
D8026	D8058	D8090	D8122
D8027	D8059	D8091	D8123
D8028	D8060	D8092	D8124
D8029	D8061	D8093	D8125
D8030	D8062	D8094	D8126
D8031	D8063	D8095	D8127

Bo-Bo   "1"

Introduced: 1957.
Locomotive manufacturer: English Electric Co./Vulcan Foundry Ltd.
Total b.h.p.: 1,000.
Engine: English Electric 8 SVT Mk. II of 1,000 b.h.p. at 850 r.p.m. (continuous).
Transmission: **Electric.** Four axlehung, nose-suspended d.c. traction motors.
Weight: 72 tons.

Bo-Bo   "1"

Introduced: 1957.
Locomotive manufacturer: British Thomson-Houston Co.
Total b.h.p.: 800.
Engine: Paxman 16-cyl. YHXL "V"-type pressure charged by two Napier exhaust gas-driven turbo chargers. 800 b.h.p. at 1,250 r.p.m.
Transmission: **Electric.** Four B.T.H. nose-suspended traction motors with single reduction gear drive.

Weight: 68 tons.
Driving Wheels: 3′ 3½″.
Maximum tractive effort: 37,500 lb.
Classified **D8/1** by the E. & N.E.R.

D8200	D8211	D8222	D8233
D8201	D8212	D8223	D8234
D8202	D8213	D8224	D8235
D8203	D8214	D8225	D8236
D8204	D8215	D8226	D8237
D8205	D8216	D8227	D8238
D8206	D8217	D8228	D8239
D8207	D8218	D8229	D8240
D8208	D8219	D8230	D8241
D8209	D8220	D8231	D8242
D8210	D8221	D8232	D8243

Bo-Bo   " I "

Introduced: 1958.
Locomotive manufacturer: North British
  Locomotive Co.
Total b.h.p.: 800.
Engine: Paxman 16-cyl. type 16YHXL
  of 800 b.h.p. at 1,250 r.p.m.
Transmission: **Electric.** Four G.E.C.
  axle-hung nose-suspended traction
  motors.
Weight: 68 tons.
Driving Wheels: 3′ 7″.
Maximum tractive effort: 42,000 lb.
Classified **D8/2** by the E. & N.E.R.

D8400	D8403	D8406	D8408
D8401	D8404	D8407	D8409
D8402	D8405		

Co-Co   Deltic " 5 "

To be introduced.
Locomotive manufacturer: English Electric
Total b.h.p.: 3,300.
Engines:
Transmission: **Electric.**
Weight:
Driving Wheels:
Maximum tractive effort:

D9000	D9006	D9012	D9018
D9001	D9007	D9013	D9019
D9002	D9008	D9014	D9020
D9003	D9009	D9015	D9021
D9004	D9010	D9016	
D9005	D9011	D9017	

Co-Co   " Deltic "

NOTE: British Railways are pro-
viding facilities for road tests of
this locomotive, which remains the
property of the manufacturer, and
is not included in B.R. stock. An
order has been placed for 22 of these
locomotives to work on the E.,
N.E. & Scottish Regions, (D9000-21)

Introduced: 1955.
Locomotive manufacturer: English Electric
Total b.h.p.: 3,300.
Engines: Two Napier "Deltic" 18 cyl.
  engines of 1,650 b.h.p.
Transmission: **Electric.** Six axle-hung
  nose-suspended traction motors.
Weight: 106 tons.
Driving Wheels: 3′ 7″
Maximum tractive effort: 60,000 lb.

Co-Co   5P/5F

Introduced: 1947.
Locomotive manufacturer: Derby Works,
  L.M.S.
Total b.h.p.: 1,600.
Engine : English Electric 16-cyl. of
  1,600 b.h.p. at 750 r.p.m. (continuous
  rating).
Transmission: **Electric.** Six nose-
  suspended motors, single reduction
  gear drive.
Weight: 127 tons 13 cwt.
Driving Wheels: 3′ 6″.
Maximum tractive effort: 41,400 lb.

| 10000 | 10001 | **Total 2** |

ICo-Col $\left\{ \begin{matrix} 10201/2 & 5P/5F \\ 10203 & 6P/6F \end{matrix} \right\}$

Introduced: $\left\{ \begin{matrix} 1951 \\ 1954* \end{matrix} \right.$
Locomotive manufacturer: Ashford
  Works, B.R.
Total b.h.p.: $\left\{ \begin{matrix} 1,750 \\ 2,000* \end{matrix} \right.$
Engine: English Electric Co. 16-cyl
  1,750 b.h.p. (2,000 b.h.p.*)
Transmission: **Electric.** six nose-
  suspended, axle-hung motors of
  260 h.p. (1-hour rating).
Weight: $\left\{ \begin{matrix} 135 \text{ tons.} \\ 132 \text{ tons*} \end{matrix} \right.$
Driving Wheels: 3′ 7″.
Maximum tractive effort: $\left\{ \begin{matrix} 48,000 \text{ lb.} \\ 50,000 \text{ lb.*} \end{matrix} \right.$

| 10201 | 10202 | *10203 |
| | | **Total 3** |

0-6-0   Shunter

Introduced: 1936.
Locomotive manufacturer: English Electric for L.M.S.
Total b.h.p.: 350.
Engine: English Electric 6-cyl. 350 b.h.p.
Transmission: **Electric.** Two nose-suspended motors, single reduction gear drive.
Weight. 51 tons.
Driving Wheels: 4′ 0½″.
Maximum tractive effort: 30,000 lb.

12000	12001	**Total 2**

0-6-0   Shunter

Introduced: 1939.
Locomotive manufacturer: Derby Works, L.M.S.
Total b.h.p.: 350.
Engine: English Electric, 6-cyl. 350 b.h.p.
Transmission: **Electric.** Single motor; jackshaft drive.
Weight: 54 tons 16 cwt.
Driving Wheels: 4′ 3″.
Maximum tractive effort: 33,000 lb.
Classified **D3/7** by the E. & N.E.R.

12003	12011	12019	12027
12004	12012	12020	12028
12005	12013	12021	12029
12006	12014	12022	12030
12007	12015	12023	12031
12008	12016	12024	12032
12009	12017	12025	
12010	12018	12026	

Total 30

0-6-0   Shunter

Introduced: 1945.
Locomotive manufacturer: **L.M.S.** and **B.R.**
Total b.h.p.: 350.
Engine: English Electric, 6-cyl. 350 b.h.p.
Transmission: **Electric.** Two 135 h.p., nose-suspended motors, double reduction gear drive.
Weight: 47 tons 5 cwt.
Driving Wheels: 4′ 0½″.
Maximum tractive effort: 35,000 lb.
Classified **D3/8** by the E. & N.E.R.

12033	12060	12087	12114
12034	12061	12088	12115
12035	12062	12089	12116
12036	12063	12090	12117
12037	12064	12091	12118
12038	12065	12092	12119
12039	12066	12093	12120
12040	12067	12094	12121
12041	12068	12095	12122
12042	12069	12096	12123
12043	12070	12097	12124
12044	12071	12098	12125
12045	12072	12099	12126
12046	12073	12100	12127
12047	12074	12101	12128
12048	12075	12102	12129
12049	12076	12103	12130
12050	12077	12104	12131
12051	12078	12105	12132
12052	12079	12106	12133
12053	12080	12107	12134
12054	12081	12108	12135
12055	12082	12109	12136
12056	12083	12110	12137
12057	12084	12111	12138
12058	12085	12112	12139
12059	12086	12113	

Total 106

0-6-0   Shunter

Introduced: 1944.
Locomotive manufacturer: Doncaster Works, L.N.E.R.
Total b.h.p.: 350.
Engine: English Electric, 6-cyl. 350 b.h.p.
Transmission: **Electric.** Two 135 h.p. nose-suspended motors, double reduction gear drive.
Weight: 50 tons.
Driving Wheels: 4′ 0″.
Maximum tractive effort: 32,000 lb.
Classified **D3/9** by the E. & N.E.R.

15000	15001	15002	15003

Total 4

0-6-0   Shunter

Introduced: 1949.
Locomotive manufacturer: Doncaster
  Works, B.R.
Total b.h.p.: 360.
Engine: Petter SS4 4-cyl. 360 b.h.p.
Transmission: **Electric.** Two 135 h.p.
  nose-suspended traction motors
  double reduction gear drive.
Weight: 51 tons.
Driving Wheels: 4′ 0″.
Maximum tractive effort: 32,000 lb.
Classified **D3/14** by the E. & N.E.R.

15004	Total 1

0-6-0   Shunter

Introduced: 1936.
Locomotive manufacturer: English Elec-
  tric for G.W.R.
Total b.h.p.: 350.
Engine: English Electric, 6-cyl. 350 b.h.p.
Transmission: **Electric.** Two nose-
  suspended motors, single reduction
  gear drive.
Weight: 51 tons 10 cwt.
Driving Wheels: 4′ 1″.
Maximum tractive effort: 30,000 lb.

15100	Total 1

0-6-0   Shunter

Introduced: 1948.
Locomotive manufacturer: Swindon
  Works, B.R.
Total b.h.p.: 350.
Engine: English Electric, 6-cyl. 350 b.h.p.
Transmission: **Electric.** Two 135 h.p.
  nose-suspended motors, double
  reduction gear drive.
Weight: 50 tons.
Driving Wheels: 4′ 0½″.
Maximum tractive effort: 33,500 lb.

15101	15103	15105	
15102	15104	15106	**Total 6**

0-6-0   Shunter

Introduced: 1937.
Locomotive manufacturer: Ashford
  Works, S.R.
Total b.h.p.: 350.
Engine: English Electric, 6-cyl. 350 b.h.p.
Transmission: **Electric.** Two nose-
  suspended motors, single reduction
  gear drive.
Weight: 55 tons 5 cwt.
Driving Wheels: 4′ 6″.
Maximum tractive effort: 30,000 lb.

15201	15202	15203	**Total 3**

0-6-0   Shunter

Introduced: 1949.
Locomotive manufacturer: Ashford
  Works, B.R.
Total b.h.p.: 350.
Engine: English Electric, 6-cyl. 350 b.h.p.
Transmission: **Electric.** Two 135 h.p.
  nose-suspended motors, double
  reduction gear drive.
Weight: 45 tons.
Driving Wheels: 4′ 6″.
Maximum tractive effort: 24,000 lb.

15211	15218	15225	15232
15212	15219	15226	15233
15213	15220	15227	15234
15214	15221	15228	15235
15215	15222	15229	15236
15216	15223	15230	
15217	15224	15231	

Total 26

**NOTE: British Railways are pro-
viding facilities for road tests of
the following two locomotives,
which remain the property of the
manufacturer and are not included
in B.R. stock.**

0-6-0   Shunter

Introduced: 1957.
Locomotive manufacturer: English Elec-
  tric.
Total b.h.p.: 500.
Engine: English Electric 6RKT of 500
  b.h.p. at 750 r.p.m.

Transmission: **Electric.** One English Electric traction motor coupled to double-reduction gear box final drive.
Weight: 48 tons.
Driving Wheels: 4′ 0″.
Maximum tractive effort: 33,000 lb.

D0226

0-6-0 Shunter

Introduced: 1957.
Locomotive manufacturer: English Electric.
Total b.h.p.: 500.
Engine: English Electric, 6RKT of 500 b.h.p. at 750 r.p.m.
Transmission: **Hydraulic.** Lysholm-Smith torque-converter and three-speed reduction gear to final drive.
Weight: 48 tons.

Driving Wheels: 4′ 0″.
Maximum tractive effort: 33,000 lb.

D0227

AIA-AIA Gas Turbine

Introduced: 1949.
Locomotive manufacturer: Swiss Locomotive & Machine Works, Winterthur.
Total b.h.p.: 2,500.
Engine: Brown-Boveri 2,500 b.h.p. Gas Turbine.
Transmission: **Electric.** Four frame-mounted traction motors driving through spring drive.
Weight: 115 tons.
Driving Wheels: 4′ 0½″.
Maximum tractive effort: 60,000 lb.

18000

SERVICE LOCOMOTIVES

Western Region

0-4-0

Introduced: 1957.
Locomotive manufacturer: Ruston & Hornsby.
Total b.h.p.: 88.
Engine: Ruston & Hornsby 4-cyl. type of 88 b.h.p.
Transmission: **Mechanical.** Chain driven from gearbox.
Weight: 17 tons.
Wheel Diameter: 3′ 0″.
Maximum tractive effort: 9,500 lb.

20

0-6-0

Introduced: 1953.
Locomotive manufacturer: Ruston & Hornsby.
Total b.h.p.: 165.
Engine: Ruston & Hornsby 6-cyl. type of 165 b.h.p.
Transmission: **Electric.** One B.T.H. nose-suspended traction motor.
Weight: 30 tons.
Driving Wheels: 3′ 2½″.
Maximum tractive effort: 17,000 lb.

PWM650 | PWM652 | PWM654
PWM651 | PWM653 |

Also Petrol Locomotives 24 and 27.

Southern Region

0-4-0

Introduced: 1947.
Locomotive manufacturer: John Fowler & Co.
Total b.h.p.: 150.
Engine: Fowler.
Transmission: **Mechanical.** Four-speed gearbox.
Weight: 29 tons.
Driving Wheels: 3′ 3″.
Maximum tractive effort: 15,000 lb.

DS600

0-4-0

Introduced:
Locomotive manufacturer: Ruston & Hornsby.
Total b.h.p.:
Engine:
Transmission:
Weight:
Driving Wheels:
Maximum tractive effort:

DS1169

0-6-0

Introduced: 1947.
Locomotive manufacturer: Drewry.
Total b.h.p.: 204.
Engine: Gardner 8L3 or 204 b.h.p.
Transmission: **Mechanical.** Five-speed gearbox.
Weight: 24 tons 15 cwt.
Driving Wheels: 3′ 3″.
Maximum tractive effort: 16,850 lb.
DS1173

London Midland Region

0-4-0

Introduced: 1936.
Locomotive manufacturer: John Fowler & Co.
Total b.h.p.: 88.
Engine: Ruston & Hornsby 6-cyl. type VQ of 88 b.h.p.
Transmission: **Mechanical.** Four-speed constant-mesh gearbox with multiple-disc dry clutch manually operated.
Weight: 25 tons.
Driving Wheels: 3′ 0″.
Maximum tractive effort: 8,940 lb.
ED1

0-4-0

Introduced: 1936.
Locomotive manufacturer: John Fowler & Co.
Total b.h.p.: 150.
Engine: Fowler type 4C vertical or 150 b.h.p. at 1,000 r.p.m. (1 hr. rating).
Transmission: **Mechanical.** Four speed gearbox.
Weight: 29 tons.
Driving Wheels: 3′ 3″.
Maximum tractive effort: 15,000 lb.

| ED2 | ED4 | ED6 |
| ED3 | ED5 | |

0-4-0

Introduced: 1955.
Locomotive manufacturer John Fowler & Co.
Total b.h.p.: 150.
Engine: Fowler 4-cyl. type C of 150 b.h.p.

Transmission: **Mechanical.** Three-lobe synchromesh gearbox with multiple disc dry clutch manually operated.
Weight: 29 tons.
Driving Wheels: 3′ 3″.
Maximum tractive effort: 15,000 lb.
ED7

0-4-0

Introduced: 1958.
Locomotive manufacturer: Ruston & Hornsby.
Total b.h.p.:
Engine: Ruston type 4YCL.
Transmission: **Mechanical.** Chain drive.
Weight: 8 tons 4 cwt.
Driving Wheel: 2′ 6″.
Maximum tractive effort: 4,200 lb
Gauge: 3′ 0″.
ED10

0-4-0

Introduced: 1958.
Locomotive manufacturer: Ruston & Hornsby.
Total b.h.p.: 20.
Engine:
Transmission:
Weight: 3 tons 10 cwt.
Driving Wheels:
Maximum tractive effort: 1 890 lb.
Gauge: 1′ 6″.
ZM32

Eastern Region

0-4-0

Introduced: 1950.
Locomotive manufactuer: Hibberd & Co.
Total b.h.p.: 52.
Engine: English National 4-cyl. Gas type. DA4 of 52 b.h.p. at 1,250 r.p.m.
Transmission: **Mechanical.** Spur-type three-speed gearbox with roller chains.
Weight: 11 tons.
Driving Wheels:
Maximum tractive effort:
52 (11104)

0-4-0

Introduced: 1955.
Locomotive manufacturer: Ruston & Hornsby.
Total b.h.p.: 88.
Engine: Ruston & Hornsby Mark 4V vertical 4-cyl. of 88 b.h.p.
Transmission: **Mechanical.**
Weight: 17 tons.
Driving Wheels: 3′ 0″.
Maximum tractive effort: 9,500 lb.

56

0-4-0

Introduced: 1958.
Locomotive manufacturer: Andrew Barclay.
Total b.h.p.: 150.
Engine:
Transmission: **Mechanical.**
Weight:
Driving Wheels:
Maximum tractive effort:

81

0-4-0

Introduced: 1959.
Locomotive manufacturer: Ruston & Hornsby.
Total b.h.p.:
Engine:
Transmission:
Weight:
Driving Wheels:
Maximum tractive effort:

85

0-6-0

Introduced: 1958.
Locomotive manufacturer: Swindon Works, B.R.
Total b.h.p.: 200.
Engine: Gardner type 8L3 of 204 b.h.p at 1,200 r.p.m.
Transmission. **Mechanical.** Wilson-Drewry Director air-operated epicyclic gearbox. R.F.11 Spiral Bevel reverse/final drive unit.
Weight: 30 tons 4 cwt.
Driving Wheels: 3′ 7″.
Maximum tractive effort: 15,300 lb.

91   92

WARNING!

ON ALL LINES

It is dangerous to climb signal posts and masts supporting overhead wires or to touch conductor rails.

Diesel and electric trains approach quickly and silently.

DO NOT TRESPASS
ON THE RAILWAY

DIESEL MULTIPLE UNITS

The numbers of diesel cars have been checked to July 16th, 1960

Unless otherwise stated, all multiple-unit trains are gangwayed within each set, with guard's and luggage compartment at the inner end of motor brake coaches, and seating is in open saloons with centre and/or end doors. The letter L in the headings indicates an open vehicle fitted with toilet facilities : K indicates a different side corridor vehicle with toilet. Two standard lengths of underframe are in use, namely 56 ft. 11 in. and 63 ft. 5 in. but the actual body lengths vary by a few inches for the same type of underframe. The dimensions shown are the length over body and the overall width.

Several of the types listed are sub-divided by reason of detail or mechanical differences. For example, a certain number of cars in a class may have a different seating arrangement or a different make of engine but are otherwise similar to the main batch. Such differences are noted in the heading to the class and given a reference mark by which the relevant dimensions or details and the cars concerned can be identified. The type of set in which each class is formed on delivery is shown at the head of the details for that class, although it should be noted that changes may occur owing to varying operating conditions, even to the extent of coupling different makes of car in the same set or running power cars without intermediate trailers.

COUPLING OF DIESEL MULTIPLE UNITS

Although several multiple-unit diesel sets can be coupled together and driven by one man in the leading cab, for various reasons it is not possible for all types of diesel unit to work together. In order to distinguish cars that can run together, all have painted under the left and right headlights a colour code symbol. This is repeated at the inner end of the car in similar positions and a miniature symbol also appears on the plug socket covers. Only units bearing the same symbol can be coupled together.

- ▲ **RED TRIANGLE**
- ◆ **YELLOW DIAMOND**
- ● **WHITE CIRCLE**
- ▩ **BLUE SQUARE**
- ★ **ORANGE STAR**

Motor Brake Second ∎
(TWIN UNITS)

Built by: **Derby Works, B.R.**

Engines: Two B.U.T. (Leyland) 6-cyl.
horizontal type of 230 b.h.p.
*Two Rolls Royce 8-cyl. horizontal
type of 238 b.h.p.
†Two B.U.T. (Leyland) 6-cyl. horizontal type of 230 b.h.p.

Transmission: **Mechanical.** Cardan
shaft and freewheel to four-speed
epicyclic gearbox and further cardan
shaft to final drive.
***Hydraulic.** Twin Disc Torque
converter
†**Mechanical.** Cardan shaft and free
wheel to Self Changing Gears Ltd.
automatic four-speed gearbox and
further cardan shaft to final drive.

Body: 64′ 6″ × 9′ 3″.

Weight: { 35 tons 10 cwt.
37 tons 10 cwt.†

Seats 2nd: 62

E50000*	E50017	E50034
E50001	E50018	E50035
E50002	E50019	E50036
E50003	E50020	E50037
E50004	E50021	E50038
E50005	E50022	E50039
E50006	E50023	E50040
E50007	E50024	E50041
E50008	E50025	E50042
E50009	E50026	E50043
E50010	E50027	E50044
E50011	E50028	E50045
E50012	E50029	E50046
E50013	E50030	E50047
E50014	E50031	E50048
E50015	E50032	E50049†
E50016	E50033	

Motor Brake Second ∎
(THREE-CAR SUBURBAN)

Built by: **Derby Works, B.R.**
Engines: Two B.U.T. (Leyland) 6-cyl.
horizontal type of 150 b.h.p.
Transmission: **Mechanical.** Cardan
shaft and freewheel to four-speed
epicyclic gearbox and further cardan
shaft to final drive.
Body: 64′ 0″ × 9′ 3″. Non-gangwayed,
side doors to each seating bay.

Weight: 35 tons 10 cwt.
Seats 2nd : 65.

W50050	W50064	W50078
W50051	W50065	W50079
W50052	W50066	W50080
W50053	W50067	W50081
W50054	W50068	W50082
W50055	W50069	W50083
W50056	W50070	W50084
W50057	W50071	W50085
W50058	W50072	W50086
W50059	W50073	W50087
W50060	W50074	W50088
W50061	W50075	W50089
W50062	W50076	W50090
W50063	W50077	W50091

Motor Second ∎
(THREE-CAR SUBURBAN)

Built by: **Derby Works, B.R.**

Engines: Two B.U.T. (Leyland) 6-cyl.
horizontal type of 150 b.h.p.

Transmission: **Mechanical.** Cardan
shaft and freewheel to four-speed
epicyclic gearbox and further cardan
shaft to final drive.

Body: 64′ 0″ × 9′ 3″. Non-gangwayed,
side doors to each seating bay.

Weight: 35 tons 10 cwt.

Seats 2nd: 95.

W50092	W50106	W50120
W50093	W50107	W50121
W50094	W50108	W50122
W50095	W50109	W50123
W50096	W50110	W50124
W50097	W50111	W50125
W50098	W50112	W50126
W50099	W50113	W50127
W50100	W50114	W50128
W50101	W50115	W50129
W50102	W50116	W50130
W50103	W50117	W50131
W50104	W50118	W50132
W50105	W50119	W50133

Motor Brake Second ■
(TWIN UNITS)

Built by: **Metropolitan Cammell.**
Engines: Two Rolls Royce 6-cyl. horizontal type of 180 b.h.p.
*Two Rolls Royce 6-cyl. type supercharged to 230 b.h.p.
Transmission: **Mechanical.** Cardan shaft and freewheel to four-speed epicyclic gearbox and further cardan shaft to final drive.
Body: 57′ 0″ × 9′ 3″.
Weight: 33 tons.
Seats 2nd: 52.

M50134	M50136 *	M50137
M50135		

Motor Composite (L) ■
(FOUR-CAR UNITS)

Built by: **Metropolitan Cammell.**
Engines: Two B.U.T. (A.E.C.) 6-cyl. horizontal type of 150 b.h.p.
Transmission: **Mechanical.** Cardan shaft and freewheel to four-speed epicyclic gearbox and further cardan shaft to final drive.
Body: 57′ 0″ × 9′ 3″
Weight: 32 tons.
Seats 1st: 12.
 2nd: 45.

E50138	E50143	E50148
E50139	E50144	E50149
E50140	E50145	E50150
E50141	E50146	E50151
E50142	E50147	

Motor Brake Second ■
TWIN UNITS)

Built by: **Metropolitan Cammell.**
Engines: Two B.U.T. (A.E.C.) 6 cyl. horizontal type of 150 b.h.p.
Transmission: **Mechanical.** Cardan shaft and freewheel to four-speed epicyclic gearbox and further cardan shaft to final drive.
Body: 57′ 0″ × 9′ 3″.
Weight: 31 tons 10 cwt.
Seats: 2nd: 52.

E50152	E50154	E50156
E50153	E50155	E50157

Motor Composite (L) ■
(TWIN UNITS)

Built by: **Metropolitan Cammell.**
Engines: Two B.U.T. (A.E.C.) 6-cyl. horizontal type of 150 b.h.p.
Transmission: **Mechanical.** Cardan shaft and freewheel to four-speed epicyclic gearbox and further cardan shaft to final drive.
Body: 57′ 0″ × 9′ 3″.
Weight: 32 tons.
Seats: 1st: 12.
 2nd: 53.

E50158	E50160	E50162
E50159	E50161	E50163

Motor Brake Second ■
(TWIN UNITS)
For Details see E50152-7

E50164	E50166	E50167
E50165		

Motor Composite (L) ■
(TWIN UNITS)
For Details see E50158-63

E50168	E50170	E50171
E50169		

Motor Composite (L) ■
(FOUR-CAR UNITS)

Built by: **Metropolitan Cammell.**
Engines: B.U.T. (A.E.C.), 6-cyl. horizontal type of 150 b.h.p.
Transmission: **Mechanical.** Cardan shaft and freewheel to four-speed epicyclic gearbox and further cardan shaft to final drive.
Body: 57′ 0″ × 9′ 3″
Weight: 32 tons.
Seats 1st: 12.
 2nd: 53.

E50172	E50182	E50191
E50174	E50183	E50192
E50175	E50184	E50193
E50176	E50185	E50194
E50177	E50186	E50195
E50178	E50187	E50196
E50179	E50188	E50197
E50180	E50189	
E50181	E50190	

Motor Brake Second ■
(TWIN UNITS)

Built by: **Metropolitan Cammell.**
Engines: Two B.U.T. (A.E.C.) 6-cyl
horizontal type of 150 b.h.p
Transmission: **Mechanical.** Cardan
shaft and freewheel to four-speed
epicyclic gearbox and further cardan
shaft to final drive.
Body: 57' 0" × 9' 3"
Weight: 32 tons.
Seats 2nd: 52.

E50198	E50210	E50222
E50199	E50211	E50223
E50200	E50212	E50224
E50201	E50213	E50225
E50202	E50214	E50226
E50203	E50215	E50227
E50204	E50216	E50228
E50205	E50217	E50229
E50206	E50218	E50230
E50207	E50219	E50231
E50208	E50220	E50232
E50209	E50221	E50233

Motor Composite (L) ■
(FOUR-CAR UNITS)
For Details see E50138-45

E50234	E50238	E50242
E50235	E50239	E50243
E50236	E50240	E50244
E50237	E50241	E50245

Motor Brake Second ■
(TWIN UNITS)

Built by: **Metropolitan Cammell.**
Engines: Two B.U.T. (A.E.C.) 6-cyl.
horizontal type of 150 b.h.p.
Transmission: **Mechanical.** Cardan
shaft and freewheel to four-speed
epicyclic gearbox and further cardan
shaft to final drive.
Body: 57' 0" × 9' 3".
Weight: 31 tons 10 cwt.
Seats 2nd: 44.

E50246	E50247	E50248

Motor Brake Second ■
(FOUR-CAR UNITS)

Built by: **Cravens.**
Engines: Two B.U.T. (A.E.C.) 6-cyl.
horizontal type of 150 b.h.p.
Transmission: **Mechanical.** Cardan
shaft and freewheel to four-speed
epicyclic gearbox and further cardan
shaft to final drive.
Body: 57' 6" × 9' 3".
Weight: 30 tons.
Seats 2nd: 52.

E50249

Motor Brake Second ■
(TWIN UNITS)

Built by: **Metropolitan Cammell.**
Engines: Two B.U.T. (A.E.C.) 6-cy'.
horizontal type of 150 b.h.p.
Transmission: **Mechanical.** Cardan
shaft and freewheel to four-speed
epicyclic gearbox and further cardan
shaft to final drive.
Body: 57' 0" × 9' 3".
Weight: 31 tons 10 cwt.
Seats 2nd: 52.

E50250	E50254	E50258
E50251	E50255	E50259
E50252	E50256	
E50253	E50257	

Motor Composite (L) ■
(TWIN UNITS)

Built by: **Metropolitan Cammell.**
Engines: Two B.U.T. (A.E.C.) 6 cyl.
horizontal type of 150 b.h.p.
Transmission: **Mechanical.** Cardan
shaft and freewheel to four-speed
epicyclic gearbox and further cardan
shaft to final drive.
Body: 57' 0" × 9' 3".
Weight: 31 tons 10 cwt.
Seats 1st: 12.
      2nd: 53.

E50260	E50264	E50268
E50261	E50265	E50269
E50262	E50266	
E50263	E50267	

Motor Composite (L) ∎
(THREE-CAR UNITS)

Built by: **Metropolitan Cammell.**
Engines: Two Rolls Royce 6-cyl. horizontal type of 180 b.h.p.
Transmission: **Mechanical.** Cardan shaft and freewheel to four-speed epicyclic gearbox and further cardan shaft to final drive.
Body: 57′ 0″ × 9′ 3″.
Weight: 32 tons
Seats 1st: 12.
 2nd: 53.

E50270	E50274	E50278
E50271	E50275	E50279
E50272	E50276	
E50273	E50277	

Motor Brake Second ∎
(THREE-CAR UNITS)

Built by: **Metropolitan Cammell.**
Engine: Two Rolls Royce 6-cyl. horizontal type of 180 b.h.p.
Transmission: **Mechanical.** Cardan shaft and freewheel to four-speed epicyclic gearbox and further cardan shaft to final drive.
Body: 57′ 0″ × 9′ 3″.
Weight: 33 tons.
Seats 2nd: 52.

E50280	E50285	E50290
E50281	E50286	E50291
E50282	E50287	E50292
E50283	E50288	
E50284	E50289	

Motor Brake Second ∎
(TWIN UNITS)

Built by: **Metropolitan Cammell.**
Engines: Two B.U.T. (A.E.C.) 6-cyl. horizontal type of 150 b.h.p.
Transmission: **Mechanical.** Cardan shaft and freewheel to four-speed epicyclic gearbox and further cardan shaft to final drive.
Body: 57′ 0″ × 9′ 3″.
Weight: 31 tons 10 cwt.
Seats 2nd: 52.

E50293	E50295	E50296
E50294		

Motor Brake Second ∎
(THREE-CAR UNITS)

Built by: **Metropolitan Cammell.**
Engines: Two B.U.T. 6-cyl. horizontal type of 150 b.h.p.
Transmission: **Mechanical.** Cardan shaft and freewheel to four-speed epicyclic gearbox and further cardan shaft to final drive.
Body: 57′ 0″ × 9′ 3″.
Weight: 31 tons 10 cwt.
Seats 2nd: 52.

M50303	M50309	M50315
M50304	M50310	M50316
M50305	M50311	M50317
M50306	M50312	M50318
M50307	M50313	M50319
M50308	M50314	M50320

Motor Composite (L) ∎
(THREE-CAR UNITS)

Built by: **Metropolitan Cammell.**
Engines: Two B.U.T. 6-cyl. horizontal type of 150 b.h.p.
Transmission: **Mechanical.** Cardan shaft and freewheel to four-speed epicyclic gearbox and further cardan shaft to final drive.
Body: 57′ 0″ × 9′ 3″.
Weight: 31 tons 10 cwt.
Seats 1st: 12.
 2nd: 53.

M50321	M50327	M50333
M50322	M50328	M50334
M50323	M50329	M50335
M50324	M50330	M50336
M50325	M50331	M50337
M50326	M50332	M50338

Motor Brake Second ∎
(TWIN UNITS)

Built by: **Gloucester R.C. & W. Co.**
Engines: Two B.U.T. (A.E.C.) 6-cyl. horizontal type of 150 b.h.p.
Transmission: **Mechanical.** Cardan shaft and freewheel to four-speed epicyclic gearbox and further cardan shaft to final drive.
Body: 57′ 6″ × 9′ 3″.
Weight: 30 tons 5 cwt.
Seats. 2nd: 52.

SC50339	SC50346	M50353	M50395	M50402	M50409
SC50340	SC50347	M50354	M50396	M50403	M50410
SC50341	SC50348	M50355	M50397	M50404	M50411
SC50342	SC50349	M50356	M50398	M50405	M50412
SC50343	M50350	M50357	M50399	M50406	M50413
SC50344	M50351	M50358 *	M50400	M50407	M50414
SC50345	M50352		M50401	M50408	

*Fitted with C.A.V. Ltd. automatic gear change equipment.

Motor Brake Second ■
(TWIN UNITS)

Built by: **Cravens.**
Engines: Two B.U.T. (Leyland) (A.E.C.*) 6-cyl. horizontal type of 150 b.h.p.
Transmission: **Mechanical.** Cardan shaft and freewheel to four-speed epicyclic gearbox and further cardan shaft to final drive.
Body: 57′ 6″ × 9′ 3″.
Weight: 29 tons.
Seats 2nd: 52.

E50359	E50371*	E50383*
E50360	E50372*	E50384*
E50361	E50373*	E50385*
E50362	E50374*	E50386*
E50363	E50375*	E50387*
E50364	E50376*	E50388*
E50365	E50377*	E50389*
E50366	E50378*	M50390*
E50367	E50379*	M50391*
E50368	E50380*	M50392*
E50369	E50381*	M50393*
E50370	E50382*	M50394*

Motor Brake Second ■
(TWIN UNITS)

Built by: **Park Royal Vehicles.**
Engines: Two B.U.T. (A.E.C.) 6-cyl. horizontal type of 150 b.h.p.
Transmission: **Mechanical.** Cardan shaft and freewheel to four-speed epicyclic gearbox and further cardan shaft to final drive.
Body: 57′ 6″ × 9′ 3′.
Weight: 33 tons 8 cwt.
Seats 2nd: 52.

Motor Brake Second ■
(TWIN UNITS)

Built by: **D. Wickham & Co. Ltd.**
Engines: Two B.U.T. (Leyland) 6-cyl. horizontal type of 150 b.h.p.
Transmission: **Mechanical.** Cardan shaft and freewheel to four-speed epicyclic gearbox and further cardan shaft to final drive.
Body: 57′ 0″ × 9′ 3″.
Weight: 27 tons 10 cwt.
Seats 2nd: 59.

| E50415 | E50417 | E50419 |
| E50416 | E50418 | |

Motor Brake Second ■
(L.M. THREE-CAR UNITS)

Built by: **Birmingham R.C. & W. Co.**
Engines: Two B.U.T. (Leyland) 6-cyl. horizontal type of 150 b.h.p.
Transmission: **Mechanical.** Cardan shaft and freewheel to four-speed epicyclic gearbox and further cardan shaft to final drive.
Body: 57′ 6″ × 9′ 3″.
Weight: 31 tons.
Seats 2nd: 52.

| M50420 | M50422 | M50423 |
| M50421 | | |

Motor Composite (L) ■
(THREE-CAR UNITS)

Built by: **Birmingham R. C. & W. Co.**
Engines: Two B.U.T. (Leyland) 6-cyl. horizontal type of 150 b.h.p.
Transmission: **Mechanical.** Cardan shaft and freewheel to four-speed epicyclic gearbox and further cardan shaft to final drive.
Body: 57′ 6″ × 9′ 3″
Weight: 31 tons.
Seats 1st: 12.
  2nd: 54.

| M50424 | M50426 | M50427 |
| M50425 | | |

Motor Brake Second ■
(THREE-CAR UNITS)
For Details see M50420-3

M50428	M50446	M50464
M50429	M50447	M50465
M50430	M50448	M50466
M50431	M50449	M50467
M50432	M50450	M50468
M50433	M50451	M50469
M50434	M50452	M50470
M50435	M50453	M50471
M50436	M50454	M50472
M50437	M50455	M50473
M50438	M50456	M50474
M50439	M50457	M50475
M50440	M50458	M50476
M50441	M50459	M50477
M50442	M50460	M50478
M50443	M50461	M50479
M50444	M50462	
M50445	M50463	

Motor Composite (L) ■
(THREE-CAR UNITS)
For Details see M50424-7.

M50480	M50498	M50516
M50481	M50499	M50517
M50482	M50500	M50518
M50483	M50501	M50519
M50484	M50502	M50520
M50485	M50503	M50521
M50486	M50504	M50522
M50487	M50505	M50523
M50488	M50506	M50524
M50489	M50507	M50525
M50490	M50508	M50526
M50491	M50509	M50527
M50492	M50510	M50528
M50493	M50511	M50529
M50494	M50512	M50530
M50495	M50513	M50531
M50496	M50514	
M50497	M50515	

Motor Brake Second ■
(TWIN UNITS)

Built by: **Birmingham R. C. & W. Co.**
Engines: Two B.U.T. (Leyland) 6-cyl. horizontal type of 150 b.h.p .
Transmission: **Mechanical.** Cardan shaft and freewheel to four-speed epicyclic gearbox and further cardan shaft to final drive.
Body: 57′ 6″ × 9′ 3″
Weight: 31 tons.
Seats 2nd: 52.

M50532	M50536	M50540
M50533	M50537	M50541
M50534	M50538	
M50535	M50539	

Motor Composite (L) ■
(FOUR-CAR UNITS)

Built by: **Birmingham R. C. & W. Co.**
Engines: Two B.U.T. (Leyland) 6-cyl. horizontal type of 150 b.h.p.
Transmission: **Mechanical.** Cardan shaft and freewheel to four-speed epicyclic gearbox and further cardan shaft to final drive.
Body: 57′ 6″ × 9′ 3″.
Weight: 31 tons.
Seats 1st: 12.
2nd: 41.

E50542	E50560	E50578
E50543	E50561	E50579
E50544	E50562	E50580
E50545	E50563	E50581
E50546	E50564	E50582
E50547	E50565	E50583
E50548	E50566	E50584
E50549	E50567	E50585
E50550	E50568	E50586
E50551	E50569	E50587
E50552	E50570	E50588
E50553	E50571	E50589
E50554	E50572	E50590
E50555	E50573	E50591
E50556	E50574	E50592
E50557	E50575	E50593
E50558	E50576	
E50559	E50577	

Motor Brake Second ■
(TWIN UNITS)
Built by: **Birmingham R. C. & W. Co.**
Engines: Two B.U.T. (Leyland) 6-cyl.
horizontal type of 150 b.h.p.
Transmission: **Mechanical.** Cardan
shaft and freewheel to four-speed
epicyclic gearbox and further cardan
shaft to final drive.
Body: 57′ 6″ × 9′ 3″.
Weight: 31 tons.
Seats 2nd: 52.

E50594	E50596	E50598
E50595	E50597	

Motor Brake Second ■
(TWIN OR THREE*-CAR UNITS)
Built by: **Derby Works, B.R.**
Engines: Two B.U.T. (A.E.C.) 6-cyl.
horizontal type of 150 b.h.p.
Transmission: **Mechanical.** Cardan
shaft and freewheel to four-speed
epicyclic gearbox and further cardan
shaft to final drive.
Body: 57′ 6″ × 9′ 2″.
Weight: 28 tons 10 cwt.
Seats 2nd: 52.

E50599	E50610	E50621*
E50600	E50611	E50622*
E50601	E50612	E50623*
E50602	E50613	E50624*
E50603	E50614	M50625
E50604	E50615	M50626
E50605	E50616	M50627
E50606	E50617	M50628
E50607	E50618	M50629
E50608	E50619	
E50609	E50620*	

Motor Composite (L) ■
(THREE* AND FOUR-CAR UNITS)
Built by: **Derby Works, B.R.**
Engines: Two B.U.T. (A.E.C.) 6-cyl.
horizontal type of 150 b.h.p.
Transmission: **Mechanical.** Cardan
shaft and freewheel to four-speed
epicyclic gearbox and further cardan
shaft to final drive.
Body: 57′ 6″ × 9′ 2″.
Weight: 28 tons.
Seats 2nd: 12.
2nd: 50

E50630	E50636	E50642*
E50631	E50637	E50643*
E50632	E50638	E50644*
E50633	E50639	E50645*
E50634	E50640	E50646*
E50635	E50641	

Motor Second (L) ■
(THREE-CAR CROSS-COUNTRY)
Built by: **Swindon Works B.R.**
Engines: Two B.U.T. 6-cyl. horizontal
type of 150 b.h.p.
Transmission: **Mechanical.** Cardan
shaft and freewheel to four-speed
epicyclic gearbox and further cardan
shaft to final drive.
Body: 64′ 6″ × 9′ 3″.
Weight: 36 tons 10 cwt.
Seats 2nd: 63.

W50647	W50664	W50681
W50648	W50665	W50682
W50649	W50666	W50683
W50650	W50667	W50684
W50651	W50668	W50685
W50652	W50669	W50686
W50653	W50670	W50687
W50654	W50671	W50688
W50655	W50672	W50689
W50656	W50673	W50690
W50657	W50674	W50691
W50658	W50675	W50692
W50659	W50676	W50693
W50660	W50677	W50694
W50661	W50678	W50695
W50662	W50679	
W50663	W50680	

Motor Brake Composite ■
(THREE-CAR CROSS-COUNTRY)
Built by: **Swindon Works B.R.**
Engines: Two B.U.T. 6-cyl. horizontal
type of 150 b.h.p.
Transmission: **Mechanical.** Cardan
shaft and freewheel to four-speed
epicyclic gearbox and further cardan
shaft to final drive.
Body: 64′ 6″ × 9′ 3″.
Weight: 36 tons 7 cwt.
Seats 1st: 18.
2nd: 16.

W50696	W50713	W50730
W50697	W50714	W50731
W50698	W50715	W50732
W50699	W50716	W50733
W50700	W50717	W50734
W50701	W50718	W50735
W50702	W50719	W50736
W50703	W50720	W50737
W50704	W50721	W50738
W50705	W50722	W50739
W50706	W50723	W50740
W50707	W50724	W50741
W50708	W50725	W50742
W50709	W50726	W50743
W50710	W50727	W50744
W50711	W50728	
W50712	W50729	

Motor Composite (L) ■
(THREE-CAR UNITS)

Built by: **Metropolitan Cammell.**
Engines: Two Rolls Royce 6-cyl. horizontal type of 180 b.h.p.
Transmission: **Mechanical:** Cardan shaft and freewheel to four-speed epicyclic gearbox and further cardan shaft to final drive.
Body: 57′ 0″ × 9′ 3″.
Weight: 31 tons 10 cwt.
Seats 1st: 12.
2nd: 53.

E50745	E50746	E50747

Motor Composite (L) ▨
(N.E. FOUR-CAR UNITS)

Built by: **Metropolitan Cammell.**
Engines: Two B.U.T. (A.E.C.) 6-cyl. horizontal type of 150 b.h.p.
Transmission: **Mechanical.** Cardan shaft and freewheel to four-speed epicyclic gearbox and further cardan shaft to final drive.
Body: 57′ 0″ × 9′ 3″.
Weight: 31 tons 10 cwt.
Seats 1st: 12.
2nd: 53.

E50748	E50750	E50751
E50749		

Motor Brake Second ■
(THREE-CAR UNITS)

Built by: **Cravens.**
Engines: Two B.U.T. (Leyland) 6-cyl. horizontal type of 150 b.h.p.
Transmission: **Mechanical.** Cardan shaft and freewheel to four-speed epicyclic gearbox and further cardan shaft to final drive.
Body: 57′ 6″ × 9′ 3″
Weight: 30 tons.
Seats 2nd: 52.

M50752	M50759	M50766
M50753	M50760	M50767
M50754	M50761	M50768
M50755	M50762	M50769
M50756	M50763	M50770
M50757	M50764	
M50758	M50765	

Motor Brake Second ▨
(TWIN UNITS)

Built by: **Cravens.**
Engines: Two B.U.T. (A.E.C.) 6-cyl. horizontal type of 150 b.h.p.
Transmission: **Mechanical.** Cardan shaft and freewheel to four-speed epicyclic gearbox and further cardan shaft to final drive.
Body: 57′ 6″ × 9′ 3″.
Weight: 30 tons.
Seats 2nd: 52.

M50771	M50776	M50781
M50772	M50777	M50782
M50773	M50778	M50783
M50774	M50779	M50784
M50775	M50780	

Motor Composite (L) ■
(L.M. THREE-CAR UNITS)

Built by: **Cravens.**
Engines: Two B.U.T. (Leyland) 6-cyl. horizontal type of 150 b.h.p.
Transmission: **Mechanical.** Cardan shaft and freewheel to four-speed epicyclic gearbox and further cardan shaft to final drive.
Body: 57′ 6″ × 9′ 3″.
Weight: 30 tons.
Seats 1st: 12.
2nd: 51

M50785	M50792	M50799
M50786	M50793	M50800
M50787	M50794	M50801
M50788	M50795	M50802
M50789	M50796	M50803
M50790	M50797	
M50791	M50798	

Motor Composite (L) ■

(TWIN UNITS)

Built by: **Cravens.**
Engines: Two B.U.T. (A.E.C.) 6-cyl. horizontal type of 150 b.h.p.
Transmission: **Mechanical.** Cardan shaft and freewheel to four-speed epicyclic gearbox and further cardan shaft to final drive.
Body: 57′ 6″ × 9′ 3″.
Weight: 30 tons.
Seats 1st: 12.
2nd: 51.

M50804	M50809	M50814
M50805	M50810	M50815
M50806	M50811	M50816
M50807	M50812	M50817
M50808	M50813	

Motor Brake Second ■

(THREE-CAR SUBURBAN)
For Details see W50050-91

W50818	W50836	W50854
W50819	W50837	W50855
W50820	W50838	W50856
W50821	W50839	W50857
W50822	W50840	W50858
W50823	W50841	W50859
W50824	W50842	W50860
W50825	W50843	W50861
W50826	W50844	W50862
W50827	W50845	W50863
W50828	W50846	W50864
W50829	W50847	W50865
W50830	W50848	W50866
W50831	W50849	W50867
W50832	W50850	W50868
W50833	W50851	W50869
W50834	W50852	W50870
W50835	W50853	

Motor Second ■

(THREE-CAR SUBURBAN)
For Details see W50092-50133

W50871	W50889	W50907
W50872	W50890	W50908
W50873	W50891	W50909
W50874	W50892	W50910
W50875	W50893	W50911
W50876	W50894	W50912
W50877	W50895	W50913
W50878	W50896	W50914
W50879	W50897	W50915
W50880	W50898	W50916
W50881	W50899	W50917
W50882	W50900	W50918
W50883	W50901	W50919
W50884	W50902	W50920
W50885	W50903	W50921
W50886	W50904	W50922
W50887	W50905	W50923
W50888	W50906	

Motor Brake Second ■

(TWIN UNITS)

Built by: **Derby Works, B.R.**
Engines: Two B.U.T. (A.E.C.) 6-cyl. horizontal type of 150 b.h.p.
Transmission: **Mechanical.** Cardan shaft and freewheel to four-speed epicyclic gearbox and further cardan shaft to final drive.
Body: 57′ 6″ × 9′ 2″.
Weight: 28 tons 10 cwt.
Seats 2nd: 52.

M50924	M50928	M50932
M50925	M50929	M50933
M50926	M50930	M50934
M50927	M50931	M50935

Motor Second (L) ●
(INTER CITY UNITS)

Built by: **Swindon Works, B.R.**
Engines: Two B.U.T. 6-cyl. horizontal
type of 150 b.h.p.
Transmission: **Mechanical.** Cardan
shaft and freewheel to four-speed
epicyclic gearbox and further cardan
shaft to final drive.
Body: 64' "6 × 9' 3" Gangwayed both
ends, side driving compartment at
one end.
Weight:
Seats 2nd: 64.

SC50936

Motor Second ★
(THREE-CAR SUBURBAN)

Built by: **Derby Works, B.R.**
Engines: Two Rolls Royce horizontal
type of 238 b.h.p.
Transmission: **Hydraulic.** Twin-disc
torque converter.
Body: 64' 0" × 9' 3". Non-gangwayed,
side doors to each seating bay.
Weight: 39 tons 10 cwt.
Seats 2nd: 95.

E50988	E50995	E51002
E50989	E50996	E51003
E50990	E50997	E51004
E50991	E50998	E51005
E50992	E50999	E51006
E50993	E51000	E51007
E50994	E51001	

Motor Brake Second ■
(TWIN UNITS)

Built by: **Derby Works, B.R.**
Engines: Two B.U.T. (A.E.C.) 6-cyl.
horizontal type of 150 b.h.p.
Transmission: **Mechanical.** Cardan
shaft and freewheel to four-speed
epicyclic gearbox and further cardan
shaft to final drive.
Body: 57' 6" × 9' 2".
Weight:
Seats 2nd:

M50938	M50955	M50972
M50939	M50956	M50973
M50940	M50957	M50974
M50941	M50958	M50975
M50942	M50959	M50976
M50943	M50960	M50977
M50944	M50961	M50978
M50945	M50962	M50979
M50946	M50963	M50980
M50947	M50964	M50981
M50948	M50965	M50982
M50949	M50966	M50983
M50950	M50967	M50984
M50951	M50968	M50985
M50952	M50969	M50986
M50953	M50970	M50987
M50954	M50971	

Motor Second (L) ●
(INTER CITY UNITS)

Built by : **Swindon Works, B.R.**
Engines: Two B.U.T. 6-cyl. horizontal
type of 150 b.h.p.
Transmission: **Mechanical.** Cardan
shaft and freewheel to four-speed
epicyclic gearbox and further cardan
shaft to final drive.
Body: 64' 6" × 9' 3". Gangwayed both
ends, side driving compartment at
one end.
Weight:
Seats 2nd: 64.

SC51008	SC51016	SC51024
SC51009	SC51017	SC51025
SC51010	SC51018	SC51026
SC51011	SC51019	SC51027
SC51012	SC51020	SC51028
SC51013	SC51021	SC51029
SC51014	SC51022	
SC51015	SC51023	

Motor Brake Second (L) ●
(INTER CITY UNITS)

Built by : **Swindon Works, B.R.**
Engines: Two B.U.T. (A.E.C.) 6-cyl.
horizontal type of 150 b.h.p.
Transmission: **Mechanical.** Cardan
shaft and freewheel to four-speed
epicyclic gearbox and further cardan
shaft to final drive.
Body: 64' 6" × 9' 3".
Weight: 38 tons.
Seats 2nd: 52.

SC51030	SC51038	SC51046
SC51031	SC51039	SC51047
SC51032	SC51040	SC51048
SC51033•	SC51041	SC51049
SC51034	SC51042	SC51050
SC51035	SC51043	SC51051
SC51036	SC51044	
SC51037	SC51045	

W51089	W51096	W51103
W51090	W51097	W51104
W51091	W51098	W51105
W51092	W51099	W51106
W51093	W51100	W51107
W51094	W51101	
W51095	W51102	

Motor Brake Composite ■
(THREE-CAR CROSS-COUNTRY)

Built by: **Gloucester R.C. & W. Co.**
Engines: Two B.U.T. 6-cyl. horizontal type of 150 b.h.p.
Transmission: **Mechanical.** Cardan shaft and freewheel to four-speed epicyclic gearbox and further cardan shaft to final drive.
Body: 64' 6" × 9' 3".
Weight: 36 tons 19 cwt.
Seats 1st: 18.
2nd: 16.

W51052	W51062	W51072
W51053	W51063	W51073
W51054	W51064	W51074
W51055	W51065	W51075
W51056	W51066	W51076
W51057	W51067	W51077
W51058	W51068	W51078
W51059	W51069	W51079
W51060	W51070	
W51061	W51071	

Motor Second (L) ■
(THREE-CAR CROSS-COUNTRY)

Built by: **Gloucester R.C. & W. Co.**
Engines: Two B.U.T. 6-cyl. horizontal type of 150 b.h.p.
Transmission: **Mechanical.** Cardan shaft and freewheel to four-speed epicyclic gearbox and further cardan shaft to final drive.
Body: 64' 6" × 9' 3".
Weight: 37 tons 10 cwt.
Seats 2nd: 68.

W51080	W51083	W51086
W51081	W51084	W51087
W51082	W51085	W51088

Motor Brake Second ■
(TWIN UNITS)
For Details see SC50339-M50358

SC51108	SC51115	SC51122
SC51109	SC51116	SC51123
SC51110	SC51117	SC51124
SC51111	SC51118	SC51125
SC51112	SC51119	SC51126
SC51113	SC51120	SC51127
SC51114	SC51121	

Motor Brake Second ■
(THREE-CAR SUBURBAN)
For Details see W50050-91

W51128	W51133	W51138
W51129	W51134	W51139
W51130	W51135	W51140
W51131	W51136	
W51132	W51137	

Motor Second ■
(THREE-CAR SUBURBAN)
For Details see W50092-50133

W51141	W51146	W51151
W51142	W51147	W51152
W51143	W51148	W51153
W51144	W51149	
W51145	W51150	

Motor Brake Second ★
(E.R. THREE-CAR SUBURBAN)

Built by: **Derby Works, B.R.**
Engines: Two Rolls Royce horizontal type of 238 b.h.p.
Transmission: **Hydraulic.** Twin-disc torque converter.
Body: 64' 0" × 9' 3". Non-gangwayed side doors to each seating bay.
Weight: 39 tons 10 cwt.
Seats 2nd: 65

E51154	E51161	E51168
E51155	E51162	E51169
E51156	E51163	E51170
E51157	E51164	E51171
E51158	E51165	E51172
E51159	E51166	E51173
E51160	E51167	

Motor Brake Second ■
(TWIN UNITS)

Built by: **Metropolitan Cammell.**
Engines: Two B.U.T. (A.E.C.) 6-cyl. horizontal type of 150 b.h.p.
Transmission: **Mechanical.** Cardan shaft and freewheel to four-speed epicyclic gearbox and further cardan shaft to final drive.
Body: 57′ 0″ × 9′ 3″.
Weight: 32 tons.
Seats 2nd: 52.

M51174	M51201	SC51228
M51175	M51202	SC51229
M51176	M51203	SC51230
M51177	E51204	SC51231
M51178	E51205	SC51232
M51179	E51206	SC51233
M51180	E51207	SC51234
M51181	E51208	SC51235
M51182	E51209	SC51236
M51183	E51210	SC51237
M51184	E51211	SC51238
M51185	E51212	SC51239
M51186	E51213	SC51240
M51187	E51214	SC51241
M51188	E51215	SC51242
M51189	E51216	SC51243
M51190	E51217	SC51244
M51191	E51218	SC51245
M51192	E51219	SC51246
M51193	E51220	SC51247
M51194	E51221	SC51248
M51195	E51222	SC51249
M51196	E51223	SC51250
M51197	SC51224	SC51251
M51198	SC51225	SC51252
M51199	SC51226	SC51253
M51200	SC51227	

Motor Brake Second ■
(TWIN UNITS)

Built by: **Cravens.**
Engines: Two B.U.T. (A.E.C.) 6-cyl. horizontal type of 150 b.h.p.
Transmission: **Mechanical.** Cardan shaft and freewheel to four-speed epicyclic gearbox and further cardan shaft to final drive.
Body: 57′ 6″ × 9′ 3″.
Weight: 30 tons.
Seats 2nd: 52.

E51254	E51270	E51286
E51255	E51271	E51287
E51256	E51272	E51288
E51257	E51273	E51289
E51258	E51274	E51290
E51259	E51275	E51291
E51260	E51276	E51293
E51261	E51277	E51293
E51262	E51278	E51294
E51263	E51279	E51295
E51264	E51280	E51296
E51265	E51281	E51297
E51266	E51282	E51298
E51267	E51283	E51299
E51268	E51284	E51300
E51269	E51285	E51301

Motor Brake Second ■

Built by: **Birmingham R.C. & W. Co.**
Engines:
Transmission: **Mechanical.** Cardan shaft and freewheel to four-speed epicyclic gearbox and further cardan shaft to final drive.
Body: 64′ 0″. × 9′ 3″. Non-gangwayed, side doors to each seating bay.
Weight:
Seats: 2nd.

W51302	W51307	W51312
W51303	W51308	W51313
W51304	W51309	W51314
W51305	W51310	
W51306	W51311	

Motor Second ■

Built by: **Birmingham R.C. & W. Co.**
Engines:
Transmission: **Mechanical.** Cardan shaft and freewheel to four-speed epicyclic gearbox and further cardan shaft to final drive.

Body: 64' 0" × 9' 3". Non-gangwayed, side doors to each seating bay.
Weight:
Seats 2nd:

W51317	W51322	W51326
W51318	W51323	W51327
W51319	W51324	W51328
W51320	W51325	W51329
W51321		

Motor Brake Second ■
(THREE-CAR SUBURBAN)

Built by: **Pressed Steel Co.**
Engines: Two B.U.T. 6-cyl. horizontal type of 150 b.h.p.
Transmission: **Mechanical.** Cardan shaft and freewheel to four-speed epicyclic gearbox and further cardan shaft to final drive.
Body: 64' 0" × 9' 3". Non-gangwayed, side doors to each seating bay.
Weight:
Seats 2nd:

W51332	W51341	W51350
W51333	W51342	W51351
W51334	W51343	W51352
W51335	W51344	W51353
W51336	W51345	W51354
W51337	W51346	W51355
W51338	W51347	W51356
W51339	W51348	W51357
W51340	W51349	W51358

Motor Second ■
(THREE-CAR SUBURBAN)

Built by: **Pressed Steel Co.**
Engines: Two B.U.T. 6-cyl. horizontal type of 150 b.h.p.
Transmission: **Mechanical.** Cardan shaft and freewheel to four-speed epicyclic gearbox and further cardan shaft to final drive.
Body: 64' 0" × 9' 3". Non-gangwayed, side doors to each seating bay.
Weight:
Seats 2nd:

W51374	W51377	W51380
W51375	W51378	W51381
W51376	W51379	W51382

W51383	W51389	W51395
W51384	W51390	W51396
W51385	W51391	W51397
W51386	W51392	W51398
W51387	W51393	W51399
W51388	W51394	W51400

Motor Brake Second ■
(TWIN UNITS)

Built by: **Derby Works, B.R.**
Engines: Two B.U.T. (A.E.C.) 6-cyl. horizontal type of 150 b.h.p.
Transmission: **Mechanical.** Cardan shaft and freewheel to four-speed epicyclic gearbox and further cardan shaft to final drive.
Body: 57' 6" × 9' 2".
Weight:
Seats 2nd:

M51416	M51419	M51422
M51417	M51420	M51423
M51418	M51421	M51424

Motor Brake Second ■
(TWIN UNITS)

Built by: **Metropolitan Cammell.**
Engines: Two B.U.T. (A.E.C.) 6-cyl. horizontal type of 150 b.h.p.
Transmission: **Mechanical.** Cardan shaft and freewheel to four-speed epicyclic gearbox and further cardan shaft to final drive.
Body: 57' 0" × 9' 3".
Weight: 31 tons 10 cwt.
Seats 2nd: 52.

E51425	E51429	E51433
E51426	E51430	E51434
E51427	E51431	
E51428	E51432	

Motor Brake Second ■
(THREE OR *FOUR-CAR UNITS)

Built by: **Metropolitan Cammell.**
Engines: Two B.U.T. (A.E.C.) 6-cyl. horizontal type of 150 b.h.p.
Transmission: **Mechanical.** Cardan shaft and freewheel to four-speed epicyclic gearbox and further cardan shaft to final drive.
Body: 57' 0" × 9' 3".
Weight: 32 tons.
Seats 2nd: 52.

E51435*	SC51447	SC51459
E51436*	SC51448	SC51460
E51437*	SC51449	SC51461
E51438*	SC51450	SC51462
E51439*	SC51451	SC51463
E51440*	SC51452	SC51464
E51441*	SC51453	SC51465
E51442*	SC51454	SC51466
E51443*	SC51455	SC51467
E51444*	SC51456	SC51468
SC51445	SC51457	SC51469
SC51446	SC51458	SC51470

Motor Brake Second ■
(TWIN UNITS)

Built by: **Cravens.**
Engines: Two B.U.T. (A.E.C.) 6-cyl. horizontal type of 150 b.h.p.
Transmission: **Mechanical.** Cardan shaft and freewheel to four-speed epicyclic gearbox and further cardan shaft to final drive.
Body: 57′ 6″ × 9′ 3″.
Weight:
Seats 2nd:

E51471	SC51479	SC51487
E51472	SC51480	SC51488
SC51473	SC51481	SC51489
SC51474	SC51482	SC51490
SC51475	SC51483	SC51491
SC51476	SC51484	SC51492
SC51477	SC51485	SC51493
SC51478	SC51486	SC51494

Motor Composite (L) ■
(TWIN UNITS)

Built by: **Metropolitan Cammell.**
Engines: Two B.U.T. (A.E.C.) 6-cyl. horizontal type of 150 b.h.p.
Transmission: **Mechanical.** Cardan shaft and freewheel to four-speed epicyclic gearbox and further cardan shaft to final drive.
Body: 57′ 0″ × 9′ 3″.
Weight: 31 tons 10 cwt.
Seats 1st: 12.
2nd: 53.

E51495	E51499	E51503
E51496	E51500	E51504
E51497	E51501	
E51498	E51502	

Motor Composite (L) ■
(THREE OR *FOUR-CAR UNITS)

Built by: **Metropolitan Cammell.**
Engines: Two B.U.T. (A.E.C.) 6-cyl. horizontal type of 150 b.h.p.
Transmission: **Mechanical.** Cardan shaft and freewheel to four-speed epicyclic gearbox and further cardan shaft to final drive.
Body: 57′ 0″ × 9′ 3″.
Weight: 31 tons 10 cwt.
Seats 1st: 12.
2nd: 53.

E51505*	SC51517	SC51529
E51506*	SC51518	SC51530
E51507*	SC51519	SC51531
E51508*	SC51520	SC51532
E51509*	SC51521	SC51533
E51510*	SC51522	SC51534
E51511*	SC51523	SC51535
E51512*	SC51524	SC51536
E51513*	SC51525	SC51537
E51514*	SC51526	SC51538
SC51515	SC51527	SC51539
SC51516	SC51528	SC51540

Motor Brake Second ■
(THREE-CAR UNITS)
For Details see E51435-SC51470

E51541	E51544	E51547
E51542	E51545	
E51543	E51546	

Motor Brake Second ■
(TWIN UNITS)

Built by: **Metropolitan Cammell.**
Engines: Two B.U.T. (A.E.C.) 6-cyl horizontal type of 150 b.h.p.
Transmission: **Mechanical.** Cardan shaft and freewheel to four-speed epicyclic gearbox and further cardan shaft to final drive.
Body: 57′ 0″ × 9′ 3″.
Weight: 31 tons 10 cwt.
Seats 2nd: 52.

M51548   M51549   M51550

Motor Composite (L) ■
(THREE-CAR UNITS)
For Details see E51505-SC51540

E51551	E51554	E51557
E51552	E51555	
E51553	E51556	

Motor Composite (L) ■
(TWIN UNITS)

Built by: **Metropolitan Cammell.**
Engines: Two B.U.T. (A.E.C.) 6-cyl. horizontal type of 150 b.h.p.
Transmission: **Mechanical.** Cardan shaft and freewheel to four-speed epicyclic gearbox and further cardan shaft to final drive.
Body: 57′ 0″ × 9′ 3″.
Weight: 31 tons 10 cwt.
Seats 1st: 12
      2nd: 53.

| E51558 | E51559 | E51560 |

Motor Composite (L) ■
(TWIN UNITS)

Built by: **Derby Works, B.R.**
Engines: Two B.U.T. (A.E.C.) 6-cyl. horizontal type of 150 b.h.p.
Transmission: **Mechanical.** Cardan shaft and freewheel to four-speed epicyclic gearbox and further cardan shaft to final drive.
Body: 57′ 6″ × 9′ 2″.
Weight: 27 tons.
Seats 1st: 12.
      2nd: 53.

E51561	E51565	E51569
E51562	E51566	E51570
E51563	E51567	E51571
E51564	E51568	E51572

Motor Brake Second ■
(FOUR-CAR SUBURBAN)

Built by: **Derby Works, B.R.**
Engines: Two Rolls Royce 8-cyl. horizontal type of 238 b.h.p.
Transmission: **Hydraulic.** Torque converter.
Body: 64′ 0″ × 9′ 3″.
  Non-gangwayed, side doors to each seating bay.
Weight:
Seats 2nd: 76.

M51591	M51594	M51597
M51592	M51595	M51598
M51593	M51596	M51599

M51600	M51617	M51634
M51601	M51618	M51635
M51602	M51619	M51636
M51603	M51620	M51637
M51604	M51621	M51638
M51605	M51622	M51639
M51606	M51623	M51640
M51607	M51624	M51641
M51608	M51625	M51642
M51609	M51626	M51643
M51610	M51627	M51644
M51611	M51628	M51645
M51612	M51629	M51646
M51613	M51630	M51647
M51614	M51631	M51648
M51615	M51632	M51649
M51616	M51633	M51650

Motor Brake Second ■
(FOUR-CAR SUBURBAN)

Built by: **Derby Works, B.R.**
Engines: Two B.U.T. 6-cyl. horizontal type of 230 b.h.p.
Transmission: **Mechanical.** Cardan shaft and freewheel to four-speed epicyclic gearbox and further cardan shaft to final drive.
Body: 64′ 0″ × 9′ 3″. Non-gangwayed side doors to each seating bay.
Weight:
Seats 2nd:

M51651	M51661	M51671
M51652	M51662	M51672
M51653	M51663	M51673
M51654	M51664	M51674
M51655	M51665	M51675
M51656	M51666	M51676
M51657	M51667	M51677
M51658	M51668	M51678
M51659	M51669	M51679
M51660	M51670	M51680

Motor Brake Second ■
(TWIN UNITS)

Built by: **Cravens.**
Engine: One Rolls Royce 8-cyl. horizontal type of 238 b.h.p.
Transmission:
Body: 57′ 6″ × 9′ 3″
Weight:
Seats 2nd: 52.

M51681	M51690	M51699
M51682	M51691	M51700
M51683	M51692	M51701
M51684	M51693	M51702
M51685	M51694	M51703
M51686	M51695	M51704
M51687	M51696	M51705
M51688	M51697	
M51689	M51698	

Motor Composite (L)
(TWIN UNITS)

Built by: **Cravens.**
Engine: One Rolls Royce 8-cyl. horizontal type of 238 b.h.p.
Transmission:
Body: 57′ 6″ × 9′ 3″.
Weight:
Seats 1st: 12.
2nd: 51.

M51706	M51715	M51724
M51707	M51716	M51725
M51708	M51717	M51726
M51709	M51718	M51727
M51710	M51719	M51728
M51711	M51720	M51729
M51712	M51721	M51730
M51713	M51722	
M51714	M51723	

Motor Brake Second
(TWIN UNITS)

Built by: **Cravens.**
Engines: One Rolls Royce 8-cyl. horizontal type of 238 b.h.p.
Transmission: **Hydraulic.** Torque converter.
Body: 57′ 6″ × 9′ 3″.
Weight:
Seats 2nd: 52.

M51731	M51740	M51749
M51732	M51741	M51750
M51733	M51742	M51751
M51734	M51743	M51752
M51735	M51744	M51753
M51736	M51745	M51754
M51737	M51746	M51755
M51738	M51747	
M51739	M51748	

Motor Composite (L)
(TWIN UNITS)

Built by: **Cravens.**
Engine: One Rolls Royce 8-cyl. horizontal type of 238 b.h.p.
Transmission: **Hydraulic.** Torque converter.
Body: 57′ 6″ × 9′ 3″.
Weight:
Seats 1st: 12.
2nd: 51.

M51756	M51765	M51774
M51757	M51766	M51775
M51758	M51767	M51776
M51759	M51768	M51777
M51760	M51769	M51778
M51761	M51770	M51779
M51762	M51771	M51780
M51763	M51772	
M51764	M51773	

Motor Brake Composite ■
(THREE-CAR CROSS-COUNTRY)

Built by: **Swindon Works, B.R.**
Engines: Two B.U.T. 6-cyl. horizontal type of 150 b.h.p.
Transmission: **Mechanical.** Cardan shaft and freewheel to four-speed epicyclic gearbox and further cardan shaft to final drive.
Body: 64′ 6″ × 9′ 3″.
Weight: 36 tons 7 cwt.
Seats 1st: 18.
2nd: 16.

SC51781	SC51784	SC51787
SC51782	SC51785	
SC51783	SC51786	

Motor Second (L) ■
(THREE-CAR CROSS-COUNTRY)

Built by: **Swindon Works, B.R.**
Engines: Two B.U.T. 6-cyl. horizontal type of 150 b.h.p.
Transmission: **Mechanical.** Cardan shaft and freewheel to four-speed epicyclic gearbox and further cardan shaft to final drive.
Body: 64′ 6″ × 9′ 3″.
Weight: 36 tons 10 cwt
Seats 2nd: 68.

SC51788	SC51791	SC51794
SC51789	SC51792	
SC51790	SC51793	

Motor Brake Second ■
(THREE-CAR UNITS)
Built by: **Metropolitan Cammell.**
Engines: Two B.U.T. (A.E.C.) 6-cyl.
  horizontal type of 150 b.h.p.
Transmission: **Mechanical.** Cardan
  shaft and freewheel to four-speed
  epicyclic gearbox and further cardan
  shaft to final drive.
Body: 57′ 0″ × 9′ 3″.
Weight: 32 tons.
Seats 2nd: 52.

SC51795	SC51798	SC51801
SC51796	SC51799	
SC51797	SC51800	

Motor Composite (L) ■
(THREE-CAR UNITS)
Built by: **Metropolitan Cammell.**
Engines: Two B.U.T. (A.E.C.) 6-cyl.
  horizontal type of 150 b.h.p.
Transmission: **Mechanical.** Cardan
  shaft and freewheel to four-speed
  epicyclic gearbox and further cardan
  shaft to final drive.
Body: 57′ 0″ × 9′ 3″.
Weight: 31 tons 10 cwt.
Seats 1st: 12.
  2nd: 53.

SC51802	SC51805	SC51808
SC51803	SC51806	
SC51804	SC51807	

Motor Brake Second ■
(FOUR-CAR SUBURBAN)
Built by: **Derby Works, B.R.**
Engines: Two B.U.T. 6-cyl. horizontal
  type of 230 b.h.p.
Transmission: **Mechanical.** Cardan
  shaft and freewheel to four-speed
  epicyclic gearbox and further cardan
  shaft to final drive.
Body: 64′ 0″ × 9′ 3″.
  Non-gangwayed, side doors to each
  seating bay.
Weight:
Seats 2nd:

M51849	M51857	M51865
M51850	M51858	M51866
M51851	M51859	M51867
M51852	M51860	M51868
M51853	M51861	M51869
M51854	M51862	M51870
M51855	M51863	M51871
M51856	M51864	M51872

M51873	M51883	M51893
M51874	M51884	M51894
M51875	M51885	M51895
M51876	M51886	M51896
M51877	M51887	M51897
M51878	M51888	M51898
M51879	M51889	M51899
M51880	M51890	M51900
M51881	M51891	
M51882	M51892	

Motor Brake Second ■
(TWIN UNITS)
Built by: **Derby Works, B.R.**
Engines: Two B.U.T. (A.E.C.) 6-cyl.
  horizontal type of 150 b.h.p.
Transmission: **Mechanical.** Cardan
  shaft and freewheel to four-speed
  epicyclic gearbox and further cardan
  shaft to final drive.
Body: 57′ 6″ × 9′ 2″.
Weight: 28 tons 10 cwt.
Seats 2nd: 52.

M51901	M51909	M51917
M51902	M51910	M51918
M51903	M51911	M51919
M51904	M51912	M51920
M51905	M51913	M51921
M51906	M51914	M51922
M51907	M51915	M51923
M51908	M51916	

Motor Composite ■
(INTER CITY UNITS)
Built by: **Swindon Works, B.R.**
Engines: Two B.U.T. 6-cyl. horizontal
  type of 230 b.h.p.
Transmission: **Mechanical.** Cardan
  shaft and freewheel to four-speed
  epicyclic gearbox and further cardan
  shaft to final drive.
Body: 64′ 6″ × 9′ 3″.
Weight:
Seats 1st: 21
  2nd: 36.

E51951	E51952

Motor Brake Second (L) ■
(non-driving)
(INTER-CITY UNITS)
Built by: **Swindon Works, B.R.**
Engines: Two B.U.T. 6-cyl. horizontal type of 230 b.h.p.
Transmission: **Mechanical.** Cardan shaft and freewheel to four-speed epicyclic gearbox and further cardan shaft to final drive.
Body: 64' 6" × 9' 3".
Weight:
Seats 2nd:

E51968   E51969

Motor Composite (L) ■
(TWIN UNITS)
Built by: **Derby Works, B.R.**
Engines: Two B.U.T. 6-cyl. horizontal type of 150 b.h.p.
Transmission: **Mechanical.** Cardan shaft and freewheel to four-speed epicyclic gearbox and further cardan shaft to final drive.
Body: 57' 6" × 9' 2".
Weight:
Seats 1st: 12.
     2nd: 53.

M52037   M52038

Motor Brake Second ■
(SINGLE UNITS)
Built by: **Gloucester R.C. & W. Co.**
Engines: Two B.U.T. (A.E.C.) 6-cyl. horizontal type of 150 b.h.p.
Transmission: **Mechanical.** Cardan shaft and freewheel to four-speed epicyclic gearbox and further cardan shaft to final drive.
Body: 64' 6" × 9' 3".
Non-gangwayed, side doors to each seating bay.
Weight: 35 tons.
Seats 2nd: 65.

W55000	W55007	W55014
W55001	W55008	W55015
W55002	W55009	W55016
W55003	W55010	W55017
W55004	W55011	W55018
W55005	W55012	W55019
W55006	W55013	

Motor Parcels Van ■
Built by: **Gloucester R.C. & W. Co.**
Engines: Two B.U.T. (A.E.C.) 6-cyl. horizontal type of 230 b.h.p.

Transmission: **Mechanical.** Cardan shaft and freewheel to four-speed epicyclic gearbox and further cardan shaft to final drive.
Body: 64' 6" × 9' 3".
Non-gangwayed.
Weight: 40 tons.

M55987   M55988   M55990

Motor Parcels Van ■
Built by: **Gloucester R.C. & W. Co.**
Engines: Two B.U.T. (A.E.C.) 6-cyl. horizontal type of 230 b.h.p.
Transmission: **Mechanical.** Cardan shaft and freewheel to four-speed epicyclic gearbox and further cardan shaft to final drive.
Body: 64' 6" × 9' 3".
Weight: 41 tons.

| W55991 | W55993 | W55995 |
| W55992 | W55994 | W55996 |

Motor Parcels Van ◆
Built by: **Cravens.**
Engines: Two B.U.T. (A.E.C.) 6-cyl. horizontal type of 150 b.h.p.
Transmission. **Mechanical.** Cardan shaft and freewheel to four-speed epicyclic gearbox and further cardan shaft to final drive.
Body: 57' 6" × 9' 3".
Non-gangwayed.
Weight: 30 tons.

M55997   M55998   M55999

Driving Trailer Composite (L) ■
(TWIN UNITS)
Built by: **Derby Works, B.R.**
Body: 64' 6" × 9' 3".
Weight: 29 tons 10 cwt.
Seats 1st: 12.
     2nd: 62.

E56000	E56012	E56024
E56001	E56013	E56025
E56002	E56014	E56026
E56003	E56015	E56027
E56004	E56016	E56028
E56005	E56017	E56029
E56006	E56018	E56030
E56007	E56019	E56031
E56008	E56020	E56032
E56009	E56021	E56033
E56010	E56022	E56034
E56011	E56023	E56035

E56036	E56041	E56046
E56037	E56042	E56047
E56038	E56043	E56048
E56039	E56044	E56049
E56040	E56045	

Driving Trailer ■
Composite (L)
(TWIN UNITS)
Built by: **Metropolitan Cammell.**
Body: 57′ 0″ × 9′ 3″.
Weight: 24 tons 4 cwt.
Seats 1st: 12.
    2nd: 53.

E56050	E56065	E56080
E56051	E56066	E56081
E56052	E56067	E56082
E56053	E56068	E56083
E56054	E56069	E56084
E56055	E56070	E56085
E56056	E56071	E56086
E56057	E56072	E56087
E56058	E56073	E56088
E56059	E56074	E56089
E56060	E56075	M56090
E56061	E56076	M56091
E56062	E56077	M56092
E56063	E56078	M56093
E56064	E56079	

Driving Trailer ■
Composite (L)
(TWIN UNITS)
Built by: **Gloucester R.C. & W. Co.**
Body: 57′ 6″ × 9′ 3″.
Weight: 24 tons 15 cwt.
Seats 1st: 12.
    2nd: 54.

SC56094	SC56101	M56108
SC56095	SC56102	M56109
SC56096	SC56103	M56110
SC56097	SC56104	M56111
SC56098	M56105	M56112
SC56099	M56106	M56113
SC56100	M56107	

Driving Trailer ■
Composite (L)
(TWIN UNITS)
Built by: **Cravens.**
Body: 57′ 6″ × 9′ 3″.
Weight: 23 tons.
Seats 1st: 12.
    2nd: 51.
       54*.

E56114	E56126	E56138
E56115	E56127	E56139
E56116	E56128	E56140
E56117	E56129	E56141
E56118	E56130	E56142
E56119	E56131	E56143
E56120	E56132	E56144
E56121	E56133	M56145*
E56122	E56134	M56146*
E56123	E56135	M56147*
E56124	E56136	M56148*
E56125	E56137	M56149*

Driving Trailer ■
Composite (L)
(TWIN UNITS)
Built by: **Park Royal Vehicles.**
Body: 57′ 6″ × 9′ 3″.
Weight: 26 tons 7 cwt.
Seats 1st: 16.
    2nd: 48.

M56150	M56157	M56164
M56151	M56158	M56165
M56152	M56159	M56166
M56153	M56160	M56167
M56154	M56161	M56168
M56155	M56162	M56169
M56156	M56163	

Driving Trailer ■
Composite (L)
(TWIN UNITS)
Built by: **D. Wickham & Co. Ltd.**
Body: 57′ 0″ × 9′ 3″.
Weight: 20 tons 10 cwt.
Seats 1st: 16.
    2nd: 50.

E56170	E56172	E56174
E56171	E56173	

Driving Trailer Composite (L) ■
(TWIN UNITS)
Built by: **Birmingham R.C. & W. Co.**
Body: 57′ 6″ × 9′ 3″.
Weight:
Seats 1st: 12.
    2nd: 54.

M56175	M56179	M56183
M56176	M56180	M56184
M56177	M56181	
M56178	M56182	

Driving Trailer Composite (L) ■
(TWIN UNITS)
Built by: **Birmingham R.C. & W. Co.**
Body: 57′ 6″ × 9′ 3″.
Weight: 24 tons.
Seats 1st: 12.
    2nd: 51.

E56185	E56187	E56189
E56186	E56188	

Driving Trailer Composite (L) ■
(TWIN UNITS)
Built by: **Derby Works, B.R.**
Body: 57′ 6″ × 9′ 2″.
Weight: 22 tons.
Seats 1st: 12.
    2nd: 53.

E56190	E56199	E56208
E56191	E56200	E56209
E56192	E56201	E56210
E56193	E56202	M56211
E56194	E56203	M56212
E56195	E56204	M56213
E56196	E56205	M56214
E56197	E56206	M56215
E56198	E56207	

Driving Trailer Composite (L) ■
(TWIN UNITS)
Built by: **Metropolitan Cammell.**
Body: 57′ 0″ × 9′ 3″.
Weight: 25 tons.
Seats 1st: 12.
    2nd: 45.

E56218	E56219	E56220

Driving Trailer Composite (L) ■
(TWIN UNITS)
Built by: **Derby Works, B.R.**
Body: 57′ 6″ × 9′ 2″.
Weight: 23 tons.
Seats 1st: 12.
    2nd: 53.

M56221	M56241	M56261
M56222	M56242	M56262
M56223	M56243	M56263
M56224	M56244	M56264
M56225	M56245	M56265
M56226	M56246	M56266
M56227	M56247	M56267
M56228	M56248	M56268
M56229	M56249	M56269
M56230	M56250	M56270
M56231	M56251	M56271
M56232	M56252	M56272
M56233	M56253	M56273
M56234	M56254	M56274
M56235	M56255	M56275
M56236	M56256	M56276
M56237	M56257	M56277
M56238	M56258	M56278
M56239	M56259	M56279
M56240	M56260	

Driving Trailer Second ■
(For use with Single Unit cars Nos. W55000, etc.)
Built by: **Gloucester R.C. & W. Co.**
Body: 64′ 0″ × 9′ 3″.
  Non-gangwayed, side doors to each seating bay.
Weight:
Seats 2nd: 95.

W56291	W56294	W56297	SC56401	SC56405	SC56409
W56292	W56295	W56298	SC56402	SC56406	SC56410
W56293	W56296	W56299	SC56403	SC56407	SC56411
			SC56404	SC56408	

Driving Trailer Composite (L) ■
(TWIN UNITS)
For Details see SC56094-M56113

SC56300	SC56307	SC56314
SC56301	SC56308	SC56315
SC56302	SC56309	SC56316
SC56303	SC56310	SC56317
SC56304	SC56311	SC56318
SC56305	SC56312	SC56319
SC56306	SC56313	

Driving Trailer Composite (L) ■

Built by: **Cravens.**
Body: 57' 6" × 9' 3".
Weight: 24 tons.
Seats 1st: 12.   *2nd:* 51.

E56412	E56436	E56460
E56413	E56437	E56461
E56414	E56438	SC56462
E56415	E56439	SC56463
E56416	E56440	SC56464
E56417	E56441	SC56465
E56418	E56442	SC56466
E56419	E56443	SC56467
E56420	E56444	SC56468
E56421	E56445	SC56469
E56422	E56446	SC56470
E56423	E56447	SC56471
E56424	E56448	SC56472
E56425	E56449	SC56473
E56426	E56450	SC56474
E56427	E56451	SC56475
E56428	E56452	SC56476
E56429	E56453	SC56477
E56430	E56454	SC56478
E56431	E56455	SC56479
E56432	E56456	SC56480
E56433	E56457	SC56481
E56434	E56458	SC56482
E56435	E56459	SC56483

Driving Trailer Composite (L) ■
(TWIN UNITS)
Built by: **Metropolitan Cammell.**
Body: 57' 0" × 9' 3".
Weight: 24 tons 4 cwt.
Seats 1st: 12.   *2nd:* 53.

M56332	M56355	E56378
M56333	M56356	E56379
M56334	M56357	E56380
M56335	M56358	E56381
M56336	M56359	SC56382
M56337	M56360	SC56383
M56338	M56361	SC56384
M56339	E56362	SC56385
M56340	E56363	SC56386
M56341	E56364	SC56387
M56342	E56365	SC56388
M56343	E56366	SC56389
M56344	E56367	SC56390
M56345	E56368	SC56391
M56346	E56369	SC56392
M56347	E56370	SC56393
M56348	E56371	SC56394
M56349	E56372	SC56395
M56350	E56373	SC56396
M56351	E56374	SC56397
M56352	E56375	SC56398
M56353	E56376	SC56399
M56354	E56377	SC56400

Driving Trailer Composite (L) ■
(TWIN UNITS)
Built by: **Derby Works, B.R.**
Body: 57' 6" × 9' 2"
Weight: 23 tons.
Seats 1st: 12
   2nd: 53.

M56484	M56486	M56488
M56485	M56487	M56489

Derby-built two-car lightweight unit

[J. E. Wilkinson

Pressed Steel three-car suburban motor brake second

[A. Swain

A Gloucester-built single unit and two cars of a Derby three-car suburban set
complete a six-car formation with a Swindon-built cross-country set   [M. Mensing

Metropolitan-Cammell three-car unit   [*J. B. Bucknall*

Gloucester-built twin unit   [*J. B. Bucknall*

Birmingham R.C. & W. three-car unit   [*M. Mensing*

Original type of Swindon-built six-car Inter-City set   [P. J. Sharpe

Swindon-built six-car Inter-City set for Hull-Liverpool service with new standard
front end   [A. H. Gray

The Midland Pullman entering St. Pancras after its inaugural run on July 4
                                                                   [British Railways

Gloucester three-car Cross-Country set   *[M. Mensing*

Two Swindon three-car Cross-Country sets   *[M. Mensing*

Gloucester R.C. & W. gangwayed parcels car No. W55993   *[J. B. Bucknall*

A six-car train of B.R. standard Euston–Watford stock approaches Wembley bound for Euston

Later type of Wirral train introduced in 1956 to replace the Mersey trains

[*G. M. Kichenside*

Southport to Liverpool train, composed of 1939 stock, at Seaforth   [*G. M. Kichenside*

B.R. three-car standard 25 kV a.c. suburban set for the Liverpool Street–Chingford/Enfield lines
[British Railways

Eastleigh-built four-car 1,500 V d.c. suburban set for the Liverpool Street–Southend lines
[P. J. Sharpe

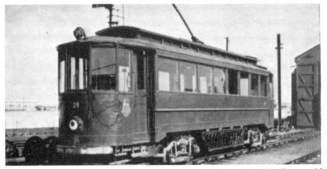

Ex-Gateshead-type tram No. 29, now working on the Grimsby–Immingham line, outside Pyewipe Depot
[J. C. W. Halliday

Ex-Southern Railway 1,470 h.p. Co-Co electric locomotive No. 20002 [L. Elsey

Doncaster-built 2,552 h.p. Bo-Bo electric locomotive No. E5003 [L. Elsey

4-CEP unit No. 7126 on a Ramsgate–Victoria train at Bromley South [P. J. Sharpe

4-COR unit No. 3115 on a Victoria–Portsmouth train passing Battersea Park
[P. J. Sharpe

5-BEL unit No. 3053 leads the Brighton Belle train through Thornton Heath
[R. Russell

6-PAN unit No. 3036 on a Victoria–Littlehampton train passing Three Bridges
[G. M. Kichenside

M56490	M56495	M56500
M56491	M56496	M56501
M56492	M56497	M56502
M56493	M56498	M56503
M56494	M56499	M56504

Trailer Composite ■
(THREE-CAR SUBURBAN)
Built by: **Derby Works, B.R.**
Body: 63' 8¾" × 9' 3". Non-gangwayed, side doors to each seating bay.
Weight: 28 tons 10 cwt.
Seats 1st: 28.
    2nd: 74.

W59000	W59011	W59022
W59001	W59012	W59023
W59002	W59013	W59024
W59003	W59014	W59025
W59004	W59015	W59026
W59005	W59016	W59027
W59006	W59017	W59028
W59007	W59018	W59029
W59008	W59019	W59030
W59009	W59020	W59031
W59010	W59021	

Trailer Second ■
(THREE-CAR SUBURBAN)
Built by: **Derby Works, B.R.**
Body: 63' 8¾" × 9' 3". Non-gangwayed, side doors to each seating bay.
Weight: 28 tons 10 cwt.
Seats 2nd: 106.

W59032	W59036	W59040
W59033	W59037	W59041
W59034	W59038	
W59035	W59039	

Trailer Second (L) ■
(FOUR-CAR UNITS)
Built by: **Metropolitan Cammell.**
Body: 57' 0" × 9' 3".
Weight: 25 tons.
Seats 2nd: 61.

E59042	E59045	E59048
E59043	E59046	
E59044	E59047	

Trailer Brake Second (L) ■
(FOUR-CAR UNITS)
Built by: **Metropolitan Cammell.**
Body: 57 0" × 9' 3".
Weight: 25 tons.
Seats 2nd: 45.

E59049	E59052	E59055
E59050	E59053	
E59051	E59054	

Trailer Second (L) ■
(FOUR-CAR UNITS)
Built by: **Metropolitan Cammell.**
Body: 57' 0" × 9' 3".
Weight: 25 tons.
Seats 2nd: 71.

E59060	E59065	E59070
E59061	E59066	E59071
E59062	E59067	E59072
E59063	E59068	
E59064	E59069	

Trailer Brake Second ■
(FOUR-CAR UNITS)
Built by: **Metropolitan Cammell.**
Body: 57' 0" × 9' 3".
Weight: 25 tons.
Seats 2nd: 53.

E59073	E59078	E59083
E59074	E59079	E59084
E59075	E59080	E59085
E59076	E59081	
E59077	E59082	

Trailer Second (L) ■
(FOUR-CAR UNITS)
For Details see E59042-8

E59086	E59088	E59090
E59087	E59089	E59091

Trailer Brake Second (L) ■
(FOUR-CAR UNITS)
For Details see E59049-55)

E59092	E59094	E59096
E59093	E59095	E59097

Trailer Second (L) ■
(THREE-CAR UNITS)
Built by: **Metropolitan Cammell.**
Body: 57' 0" × 9' 3".
Weight: 24 tons 10 cwt.
Seats 2nd: 71.

E59100	E59104	E59108
E59101	E59105	E59109
E59102	E59106	
E59103	E59107	

Trailer Brake Second (L) ■
(FOUR-CAR UNITS)
Built by: **Metropolitan Cammell.**
Body: 57' 0" × 9' 3".
Weight: 25 tons.
Seats 2nd: 53.

E59112	E59113

Trailer Composite (L) ■
(THREE-CAR UNITS)
Built by: **Metropolitan Cammell.**
Body: 57' 0" × 9' 3".
Weight: 25 tons.
Seats 1st: 12.
    2nd: 53.

M59114	M59120	M59126
M59115	M59121	M59127
M59116	M59122	M59128
M59117	M59123	M59129
M59118	M59124	M59130
M59119	M59125	M59131

Trailer Composite (L) ■
(THREE-CAR UNITS)
Built by: **Birmingham R. C. & W. Co.**
Body: 57' 0" × 9' 3".
Weight: 24 tons.
Seats 2nd: 12.
    2nd: 54.

M59132	M59151	M59170
M59133	M59152	M59171
M59134	M59153	M59172
M59135	M59154	M59173
M59136	M59155	M59174
M59137	M59156	M59175
M59138	M59157	M59176
M59139	M59158	M59177
M59140	M59159	M59178
M59141	M59160	M59179
M59142	M59161	M59180
M59143	M59162	M59181
M59144	M59163	M59182
M59145	M59164	M59183
M59146	M59165	M59184
M59147	M59166	M59185
M59148	M59167	M59186
M59149	M59168	M59187
M59150	M59169	

Trailer Second (L) ■
(FOUR-CAR UNITS)
Built by: **Birmingham R.C. & W. Co.**
Body: 57' 0" × 9' 3".
Weight: 24 tons.
Seats 2nd: 69.

E59188	E59195	E59202
E59189	E59196	E59203
E59190	E59197	E59204
E59191	E59198	E59205
E59192	E59199	E59206
E59193	E59200	E59207
E59194	E59201	E59208

Trailer Brake Second (L) ■
(FOUR-CAR UNITS)
Built by: **Birmingham R. C. & W. Co.**
Body: 57' 0" × 9' 3".
Weight: 25 tons.
Seats 2nd: 51.

E59209	E59216	E59223
E59210	E59217	E59224
E59211	E59218	E59225
E59212	E59219	E59226
E59213	E59220	E59227
E59214	E59221	E59228
E59215	E59222	E59229

Trailer Second (L) ■
(FOUR-CAR UNITS)
For Details see E59188-E59208

E59230	E59232	E59234
E59231	E59233	

Trailer Brake Second (L) ■
(FOUR-CAR UNITS)
For Details see E59209-29

E59240	E59242	E59244
E59241	E59243	

Trailer Brake Second (L) ■
(FOUR-CAR UNITS)
Built by: **Derby Works, B.R.**
Body: 57' 6" × 9' 2".
Weight: 22 tons 10 cwt
Seats 2nd: 50.

E59245	E59247	E59249
E59246	E59248	E59250

Trailer Buffet Second (L) ■
(THREE-CAR CROSS-COUNTRY)
Built by: **Swindon Works, B.R.**
Body: 64' 6" × 9' 3".
Open second with small buffet and
   counter at one end.
Weight: 30 tons 12 cwt.
Seats 2nd: 60.
      Buffet: 4.

W59255	W59271	W59287
W59256	W59272	W59288
W59257	W59273	W59289
W59258	W59274	W59290
W59259	W59275	W59291
W59260	W59276	W59292
W59261	W59277	W59293
W59262	W59278	W59294
W59263	W59279	W59295
W59264	W59280	W59296
W59265	W59281	W59297
W59266	W59282	W59298
W59267	W59283	W59299
W59268	W59284	W59300
W59269	W59285	W59301
W59270	W59286	

Trailer Second (L) ■
(THREE-CAR UNITS)
Built by: **Metropolitan Cammell.**
Body: 57' 0" × 9' 3".
Weight: 24 tons 10 cwt.
Seats 2nd: 71.

E59302	E59303	E59304

Trailer Second (L) ■
(FOUR-CAR UNITS)
Built by: **Metropolitan Cammell.**
Body: 57' 0" × 9' 3".
Weight: 25 tons.
Seats 2nd: 71.

E59305	E59306

Trailer Second (L) ■
or Trailer Composite (L)*
(THREE-CAR UNITS)
Built by **Cravens.**
Body: 57' 6" × 9' 3".
Weight: 23 tons.
Seats 2nd: 69.
     1st: 12*.
     2nd: 51*.

M59307*	M59314	M59321*
M59308	M59315	M59322*
M59309	M59316*	M59323
M59310*	M59317*	M59324
M59311	M59318*	M59325
M59312	M59319	
M59313	M59320*	

Trailer Composite ■
(THREE-CAR SUBURBAN)
For Details see W59000-31

W59326	W59343	W59360
W59327	W59344	W59361
W59328	W59345	W59362
W59329	W59346	W59363
W59330	W59347	W59364
W59331	W59348	W59365
W59332	W59349	W59366
W59333	W59350	W59367
W59334	W59351	W59368
W59335	W59352	W59369
W59336	W59353	W59370
W59337	W59354	W59371
W59338	W59355	W59372
W59339	W59356	W59373
W59340	W59357	W59374
W59341	W59358	W59375
W59342	W59359	W59376

Trailer Second (L) ■
(THREE* AND FOUR-CAR UNITS)
Built by: **Derby Works, B.R.**
Body: 57' 6" × 9' 2".
Weight: { 22 tons.
          { 22 tons 10 cwt *
Seats 2nd: 68.

E59380	E59384	E59388*
E59381	E59385	E59389*
E59382	E59386*	E59390*
E59383	E59387*	

Trailer First (K) ●
(INTER-CITY UNITS)
Built by: **Swindon Works, B.R.**
Body: 64' 6" × 9' 3".
Weight:
Seats 1st: 42.

SC59391	SC59395	SC59399
SC59392	SC59396	SC59400
SC59393	SC59397	
SC59394	SC59398	

Trailer Composite (L) ●
(INTER CITY UNITS)
Built by: **Swindon Works, B.R.**
Body: 64' 6" × 9' 3".
Weight:
Seats 1st: 18.
     2nd: 32.

SC59402	SC59406	SC59410
SC59403	SC59407	SC59411
SC59404	SC59408	SC59412
SC59405	SC59409	

Trailer Buffet Second (L) ■
(THREE-CAR CROSS COUNTRY)
Built by: **Gloucester R.C. & W. Co.**
Body: 64' 6" × 9' 3".
Open second with small buffet and counter at one end.
Weight: 31 tons 8 cwt.
Seats 2nd: 60 or 64.

W59413	W59422	W59431
W59414	W59423	W59432
W59415	W59424	W59433
W59416	W59425	W59434
W59417	W59426	W59435
W59418	W59427	W59436
W59419	W59428	W59437
W59420	W59429	
W59421	W59430	

Trailer Composite ■
(THREE-CAR SUBURBAN)
For Details see W59000-31

W59438	W59442	W59446
W59439	W59443	W59447
W59440	W59444	W59448
W59441	W59445	

Trailer Second ★
(THREE-CAR SUBURBAN)
Built by: **Derby Works, B.R.**
Body: 63' 8¾" × 9' 3". Non-gangwayed, side doors to each seating bay.
Weight: 28 tons 10 cwt.
Seats 2nd: 106.

E59449	E59456	E59463
E59450	E59457	E59464
E59451	E59458	E59465
E59452	E59459	E59466
E59453	E59460	E59467
E59454	E59461	E59468
E59455	E59462	

Trailer Composite (L) ■
Built by: **Birmingham R.C. & W. Co.**
Body:
Weight:
Seats 1st:
     2nd:

W59469	W59474	W59479
W59470	W59475	W59480
W59471	W59476	W59481
W59472	W59477	
W59473	W59478	

Trailer Composite (L) ■
(THREE-CAR SUBURBAN)
Built by: **Pressed Steel Co.**
Body:
Weight:
Seats 1st:
     2nd:

W59484	W59493	W59502
W59485	W59494	W59503
W59486	W59495	W59504
W59487	W59496	W59505
W59488	W59497	W59506
W59489	W59498	W59507
W59490	W59499	W59508
W59491	W59500	W59509
W59492	W59501	

Trailer Composite (L) ■
(THREE- OR *FOUR-CAR UNITS

Built by: **Metropolitan Cammell.**
Body: 57′ 0″ × 9′ 3″.
Weight: 25 tons.
Seats 1st: 12.
    2nd: 53.

E59523*	E59539*	SC59555
E59524*	E59540*	SC59556
E59525*	E59541*	SC59557
E59526*	E59542*	SC59558
E59527*	SC59543	SC59559
E59528*	SC59544	SC59560
E59529*	SC59545	SC59561
E59530*	SC59546	SC59562
E59531*	SC59547	SC59563
E59532*	SC59548	SC59564
E59533*	SC59549	SC59565
E59534*	SC59550	SC59566
E59535*	SC59551	SC59567
E59536*	SC59552	SC59568
E59537*	SC59553	
E59538*	SC59554	

Trailer Second (L) ■
(THREE-CAR UNITS)

Built by: **Metropolitan Cammell.**
Body: 57′ 0″ × 9′ 3″.
Weight: 24 tons 10 cwt.
Seats 2nd: 71.

E59569	E59571	E59572
E59570		

Trailer Buffet Second (L) ■

Built by: **Metropolitan-Cammell.**
Body:
Weight:
Seats 2nd:

E59573	E59575	E59577
E59574	E59576	E59578

Trailer Second (L)
(FOUR-CAR SUBURBAN)

Built by: **Derby Works, B.R.**
Body: 63′ 10″ × 9′ 3″. Non-gangwayed, side door to each seating bay. Intermediate lavatories on each side of central passageway.
Weight:
Seats 2nd: 90.

M59589	M59599	M59609
M59590	M59600	M59610
M59591	M59601	M59611
M59592	M59602	M59612
M59593	M59603	M59613
M59594	M59604	M59614
M59595	M59605	M59615
M59596	M59606	M59616
M59597	M59607	M59617
M59598	M59608	M59618

Trailer Second ■
(FOUR-CAR SUBURBAN)

Built by: **Derby Works, B.R.**
Body: 63′ 8¾″ × 9′ 3″. Non-gangwayed, side doors to each seating bay.
Weight: 28 tons 10 cwt.
Seats 2nd: 108.

M59619	M59634	M59649
M59620	M59635	M59650
M59621	M59636	M59651
M59622	M59637	M59652
M59623	M59638	M59653
M59624	M59639	M59654
M59625	M59640	M59655
M59626	M59641	M59656
M59627	M59642	M59657
M59628	M59643	M59658
M59629	M59644	M59659
M59630	M59645	M59660
M59631	M59646	M59661
M59632	M59647	M59662
M59633	M59648	M59663

Trailer Composite (L) ■
(FOUR-CAR SUBURBAN)

Built by: **Derby Works, B R.**
Body:
Weight:
Seats 1st:
    2nd:

M59664	M59669	M59674
M59665	M59670	M59675
M59666	M59671	M59676
M59667	M59672	M59677
M59668	M59673	M59678

Trailer Buffet Second (L) ■
(THREE-CAR CROSS COUNTRY)
Built by: **Swindon Works, B.R.**
Body: 64′ 6″ × 9′ 3″.
Open second with small buffet and counter at one end.
Weight: 30 tons 12 cwt.
Seats 2nd: 60.
    Buffet: 4.

SC59679	SC59682	SC59685
SC59680	SC59683	
SC59681	SC59684	

Trailer Composite (L) ■
(THREE-CAR UNITS)
Built by: **Metropolitan Cammell**.
Body: 57′ 0″ × 9′ 3″.
Weight: 25 tons.
Seats 1st: 12.
    2nd: 53.

SC59686	SC59689	SC59692
SC59687	SC59690	
SC59688	SC59691	

Trailer Second ■
(FOUR-CAR SUBURBAN)
Built by: **Derby Works, B.R.**
Body:
Weight:
Seats 2nd:

M59713	M59715	M59717
M59714	M59716	M59718

Trailer Composite (L) ■
(FOUR-CAR SUBURBAN)
Built by: **Derby Works, B.R.**
Body:
Weight:
Seats 1st:
    2nd:

M59719	M59721	M59723
M59720	M59722	M59724

Trailer Second Suburban ■
(FOUR-CAR SUBURBAN
For Details see M59713-8

M59725	M59732	M59739
M59726	M59733	M59740
M59727	M59734	M59741
M59728	M59735	M59742
M59729	M59736	M59743
M59730	M59737	M59744
M59731	M59738	

Trailer Composite ■
(FOUR-CAR SUBURBAN)
For Details see M59719-24

M59745	M59752	M59759
M59746	M59753	M59760
M59747	M59754	M59761
M59748	M59755	M59762
M59749	M59756	M59763
M59750	M59757	M59764
M59751	M59758	

Trailer Second (L)
Built by: **Swindon Works, B.R.**
Body: 64′ 6″ × 9′ 3″
Weight:
Seats: 64

E59765

Trailer Buffet First (L)
Built by: **Swindon Works, B.R.**
Body: 64′ 6″ × 9′ 3″
Weight:
Seats 1st:

E59774

Motor Brake Second
(HASTINGS UNITS)
Unit numbers 1001–7*
              1011–9†
              1031–7‡
Built by: **Eastleigh Works, B.R.**
Engine: English Electric 4-cyl. type 4SRKT Mark II of 500 b.h.p. at 850 r.p.m.
Transmission: **Electric.** Two nose-suspended axle-hung traction motors.
Body: 58′ 0″ × 8′ 2½″*
      64′ 6″ × 8′ 2½″†‡
Guard's, luggage compartment, engine room and full width driving compartment at outer end of car.

Weight: 54 tons 2 cwt.*
       55 tons 0 cwt.†‡
Seats 2nd: 22*
        30††

S60000*	S60016†	S60032‡
S60001*	S60017†	S60033‡
S60002*	S60018†	S60034‡
S60003*	S60019†	S60035‡
S60004*	S60020†	S60036‡
S60005*	S60021†	S60037‡
S60006*	S60022†	S60038‡
S60007*	S60023†	S60039‡
S60008*	S60024†	S60040‡
S60009*	S60025†	S60041‡
S60010*	S60026†	S60042‡
S60011*	S60027‡	S60043‡
S60012*	S60028†	S60044‡
S60013*	S60029†	S60045‡
S60014†	S60030†	
S60015†	S60031†	

Motor Brake First (L)
(PULLMAN UNITS)

Built by: **Metropolitan Cammell.**
Engine: One North British/M.A.N.
12-cyl. pressure-charged V-type
L12V18/21BS of 1,000 b.h.p.
Transmission. **Electric.** Two 425 h.p.
G.E.C. traction motors driving
through Brown-Boveri spring-drive.
Body: 66′ 5½″ × 9′ 3″ Guard's luggage
compartment, engine room and full
width driving cab at outer end of car.
Weight: 67 tons 10 cwt.
Seats 1st: 12.

M60090	M60092	M60093
M60091		

Motor Brake Second (L)
PULLMAN UNITS

Built by: **Metropolitan Cammell.**
Engine: One North British/M.A.N.
12-cyl. pressure-charged V-type
L12V18/21BS of 1,000 b.h.p.
Transmission. **Electric.** Two 425 h.p.
G.E.C. traction motors driving
through Brown-Boveri spring-drive.
Body: 66′ 5½″ × 9′ 3″ Guard's luggage
compartment, engine room and full
width driving cab at outer end of car.

Weight: 67 tons 10 cwt.
Seats: 2nd: 18

W60094	W60096	W60098
W60095	W60097	W60099

Motor Brake Second
TWIN* OR THREE-CAR UNITS

Unit numbers {1101-18
               {1119-22*
               {1123-6

Built by: **Eastleigh Works, B.R.**
Engine: English Electric 4-cyl. type
4SRKT Mark II of 600 b.h.p. at 850
r.p.m.
Transmission. **Electric.** Two nose-
suspended axle-hung traction motors.
Body: 64′ 0″ × 9′ 3″.
Guard's, luggage compartment, en-
gine room and full width driving
compartment at outer end of car.
Non-gangwayed, side door to each
seating bay.
Weight: 56 tons 0 cwt.
Seats 2nd: 52.

S60100	S60109	S60118*
S60101	S60110	S60119*
S60102	S60111	S60120*
S60103	S60112	S60121*
S60104	S60113	S60122
S60105	S60114	S60123
S60106	S60115	S60124
S60107	S60116	S60125
S60108	S60117	

Trailer Second (L)
(HASTINGS UNITS)

Unit numbers   1001-7*
                  1011-9†
                  1031-7‡

Built by: **Eastleigh Works, B.R.**
Body: 58′ 0″ × 8′ 2½″.*
       64′ 6″ × 8′ 2½″.††
Weight: 29 tons.*
       30 tons.††
Seats 2nd: 52.*
       60.††

S60500*	S60521†	S60542†
S60501*	S60522†	S60543†
S60502*	S60523†	S60544†
S60503*	S60524†	S60545†
S60504*	S60525†	S60546†
S60505*	S60526†	S60547†
S60506*	S60527†	S60548‡
S60507*	S60528†	S60549‡
S60508*	S60529†	S60550‡
S60509*	S60530†	S60551‡
S60510*	S60531†	S60552‡
S60511*	S60532†	S60553‡
S60512*	S60533†	S60554‡
S60513*	S60534†	S60555‡
S60514*	S60535†	S60556‡
S60515*	S60536†	S60557‡
S60516*	S60537†	S60558‡
S60517*	S60538†	S60559‡
S60518*	S60539†	S60560‡
S60519*	S60540†	S60561‡
S60520*	S60541†	

S60662	S60666	S60669
S60663	S60667	S60670
S60664	S60668	S60671
S60665		

Trailer First (K)
(HASTINGS UNITS)

Unit numbers   1001-7*
                   1011-9†
                   1031-7‡

Built by: **Eastleigh Works, B.R.**
Body: 58′ 0″ × 8′ 2½″.*
       64′ 6″ × 8′ 2½″.†‡
Side corridor with seven* (eight†‡)
first class compartments with side
door to each compartment.
Weight: 30 tons.*
          31 tons.†‡
Seats 1st: 42.*
           48.†‡

S60700*	S60708†	S60716‡
S60701*	S60709†	S60717‡
S60702*	S60710†	S60718‡
S60703*	S60711†	S60719‡
S60704*	S60712†	S60720‡
S60705*	S60713†	S60721‡
S60706*	S60714†	S60722‡
S60707†	S60715†	

Motor Kitchen First (L)
(Non-driving)
PULLMAN UNITS
Built by: **Metropolitan Cammell.**
Transmission: **Electric.** Two 425 h.p.
G.E.C. traction motors driving
through Brown-Boveri spring drive.
Body: 65′ 6″ × 9′ 3″
Weight: 49 tons.
Seats 1st: 18

M60730	M60732	M60733
M60731		

Motor Parlour Second (L)
(Non-driving)
PULLMAN UNITS
Built by: **Metropolitan Cammell.**
Transmission: **Electric.** Two 425 h.p.
G.E.C. traction motors driving through
Brown-Boveri spring drive.
Body: 65′ 6″ × 9′ 3″
Weight: 45 tons 10 cwt.
Seats 2nd: 42.

W60644	W60646	W60648
W60645	W60647	W60649

Trailer Second
(THREE-CAR UNITS)
Unit numbers 1101-18/23-26
Built by: **Eastleigh Works, B.R.**
Body: 63′ 6″ × 9′ 3″.
Weight:
Seats 2nd: 104.

S60650	S60654	S60658
S60651	S60655	S60659
S60652	S60656	S60660
S60653	S60657	S60661

Trailer Kitchen First (L)
(PULLMAN UNITS)
Built by: **Metropolitan Cammell.**
Body: 65′ 6″ × 9′ 3″
Weight: 36 tons.
Seats 1st: 18.

W60734	W60736	W60738
W60735	W60737	W60739

Trailer Parlour First (L)
(PULLMAN UNITS)
Built by: **Metropolitan Cammell.**
Body: 65' 6" × 9' 3".
Weight: 33 tons.
Seats 1st: 36

M60740	W60744	W60748
M60741	W60745	W60749
M60742	W60746	
M60743	W60747	

Trailer Buffet
(HASTINGS UNITS)
Unit numbers 1031-7
Built by: **Eastleigh Works, B.R.**
Body: 64' 6" × 8' 2½".
  Buffet with kitchen and bar; self-contained seating saloon.
Weight: 35 tons.
Seats: 21.

S60750	S60753	S60756
S60751	S60754	
S60752	S60755	

Driving Trailer Composite (L)
(TWIN* OR THREE-CAR UNITS)
Unit numbers 1101–18
  1119–22*
  1123–6
Built by: **Eastleigh Works, B.R.**
Body: 64' 0" × 9' 3".
  Non-gangwayed, side door to each seating bay or compartment. 5-bay 2nd saloon and 2 1st compartments with intermediate lavatories, also a 2nd class compartment next to driving compartment.
Weight: 32 tons 0 cwt.
Seats 1st: 13.
  2nd: 62.

S60800	S60809	S60818*
S60801	S60810	S60819
S60802	S60811	S60820*
S60803	S60812	S60821*
S60804	S60813	S60822
S60805	S60814	S60823
S60806	S60815	S60824
S60807	S60816	S60825
S60808	S60817	

Motor Brake Second ▲
(TWIN UNITS)
Built by: **Derby Works, B.R.**
Engines: Two B.U.T. (Leyland) 6-cyl. horizontal type of 125 b.h.p.
Transmission: **Hydro-Mechanical.** Lysholm Smith (Leyland) torque converter to final drive.
Body: 57' 6" × 9' 2".
Weight: 26 tons.
Seats 2nd: 61.

E79000	E79003	E79006
E79001	E79004	E79007
E79002	E79005	

Motor Brake Second ◆
(TWIN UNITS)
Built by: **Derby Works, B.R.**
Engines: Two B.U.T. (A.E.C.) 6-cyl. horizontal type of 150 b.h.p.
Transmission: **Mechanical.** Cardan shaft and freewheel to four-speed epicyclic gearbox and further cardan shaft to final drive.
Body: 57' 6" × 9' 2".
Weight: 27 tons.
Seats 1st: 61.
  56*.

M79008	E79021*	E79034*
M79009	E79022*	E79035*
M79010	E79023*	E79036*
M79011	E79024*	E79037*
M79012	E79025*	E79038*
M79013	E79026*	E79039*
M79014	E79027*	E79040*
M79015	E79028*	E79041*
M79016	E79029*	E79042*
M79017	E79030*	E79043*
M79018	E79031*	E79044*
M79019	E79032*	E79045*
M79020	E79033*	E79046*

Motor Brake Second ◆
(TWIN UNITS)
Built by: **Metropolitan Cammell.**
Engines: Two B.U.T. (A.E.C.) 6-cyl. horizontal type of 150 b.h.p.
Transmission: **Mechanical.** Cardan shaft and freewheel to four-speed epicyclic gearbox and further cardan shaft to final drive.
Body: 57' 0" × 9' 3".
Weight: 26 tons 10 cwt.
Seats 2nd: 57.
  53*.

E79047	E79059	E79071
E79048	E79060	E79072
E79049	E79061	E79073
E79050	E79062	E79074
E79051	E79063	E79075
E79052	E79064	M79076*
E79053	E79065	M79077*
E79054	E79066	M79078*
E79055	E79067	M79079*
E79056	E79068	M79080*
E79057	E79069	M79081*
E79058	E79070	M79082*

Motor Brake Second (L) ●
(INTER-CITY UNITS)
Built by: **Swindon Works, B.R.**
Engines: Two B.U.T. (A.E.C.) 6-cyl horizontal type of 150 b.h.p.
Transmission: **Mechanical.** Cardan shaft and freewheel to four-speed epicyclic gearbox and further cardan shaft to final drive.
Body: 64' 6" × 9' 3".
Guard's and luggage compartment at outer end. Two types of car; "leading"* with full width driving compartment, gangwayed at inner end only; "intermediate"† with side driving compartment gangwayed at both ends.
Weight: 38 tons.
Seats 2nd: 52.

W79083†	W79093*	SC79103*
W79084†	W79094*	SC79104*
W79085†	SC79095†	SC79105*
W79086†	SC79096*	SC79106*
W79087†	SC79097*	SC79107*
W79088†	SC79098*	SC79108*
W79089†	SC79099*	SC79109*
W79090†	SC79100*	SC79110*
W79091*	SC79101*	SC79111*
W79092*	SC79102*	

Motor Brake Second ◆
(TWIN UNITS)
Built by: **Derby Works, B.R.**
Engines: Two B.U.T. 6-cyl. horizontal type of 150 b.h.p.

Transmission: **Mechanical.** Cardan shaft and freewheel to four-speed epicyclic gearbox and further cardan shaft to final drive.
Body: 57' 6" × 9' 2".
Weight: 27 tons.
Seats 2nd: 52.

M79118	M79129	M79140
M79119	M79130	M79141
M79120	M79131	M79142
M79121	M79132	M79143
M79122	M79133	M79144
M79123	M79134	M79145
M79124	M79135 *	M79146
M79125	M79136	M79147
M79126	M79137	M79148
M79127	M79138	M79149
M79128	M79139	

Fitted with Self Changing Gears Ltd. automatic four-speed gearbox.

Motor Second
(FOUR-CAR UNITS)
Built by: **Derby Works, B.R.**
Engines: Two B.U.T. (A.E.C.) 6-cyl. horizontal type of 150 b.h.p.
Transmission: **Mechanical.** Cardan shaft and freewheel to four-speed epicyclic gearbox and further cardan shaft to final drive.
Body: 57' 6" × 9' 2".
Weight: 26 tons.
Seats 2nd: 64.

E79150	E79152	E79154
E79151	E79153	

Motor Second (L) ●
(INTER-CITY UNITS)
Built by: **Swindon Works, B.R.**
Engines: Two B.U.T. (A.E.C.) 6-cyl. horizontal type of 150 b.h.p.
Transmission: **Mechanical.** Cardan shaft and freewheel to four-speed epicyclic gearbox and further cardan shaft to final drive.
Body: 64' 6" × 9' 3".
Gangwayed both ends. Side driving compartment at one end.
Weight: 39 tons 3 cwt.
Seats 2nd: 64.

SC79155	SC79160	SC79165
SC79156	SC79161	SC79166
SC79157	SC79162	SC79167
SC79158	SC79163	SC79168
SC79159	SC79164	

Motor Brake Second ♦
(TWIN UNITS)
For Details see M79118-49

M79169	M79174	M79179
M79170	M79175	M79180
M79171	M79176	M79181
M79172	M79177	
M79173	M79178	

Motor Brake Second ♦
(TWIN UNITS)
For Details see M79008-46

M79184	M79186	M79188
M79185	M79187	

Motor Composite (L) ♦
(TWIN UNITS)
Built by: **Derby Works, B.R.**
Engines: Two B.U.T. (A.E.C.) 6-cyl. horizontal type of 150 b.h.p.
Transmission: **Mechanical.** Cardan shaft and freewheel to four-speed epicyclic gearbox and further cardan shaft to final drive.
Body: 57′ 6″ × 9′ 2″.
Weight: 27 tons.
Seats 1st: 12.
2nd: 53.

M79189	M79191	M79193
M79190	M79192	

Driving Trailer Composite (L) ♦
(TWIN UNITS)
Built by: **Derby Works, B.R.**
Body: 57′ 6″ × 9′ 2″.
Weight: 20 tons.
Seats 1st: 16.
2nd: 53.

E79250	E79255	E79260
E79251	E79256	E79261
E79252	E79257	E79262
E79253	E79258	
E79254	E79259	

Driving Trailer Second (L) ♦
(TWIN UNITS)
Built by: **Metropolitan Cammell.**
Body: 57′ 0″ × 9′ 3″.
Weight: 25 tons.
Seats 2nd: 71.

E79263	E79274	E79284
E79264	E79274	E79284
E79265	E79275	E79285
E79266	E79276	E79286
E79267	E79277	E79287
E79268	E79278	E79288
E79269	E79279	E79289
E79270	E79280	E79290
E79271	E79281	E79291
E79272	E79282	

Trailer Brake Second (L) ♦
(FOUR-CAR UNITS)
Built by: **Derby Works, B.R.**
Body: 57′ 6″ × 9′ 2″.
Weight: 20 tons 10 cwt.
Seats 2nd: 45.

E79325	E79327	E79329
E79326	E79328	

Trailer Second (L) ♦
(FOUR-CAR UNITS)
Built by: **Derby Works, B.R.**
Body: 57′ 6″ × 9′ 2″.
Weight: 20 tons 10 cwt.
Seats 2nd: 61.

E79400	E79402	E79404
E79401	E79403	

Trailer Buffet First (K) ●
(INTER-CITY UNITS)
Built by: **Swindon Works, B.R.**
Body: 64′ 6″ × 9′ 3″.
Side corridor with three first class compartments. Buffet with kitchen, bar and saloon.
Weight: 34 tons.
Seats 1st: 18.
Buffet: 12.

W79440	SC79443	SC79446
W79441	SC79444	SC79447
SC79442	SC79445	

Trailer First (K) ●
(INTER-CITY UNITS)
Built by: **Swindon Works, B.R.**
Body: 64′ 6″ × 9′ 3″.
Side corridor with seven first class compartments and end doors.
Weight: 33 tons 9 cwt.
Seats 1st: 42.

W79470	SC79475	SC79480
W79471	SC79476	SC79481
W79472	SC79477	SC79482
W79473	SC79478	
SC79474	SC79479	

Motor Composite (L) ▲
(TWIN UNITS)
Built by: **Derby Works, B.R.**
Engines: Two B.U.T. (Leyland) 6-cyl. horizontal type of 125 b.h.p.
Transmission: **Hydro-Mechanical.** Lysholm Smith (Leyland) torque converter to final drive.
Body: 57′ 6″ × 9′ 2″.
Weight:
Seats 1st: 16.
2nd: 53.

E79500	E79503	E79506
E79501	E79504	E79507
E79502	E79505	

Motor Composite ◆
(FOUR-CAR UNITS)
Built by: **Derby Works, B.R.**
Engines: Two B.U.T. (A.E.C.) 6-cyl. horizontal type of 150 b.h.p.
Transmission: **Mechanical.** Cardan shaft and freewheel to four-speed epicyclic gearbox and further cardan shaft to final drive.
Body: 57′ 6″ × 9′ 2″.
Weight: 26 tons 10 cwt.
Seats 1st: 20.
2nd: 36.

E79508	E79510	E79512
E79509	E79511	

Driving Trailer Composite (L) ◆
(TWIN UNITS)
Built by: **Derby Works, B.R.**
Body: 57′ 6″ × 9′ 2″.
Weight: 21 tons.
Seats 1st: 9.
16*.
2nd: 53.

M79600	M79609	E79618*
M79601	M79610	E79619*
M79602	M79611	E79620*
M79603	M79612	E79621*
M79604	E79613*	E79622*
M79605	E79614*	E79623*
M79606	E79615*	E79624*
M79607	E79616*	E79625*
M79608	E79617*	

Driving Trailer Composite (L) ◆
(TWIN UNITS)
Built by: **Metropolitan Cammell.**
Body: 57′ 0″ × 9′ 3″.
Weight: 25 tons.
Seats 1st: 12.
2nd: 53.

M79626	M79629	M79632
M79627	M79630	
M79628	M79631	

Driving Trailer Composite (L) ◆
(TWIN UNITS)
For Details see M79600-E79625

M79639	M79646	M79653
M79640	M79647	M79654
M79641	M79648	M79655
M79642	M79649†	M79656
M79643	M79650	M79657
M79644	M79651	E79658*
M79645	M79652	E79659*

†This vehicle has been fitted internally for use as an inspection saloon including a pantry, and is not in public service.

E79660*	M79669	M79677
E79661*	M79670	M79678
M79662	M79671	M79679
M79663	M79672	M79680
M79664	M79673	M79681
M79665	M79674	M79682
M79666	M79675	M79683
M79667	M79676	M79684
M79668		

NOTE

For reasons of clarity the 4-wheel units below are not in strict numerical order.

Some of these vehicles are now used by the L.M. Engineers Dept. and are not in public service.

Motor Second
(FOUR-WHEEL UNITS)

Built by: **British United Traction Co.**
Engine: B.U.T. (A.E.C.) 6-cyl. horizontal type of 125 b.h.p.
Transmission: **Mechanical.** Cardan shaft and freewheel to four-speed epicyclic gearbox and further cardan shaft to final drive.
Body: 37′ 6″ × 9′ 0″ Non-gangwayed. Driving compartment at each end.
Weight: 15 tons 0 cwt.
Seats 2nd: 34.

M79740   M79745   M79748

Motor Brake Second
(FOUR-WHEEL UNITS)

Built by: **British United Traction Co.**
Engine: B.U.T. (A.E.C.) 6-cyl. horizontal type of 125 b.h.p.
Transmission: **Mechanical.** Cardan shaft and freewheel to four-speed epicyclic gearbox and further cardan shaft to final drive.
Body: 37′ 6″ × 9′ 0″. Non-gangwayed. Driving compartment at each end.
Weight: 15 tons 0 cwt.
Seats 2nd: 28.

M79742   M79744   M79750
M79743

Trailer Second
(FOUR-WHEEL UNITS)

Built by: **British United Traction Co.**
Body: 37′ 6″ × 9′ 0″. Non-gangwayed.
Weight: 10 tons 10 cwt.
Seats 2nd: 48.

M79741   M79747   M79749
M79746

Motor Brake Second
(SINGLE UNITS)

Built by: **Derby Works, B.R.**
Engine: Two B.U.T. (A.E.C.) 6-cyl. horizontal type of 150 b.h.p.
Transmission: **Mechanical.** Cardan shaft and freewheel to four-speed epicyclic gearbox and further cardan shaft to final drive.
Body: 57′ 6″ × 9′ 2″. Driving compartment at each end. Non-gangwayed.
Weight: 27 tons.
Seats 2nd: 52.

M79900   M79901

Four-Wheel Railbus

Built by: **Bristol/E.C.W.**
Engine: Gardner 6.H.L.W. 6-cyl. type of 112 b.h.p. at 1,700 r.p.m.
Transmission: **Mechanical.** Cardan shaft and freewheel to Self-Changing Gears Ltd. five-speed epicyclic gearbox and further cardan shaft to final drive.
Body: 42′ 4″ × 9′ 3″. Non-gangwayed.
Weight: 13 tons 10 cwt.
Seats 2nd: 56.

SC79958   SC79959

Four-Wheel Railbus

Built by: **Waggon und Maschinenbau.**
Engine: Buessing 150 b.h.p. at 1,900 r.p.m.
Transmission: **Mechanical.** Cardan shaft to ZF electro-magnetic six-speed gearbox.
Body: 41′ 10″ × 8′ 8⅝″. Non-gangwayed.
Weight: 15 tons.
Seats 2nd: 56.

E79960	E79962	E79964
E79661	E79963	

Four-Wheel Railbus

Built by: **D. Wickham & Co.**

Engine: Meadows 6-cyl. type 6HDT500 of 105 b.h.p. at 1,800 r.p.m.

Transmission: **Mechanical.** Freeborn-Wickham disc and ring coupling driving Self-Changing Gears Ltd. four-speed epicyclic gearbox and cardan shaft to final drive.

Body: 38′ 0″ × 9′ 0″. Non-gangwayed.

Weight: 11 tons 5 cwt.

Seats 2nd: 44.

SC79965	SC79967	SC79969
SC79966	SC79968	

Four-Wheel Railbus

Built by: **Park Royal Vehicles.**

Engine: B.U.T. (A.E.C.) 6-cyl. horizontal type of 150 b.h.p.

Transmission: **Mechanical.** Cardan shaft and freewheel to Self-Changing Gears Ltd. four-speed epicyclic gearbox and further cardan shaft to final drive.

Body: 42′ 0″ × 9′ 3″. Non-gangwayed.

Weight: 15 tons.

Seats 2nd: 50.

SC79970	SC79972	SC79974
M79971	SC79973	

Four-Wheel Railbus

Built by: **A.C. Cars Ltd.**

Engine: B.U.T. (A.E.C.) 6-cyl. horizontal type of 150 b.h.p.

Transmission: **Mechanical.** Cardan shaft and freewheel to four-speed epicyclic gearbox and further cardan shaft to final drive.

Body: 36′ 0″ × 8′ 11″.

Weight: 11 tons.

Seats 2nd: 46.

W79975	W79977	W79979
W79976	W79978	

G.W.R. Railcars

Car No.	Date	Engines	Total b.h.p.	Seats 2nd:
5/7	1935	2	242	70
8	1936	2	242	70
13/4§	1936	2	242	—
15	1936	2	242	70
17*	1936	2	242	—
19-32†	1940	2	210	48
33, 38‡	1942	4	420	92
34*	1941	2	210	—
‖1096	—	–	—	64

*Parcels cars.

‡Twin-coach unit with buffet facilities. Adjoining statistics apply per 2-car unit. These cars work and a three-car set with corridor second W1096W.

†These cars may work in pairs with an additional ordinary coach between.

§Rebuilt as Parcels Cars.

‖This is an ordinary 60 ft. ex-G.W. Corridor Second adapted for use between two diesel railcars, and is painted green.

W5W	W17W	W24W	W30W
W7W	W19W	W25W	W31W
W8W	W20W	W26W	W32W
W13W	W21W	W27W	W33W
W14W	W22W	W28W	W34W
W15W	W23W	W29W	W38W
			W1096W

Battery Electric Railcar Motor Brake Second (TWIN UNIT)

Built by: **Derby/Cowlairs Works, B.R.**

Electrical Equipment: Two 100 kW Siemens-Schuckert nose-suspended traction motors powered by 216 lead-acid cell batteries of 1070 amp/hour capacity.

Body: 57′ 6″ × 9′ 2″.

Weight: 37 tons 10 cwt.

Seats 2nd: 52.

SC79998

Battery Electric Railcar Driving Trailer Composite (TWIN UNIT)

Built by: **Derby/Cowlairs Works, B.R.**

Body: 57′ 6″ × 9′ 2″.

Weight: 32 tons 10 cwt.

Seats 1st: 12. *2nd:* 53.

SC79999

ELECTRIC LOCOMOTIVES

AIA-AIA

Introduced: 1958.
Locomotive manufacturer: Metropolitan-Vickers.
Total h.p.: 2,500.
Equipment: Four 625 h.p. Metropolitan-Vickers nose-suspended traction motors.
Weight: 109 tons.
Driving Wheels: 3′ 8″.
Maximum tractive effort: 40,000 lb.
System: 25 kV. a.c. Overhead.
(Rebuilt from former Gas Turbine Loco. No. 18100.)

E2001 (formerly E1000)

Bo-Bo   " A "

introduced: 1959.
Locomotive manufacturer: British Thomson-Houston.
Total h.p.: 3,300.
Equipment: Four B.T.H. spring-borne d.c. traction motors of 847 h.p. (continuous) driving through Alsthom quill drive.
Weight: 79 tons 12 cwt.
Driving Wheels: 4′ 0″.
Maximum tractive effort: 48,000 lb.
System: 25 kV. a.c. overhead.

E3001	E3007	E3013	E3019
E3002	E3008	E3014	E3020
E3003	E3009	E3015	E3021
E3004	E3010	E3016	E3022
E3005	E3011	E3017	E3023
E3006	E3012	E3018	

Bo-Bo   " A "

Introduced: 1960.
Locomotive manufacturer: English Electric.
Total h.p.: 3,300.
Equipment: Four English Electric spring-borne d.c. traction motors of 740 h.p. (continuous) driving through S.L.M. resilient drives.
Weight: 73 tons.
Driving Wheels: 4′ 0″.
Maximum tractive effort:
System: 25 kV. a.c. overhead.

E3024	E3027	E3030	E3033
E3025	E3028	E3031	E3034
E3026	E3029	E3032	E3035

Bo-Bo   " A "

Introduced: 1960.
Locomotive manufacturer: General Electric.
Total h.p.: 3,300.
Equipment: Four G.E.C. spring-borne d.c. traction motors of 750 h.p. (continuous), driving through Brown-Boveri spring drives.
Weight: 76 tons 10 cwt.
Driving Wheels: 4′ 0″.
Maximum tractive effort: 50,000 lb.
System: 25 kV. a.c. overhead.

E3036	E3039	E3042	E3044
E3037	E3040	E3043	E3045
E3038	E3041		

Bo-Bo   " A "

Introduced: 1960
Locomotive manufacturer: Metropolitan-Vickers.
Total h.p.: 3,300.
Equipment:
Weight:
Driving Wheels:
Maximum tractive effort:
System: 25 kV. a.c. overhead.

E3046	E3049	E3052	E3054
E3047	E3050	E3053	E3055
E3048	E3051		

Bo-Bo   " A "

To be introduced:
Locomotive manufacturer: B.R., Doncaster.
Total h.p.: 3,300.
Equipment: B.T.H.
Weight:
Driving Wheels:
Maximum tractive effort:
System: 25 kV. a.c. overhead.

E3056	E3061	E3066	E3071
E3057	E3062	E3067	E3072
E3058	E3063	E3068	E3073
E3059	E3064	E3069	E3074
E3060	E3065	E3070	E3075

Bo-Bo "A"

To be introduced:
Locomotive manufacturer: B.R., Crewe.
Total h.p.: 3,300.
Equipment: B.T.H.
Weight:
Driving Wheels:
Maximum tractive effort:
System: 25 kV. a.c. overhead.

E3076	E3081	E3086	E3091
E3077	E3082	E3087	E3092
E3078	E3083	E3088	E3093
E3079	E3084	E3089	E3094
E3080	E3085	E3090	E3095

Bo-Bo "B"

To be introduced:
Locomotive manufacturer: British Thomson-Houston.
Total h.p.: 3,300.
Equipment:
Weight:
Driving Wheels:
Maximum tractive effort:
System: 25 kV. a.c. overhead.

E3301	E3302

Bo-Bo "B"

To be introduced:
Locomotive manufacturer: English Electric.
Total h.p.: 3,300.
Equipment:
Weight:
Driving Wheels:
Maximum tractive effort:
System: 25 kV. a.c. overhead.

E3303	E3304	E3305

Bo-Bo

Introduced: 1958.
Locomotive manufacturer: B.R., Doncaster.
Total h.p.: 2,552.
Equipment: Motor generator booster set and four 638 h.p. English Electric spring-borne traction motors driving through S.L.M. flexible drive.
Weight: 77 tons.
Driving Wheels: 4' 0".
Maximum tractive effort: 43,000 lb.
System: 750 V. d.c. 3rd rail and overhead.

E5000	E5006	E5012	E5018
E5001	E5007	E5013	E5019
E5002	E5008	E5014	E5020
E5003	E5009	E5015	E5021
E5004	E5010	E5016	E5022
E5005	E5011	E5017	E5023

Co-Co   Class CC

Introduced: { 1941. / 1948*.
Locomotive manufacturer: S.R., Ashford.
Total h.p.: 1,470.
Equipment: Motor generator booster set and six 245 h.p. English Electric nose-suspended traction motors.
Weight: { 99 tons 14 cwt. / 104 tons 14 cwt.*
Driving Wheels: 3' 6".
Maximum tractive effort: { 40,000 lb. / 45,000 lb.*
System: 750 V. d.c. 3rd rail and overhead.

20001	20002	20003*

Bo-Bo   Class EM1

Introduced: { 1941.* / 1950.
Locomotive manufacturer: B.R., Doncaster.
Total h.p.: 1,868.
Equipment: Four 467 h.p. Metropolitan-Vickers nose-suspended traction motors.
Weight: 87 tons 18 cwt.
Driving Wheels: 4' 2".
Maximum tractive effort: 45,000 lb.
System: 1,500 V. d.c. overhead.

26000* Tommy			
26001	26013	26024	26035
26002	26014	26025	26036
26003	26015	26026	26037
26004	26016	26027	26038
26005	26017	26028	26039
26006	26018	26029	26040
26007	26019	26030	26041
26008	26020	26031	26042
26009	26021	26032	26043
26010	26022	26033	26044
26011	26023	26034	26045
26012			

26046	Archimedes
26047	Diomedes
26048	Hector
26049	Jason
26050	Stentor
26051	Mentor
26052	Nestor
26053	Perseus
26054	Pluto
26055	Prometheus
26056	Triton
26057	Ulysses

Bo-Bo — Class ESI

Introduced: 1902.
Locomotive manufacturer: Brush Traction.
Total h.p.:
Equipment: Four B.T.H. nose-suspended traction motors.
Weight: 46 tons.
Driving Wheels:
Maximum tractive effort: 25,000 lb.
System: 630 V. d.c. overhead and 3rd rail.

| 26500 | 26501 |

Co-Co — Class EM2

Introduced: 1954.
Locomotive manufacturer: B.R., Gorton.
Total h.p.: 2,490.
Equipment: Six 415 h.p. Metropolitan-Vickers nose-suspended traction motors.
Weight: 102 tons.
Driving Wheels: 4' 2".
Maximum tractive effort: 45,000 lb.
System: 1,500 V.d.c. overhead.

27000	Electra
27001	Ariadne
27002	Aurora
27003	Diana
27004	Juno
27005	Minerva
27006	Pandora

Service Locomotives
Eastern Region
Bo-Bo — Class EBI

Introduced: 1946.
Locomotive manufacturer:
Total h.p.:
Equipment:
Weight: 74 tons 8 cwt.
Driving Wheels: 4' 0".
Maximum tractive effort: 37,600 lb.
System: 1,500 V. d.c. overhead.
100

Southern Region
DS 74   DS 75

ELECTRIC MULTIPLE UNITS

The dimensions shown are length and width over body and width overall.
The letter " L " in the headings indicates an open vehicle fitted with toilet acilities " K " indicates a side corridor vehicle with toilet.

London Midland Region

SYSTEM: 630 VOLTS D.C.
3rd & 4th RAIL

LONDON DISTRICT
THREE-CAR
COMPARTMENT SETS
Motor Brake Second

Body: 59' 0" × 8' 11" & 9' 6".
Weight: 56 tons.

Seats 2nd: 84.
Equipment: Four 280 h.p. G.E.C. or M.V traction motors.

M28001M	M28006M	M28011M
M28002M	M28007M	M28012M
M28003M	M28008M	M28013M
M28004M	M28009M	M28014M
M28005M	M28010M	M28015M

M28016M	M28020M	M28023M	M61133	M61152	M61171
M28017M	M28021M	M28024M	M61134	M61153	M61172
M28018M	M28022M	M28025M	M61135	M61154	M61173
M28019M			M61136	M61155	M61174
			M61137	M61156	M61175
			M61138	M61157	M61176

Trailer Second

Body: 57' 0" × 8' 11" & 9' 6".
Weight: 28 tons.
Seats 2nd: 108.

			M61139	M61158	M61177
M29400M	M29600M	M29611M	M61140	M61159	M61178
M29401M	M29601M	M29612M	M61141	M61160	M61179
M29402M	M29602M	M29613M	M61142	M61161	M61180
M29403M	M29603M	M29614M	M61143	M61162	M61181
M29404M	M29604M	M29615M	M61144	M61163	M61182
M29405M	M29605M	M29616M	M61145	M61164	M61183
M29406M	M29606M	M29617M	M61146	M61165	M61184
M29407M	M29607M	M29618M	M61147	M61166	M61185
M29408M	M29608M	M29619M	M61148	M61167	M61186
M29409M	M29609M	M29620M	M61149	M61168	M61187
	M29610M	M29621M	M61150	M61169	M61188
			M61151	M61170	M61189

Driving Trailer Brake Second

Body: 57' 0" × 8' 11" & 9' 6".
Weight: 30 tons.
Seats 2nd: 96.

Trailer Second

Body: 57' 1" × 9' 0" & 9' 6".
Weight: 29 tons.
Seats 2nd: 108.

M28800M	M28809M	M28817M	M70133	M70152	M70171
M28801M	M28810M	M28818M	M70134	M70153	M70172
M28802M	M28811M	M28819M	M70135	M70154	M70173
M28803M	M28812M	M28820M	M70136	M70155	M70174
M28804M	M28813M	M28821M	M70137	M70156	M70175
M28805M	M28814M	M28822M	M70138	M70157	M70176
M28806M	M28815M	M28823M	M70139	M70158	M70177
M28807M	M28816M	M28824M	M70140	M70159	M70178
M28808M			M70141	M70160	M70179

LONDON DISTRICT THREE-CAR B.R. SETS

B.R. Standard design

Motor Open Brake Second

Body: 57' 5" × 9' 0" & 9' 6"
Weight: 47 tons.
Seats 2nd: 74.
Equipment: Four 185 h.p. G.E.C. traction motors.

M70142	M70161	M70180
M70143	M70162	M70181
M70144	M70163	M70182
M70145	M70164	M70183
M70146	M70165	M70184
M70147	M70166	M70185
M70148	M70167	M70186
M70149	M70168	M70187
M70150	M70169	M70188
M70151	M70170	M70189

Driving Trailer
Open Brake Second

Body: 57' 5" × 9' 0" & 9' 6".
Weight: 30 tons.
Seats 2nd: 74.

M75133	M75152	M75171
M75134	M75153	M75172
M75135	M75154	M75173
M75136	M75155	M75174
M75137	M75156	M75175
M75138	M75157	M75176
M75139	M75158	M75177
M75140	M75159	M75178
M75141	M75160	M75179
M75142	M75161	M75180
M75143	M75162	M75181
M75144	M75163	M75182
M75145	M75164	M75183
M75146	M75165	M75184
M75147	M75166	M75185
M75148	M75167	M75186
M75149	M75168	M75187
M75150	M75169	M75188
M75151	M75170	M75189

SYSTEM: 630 VOLTS D.C. 3rd RAIL

LIVERPOOL-SOUTHPORT

TWO- AND THREE-CAR
COMPARTMENT SETS

Motor Brake Second

Body: 59' 0" × 8' 11" & 9' 3".
Weight: 56 tons.
Seats 2nd: 84.
Equipment: Four 265 h.p. Metropolitan
Vickers traction motors.

M28301M	M28305M	M28308M
M28302M	M28306M	M28309M
M28303M	M28307M	M28310M
M28304M		

Trailer Composite

Body: 57' 0" × 8' 11" & 9' 3".
Weight: 28 tons.
Seats 1st: 24.
 2nd: 72.

M29800M	M29804M	M29808M
M29801M	M29805M	M29809M
M29802M	M29806M	M29810M
M29803M	M29807M	M29811M

Driving Trailer Brake Second

Body: 57' 0" × 8' 11" & 9' 3".
Weight: 28 tons.
Seats 2nd: 96.

M29100M	M29104M	M29108M
M29101M	M29105M	M29109M
M29102M	M29106M	M29110M
M29103M	M29107M	

LIVERPOOL-SOUTHPORT

TWO- AND THREE-CAR
OPEN SETS
Motor Open Brake Second

Body: 66' 6" × 9' 3" & 9' 5".
Weight: 41 tons.
Seats 2nd: 88.
Equipment: Four 235 h.p. English
 Electric traction motors.

M28311M	M28326M	M28340M
M28312M	M28327M	M28341M
M28313M	M28328M	M28342M
M28314M	M28329M	M28343M
M28315M	M28330M	M28344M
M28316M	M28331M	M28345M
M28317M	M28332M	M28347M
M28318M	M28333M	M28348M
M28319M	M28334M	M28349M
M28321M	M28335M	M28350M
M28322M	M28336M	M28351M
M28323M	M28337M	M28352M
M28324M	M28338M	M28353M
M28325M	M28339M	M28354M

M28355M	M28360M	M28365M
M28356M	M28361M	M28366M
M28357M	M28362M	M28367M
M28358M	M28363M	M28368M
M28359M	M28364M	M28369M

Trailer Open Second

Body: 66' 6" × 9' 3" & 9' 5".
Weight: 24 tons.
Seats 2nd: 102.

M29545M	M29562M	M29579M
M29546M	M29563M	M29580M
M29547M	M29564M	M29581M
M29548M	M29565M	M29582M
M29549M	M29566M	M29583M
M29550M	M29567M	M29584M
M29551M	M29568M	M29585M
M29552M	M29569M	M29586M
M29553M	M29570M	M29587M
M29554M	M29571M	M29588M
M29555M	M29572M	M29589M
M29556M	M29573M	M29590M
M29557M	M29574M	M29591M
M29558M	M29575M	M29592M
M29559M	M29576M	M29593M
M29560M	M29577M	M29594M
M29561M	M29578M	

Trailer Open Second
(Built as Composite)

Body: 66' 6" × 9' 3" & 9' 5".
Weight: 24 tons.
Seats 2nd: 82.

M29812M	M29815M	M29818M
M29813M	M29816M	M29819M
M29814M	M29817M	M29820M

Driving Trailer Open Composite

Body: 66' 6" × 9' 3" & 9' 5".
Weight: 25 tons.
Seats 1st: 53.
      2nd: 25.

M29866M	M29878M	M29889M
M29867M	M29879M	M29890M
M29868M	M29880M	M29891M
M29869M	M29881M	M29892M
M29870M	M29882M	M29893M
M29871M	M29883M	M29894M
M29872M	M29884M	M29895M
M29873M	M29885M	M29896M
M29874M	M29886M	M29897M
M29875M	M29887M	M29898M
M29876M	M29888M	M29899M
M29877M		

LIVERPOOL-SOUTHPORT
Motor Parcels Van

Body: $\begin{cases} 57' 0" \times 8' 11" \& 9' 3"*. \\ 59' 0" \times 8' 11" \& 9' 3". \end{cases}$
Weight:
Equipment: Two 265 h.p. Metropolitan-Vickers nose-suspended traction motors.

M28496M   *M28497M

SYSTEM: 650 VOLTS D.C. 3rd RAIL

WIRRAL & MERSEY
THREE-CAR OPEN SETS
Motor Open Brake Second

Body: 58' 0" × 8' 8" & 9' 11".
Weight: 36 tons.
Seats 2nd: 58.
Equipment: Four 135 h.p. B.T.H. traction motors.

M28371M	M28380M	M28389M
M28372M	M28381M	M28390M
M28373M	M28382M	M28391M
M28374M	M28383M	M28392M
M28375M	M28384M	M28393M
M28376M	M28385M	M28394M
M28377M	M28386M	
M28378M	M28387M	M28672M
M28379M	M28388M	M28673M

M28674M	M28680M	M28686M
M28675M	M28681M	M28687M
M28676M	M28682M	M28688M
M28677M	M28683M	M28689M
M28678M	M28684M	M28690M
M28679M	M28685M	

M29155M	M29276M	M29283M
M29156M	M29277M	M29284M
	M29278M	M29285M
M29271M	M29279M	M29286M
M29272M	M29280M	M29287M
M29273M	M29281M	M29288M
M29274M	M29282M	M29289M
M29275M		

Trailer Open Composite
Body: 56′ 0″ × 8′ 8″ & 9′ 11″.
Weight: 20 tons.
Seats 1st: 40.
  2nd: 15.

M29702M	M29718M	M29833M
M29703M	M29719M	M29834M
M29704M	M29720M	M29835M
M29705M		M29836M
M29706M	M29821M	M29837M
M29707M	M29822M	M29838M
M29708M	M29823M	M29839M
M29709M	M29824M	M29840M
M29710M	M29825M	M29841M
M29711M	M29826M	M29842M
M29712M	M29827M	M29843M
M29713M	M29828M	M29844M
M29714M	M29829M	M29845M
M29715M	M29830M	M29846M
M29716M	M29831M	
M29717M	M29832M	

Driving Trailer Open Second
Body: 58′ 0″ × 8′ 8″ & 9′ 11″.
Weight: 21 tons.
Seats 2nd: 68.

M29131M	M29139M	M29147M
M29132M	M29140M	M29148M
M29133M	M29141M	M29149M
M29134M	M29142M	M29150M
M29135M	M29143M	M29151M
M29136M	M29144M	M29152M
M29137M	M29145M	M29153M
M29138M	M29146M	M29154M

SYSTEM: 1200 VOLTS D.C. SIDE CONTACT 3rd RAIL

MANCHESTER-BURY
TWO-CAR B.R. SETS
B.R. Standard design
Motor Open Brake Second
Body: 63′ 11½″ × 9′ 0″ & 9′ 3″.
Weight:
Seats 2nd: 84.
Equipment: Two 141 h.p. English Electric traction motors.

M65436	M65445	M65454
M65437	M65446	M65455
M65438	M65447	M65456
M65439	M65448	M65457
M65440	M65449	M65458
M65441	M65450	M65459
M65442	M65451	M65460
M65443	M65452	M65461
M65444	M65453	

Driving Trailer Composite
Body: 63′ 11½″ × 9′ 0″ & 9′ 3″.
Weight:
Seats 1st: 16.
  2nd: 78.

M77157	M77166	M77175
M77158	M77167	M77176
M77159	M77168	M77177
M77160	M77169	M77178
M77161	M77170	M77179
M77162	M77171	M77180
M77163	M77172	M77181
M77164	M77173	M77182
M77165	M77174	

MANCHESTER–ALTRINCHAM
THREE-CAR SETS
Motor Brake Second

Body: 58' 1" × 8' 11" & 9' 3".
Weight: 57 tons.
Seats 2nd: 72.
Equipment: Four 330 h.p. traction motors.

M28571M	M28579M	M28587M
M28572M	M28580M	M28588M
M28573M	M28581M	M28589M
M28574M	M28582M	M28590M
M28575M	M28583M	M28591M
M28576M	M28584M	M28592M
M28577M	M28585M	M28593M
M28578M	M28586M	M28594M

Trailer Composite

Body: 57' 1" × 8' 11" & 9' 3".
Weight: 30 tons.
Seats 1st: 24.
　　　2nd: 72.

M29396M	M29656M	M29664M
	M29657M	M29665M
	M29658M	M29666M
M29650M	M29659M	M29667M
M29651M	M29660M	M29668M
M29652M	M29661M	M29669M
M29653M	M29662M	M29670M
M29654M	M29663M	M29671M
M29655M		

Driving Trailer Second

Body: 58' 1" × 8' 11" & 9' 3".
Weight: 31 tons.
Seats 2nd: 108.

M29231M	M29239M	M29246M
M29232M	M29240M	M29247M
M29233M	M29241M	M29248M
M29234M	M29242M	M29249M
M29235M	M29243M	M29250M
M29236M	M29244M	M29251M
M29237M	M29245M	M29252M
M29238M		

LANCASTER–MORECAMBE–HEYSHAM
THREE-CAR OPEN SETS
Motor Open Brake Second

Body: 57' 0" × 8' 11" & 9' 6".
Weight: 57 tons.
Seats 2nd: { 28
　　　　　{ 38*.
Equipment: Four 215 h.p. English Electric traction motors.
*Four 215 h.p. Metropolitan-Vickers traction motors.

M28219M	M28221M	M28222M*
M28220M		

Trailer Open Second

Body: 57' 0" × 8' 11" & 9' 6".
Weight: 26 tons.
S ts 2nd: 62.

M29719M	M29721M	M29722M
M29720M		

Driving Trailer Open Second

Body: 57' 0" × 8' 11" & 9' 6".
Weight:
Seats 2nd: 56.

M29019M	M29021M	M29022M
M29020M		

MANCHESTER–GLOSSOP–HADFIELD
THREE-CAR OPEN SETS
Motor Open Brake Second

Body: 60' 4½" × 9' 0" & 9' 3".
Weight: 50 tons 12 cwt.
Seats 2nd: 52.
Equipment: Four 185 h.p. GEC traction motors.

M59401	M59404	M59407
M59402	M59405	M59408
M59403	M59406	

Trailer Open Second

Body: 55' 0½" × 9' 0" & 9' 3"
Weight: 26 tons 8 cwt.
Seats 2nd :

M59501	M59504	M59507
M59502	M59505	M59508
M59503	M59506	

Driving Trailer Open Second

Body: 55' 4½" × 9' 0" & 9' 3".
Weight: 27 tons 9 cwt.
Seats 2nd: 60.

M59601	M59604	M59607
M59602	M59605	M59608
M59603	M59606	

*SYSTEM: 25000 VOLTS A.C.
50 CYCLES OVERHEAD*

MANCHESTER-CREWE
LIVERPOOL-CREWE
FOUR-CAR SETS

B.R. Standard design

Driving Trailer Open Brake Second

Body: 64' 0⅜" × 9' 0" & 9' 3".
Weight: 31 tons 8 cwt.
Seats 2nd: 82.

Trailer Composite (L)

Body: 63' 6⅛ × 9' 0" & 9' 3".
Weight: 31 tons 5 cwt.
Seats 1st: 19.
　　2nd: 60.

Motor Brake Second

Body: 63' 6⅛ × 9' 0" & 9' 3".
Weight: 53 tons 12 cwt.
Seats 2nd: $\begin{cases} 96. \\ 72*. \end{cases}$
Equipment: Four 190 h.p. A.E.I.
traction motors.

Driving Trailer Open Second (L)

Body: 64' 0⅝ × 9' 0" & 9' 3".
Weight: 35 tons 12 cwt.
Seats 2nd: 80.

UNIT Nos.

001	010	019*	028*
002	011	020*	029*
003	012	021*	030*
004	013	022*	031*
005	014	023*	032*
006	015	024*	033*
007	016*	025*	034*
008	017*	026*	035*
009	018*	027*	

Eastern Region

*SYSTEM: 25000 VOLTS A.C.
50 CYCLES OVERHEAD*

LIVERPOOL ST.–
SHENFIELD
THREE-CAR OPEN UNITS

*These sets have been converted for working on 25,000 volts a.c. from 1,500 volts d.c. The centre trailers have been altered to include the guards compartment and pantograph and part of the passenger saloon thus displaced transferred to the existing motor coach. Ultimately the centre trailer will become the motor coach and the present motor coach will become a driving trailer.

Motor Open Brake Second

Body: 60' 4½" × 9' 0" & 9' 6".
Weight: 50 tons 17 cwt.
Seats 2nd: $\begin{cases} 52. \\ 62*. \end{cases}$
Equipment:

Trailer Open Second

Body: 55' 9½" × 9' 0" & 9' 6".
Weight: 26 tons.
Seats 2nd: $\begin{cases} 64. \\ 46*. \end{cases}$

Driving Trailer Open Second
Body: 55′ 4″ × 9′ 0″ & 9′ 6″.
Weight: 27 tons 10 cwt.
Seats 2nd: 60.

UNIT Nos.

001	024	047	070
002	025	048	071
003	026	049	072
004	027	050	073
005	028	051	074
006	029	052	075
007	030	053	076
008	031	054	077
009	032	055	078
010	033	056	079
011	034	057	080
012	035	058	081
013	036	059	082
014	037	060	083
015	038	061	084
016	039	062	085
017	040	063	086
018	041	064	087
019	042	065	088
020	043	066	089
021	044	067	090
022	045	068	091
023	046	069	092

LIVERPOOL ST.– SOUTHEND FOUR-CAR UNITS

These sets are being converted for working on 25,000 volts a.c. from 1,500 volts d.c. Some structural rebuilding will be necessary and sets are renumbered 1XX as they are dealt with.

B.R. Standard design

Driving Trailer Second
Body: 63′ 11½″ × 9′ 0″ & 9′ 3″.
Weight: 30 tons 5 cwt.
Seats 2nd: 108.

Trailer Composite (L)
Body: 63′ 6″ × 9′ 0″ & 9′ 3″.
Weight: 30 tons.
Seats 1st: 19.
　　　2nd: 60.

Motor Brake Second
Body: 63′ 6″ × 9′ 0″ & 9′ 3″.
Weight: 48 tons 6 cwt.
Seats 2nd: 96.
Equipment: Four 220 h.p. GEC traction motors.

Driving Trailer Open Second (L)
Body: 63′ 11½″ × 9′ 0″ & 9′ 3″.
Weight: 30 tons 19 cwt.
Seats 2nd: 80.

UNIT Nos.

01s	09s	17s	25s
02s	10s	18s	26s
103	11s	19s	27s
04s	12s	20s	28s
05s	13s	21s	29s
06s	14s	22s	30s
07s	15s	23s	31s
08s	16s	24s	32s

FENCHURCH ST.– SHOEBURYNESS FOUR-CAR UNITS

B.R. Standard design

Driving Trailer Second
Body: 63′ 11½″ × 9′ 0″ & 9′ 3″.
Weight: 32 tons.
Seats 2nd: 108.

Trailer Composite (L)
Body: 63′ 6″ × 9′ 0″ & 9′ 3″.
Weight: 31 tons.
Seats 1st: 19.
　　　2nd: 60.

Motor Brake Second
Body: 63′ 6″ × 9′ 0″ & 9′ 3″.
Weight: 56 tons 10 cwt.
Seats 2nd: 96.
Equipment: Four 240 h.p. English Electric nose-suspended traction motors.

Driving Trailer Open Second (L)
Body: 63′ 11½″ × 9′ 0″ & 9′ 3″.
Weight: 36 tons.
Seats 2nd: 80.

UNIT Nos.

201	229	257	285
202	230	258	286
203	231	259	287
204	232	260	288
205	233	261	289
206	234	262	290
207	235	263	291
208	236	264	292
209	237	265	293
210	238	266	294
211	239	267	295
212	240	268	296
213	241	269	297
214	242	270	298
215	243	271	299
216	244	272	300
217	245	273	301
218	246	274	302
219	247	275	303
220	248	276	304
221	249	277	305
222	250	278	306
223	251	279	307
224	252	280	308
225	253	281	309
226	254	282	310
227	255	283	311
228	256	284	312

———

LIVERPOOL ST.-ENFIELD AND CHINGFORD THREE-CAR UNITS

B.R. Standard design

Driving Trailer Open Second
Body: 63' 11½ in × 9' 0 " & 9' 3".
Weight:
Seats 2nd: 94.

Motor Brake Open Second
Body: 63' 6" × 9' 0" & 9' 3".
Weight:
Seats 2nd: 84.
Equipment:

Driving Trailer Open Second
Body: 63' 11½" × 9' 0" & 9' 3".
Weight:
Seats 2nd: 94.

UNIT Nos.

401	414	427	440
402	415	428	441
403	416	429	442
404	417	430	443
405	418	431	444
406	419	432	445
407	420	433	446
408	421	434	447
409	422	435	448
410	423	436	449
411	424	437	450
412	425	438	451
413	426	439	452

LIVERPOOL ST.-BISHOPS STORTFORD AND HERTFORD EAST FOUR-CAR UNITS

B.R. Standard design
Driving Trailer Second
Body: 63' 11½" × 9' 0" & 9' 3".
Weight: 32 tons.
Seats 2nd: 108.

Trailer Composite (L)
Body: 63' 6" × 9' 0" & 9' 3".
Weight: 31 tons.
Seats 1st: 19.
2nd: 60.

Motor Brake Second
Body: 63' 6" × 9' 0" & 9' 3".
Weight: 54 tons.
Seats: 2nd: 96.

Driving Trailer Open Second (L)

Body: 63' 11½" × 9' 0" & 9' 3".
Weight: 36 tons.
Seats 2nd: 80.

UNIT Nos.

501	506	511	516
502	507	512	517
503	508	513	518
504	509	514	519
505	510	515	

SYSTEM: 575 VOLTS D.C. OVERHEAD

GRIMSBY-IMMINGHAM ELECTRIC TRAMS

1	14	19	24	29
3	15	20	25	30
4	16	21	26	31
5	17	22	27	32
11	18	23	28	33
12				

North Eastern Region

SYSTEM: 600 VOLTS D.C. 3rd RAIL

SOUTH TYNESIDE TWO-CAR SETS

B.R. Standard design

Motor Open Brake Second

Body: 63' 11½" × 9' 0" & 9' 3".
Weight: 40 tons.
Seats 2nd : 74.
Equipment: Two 250 h.p. English Electric traction motors.

E65311	E65316	E65321
E65312	E65317	E65322
E65313	E65318	E65323
E65314	E65319	E65324
E65315	E65320	E65325

Driving Trailer Second

Body: 63' 11½" × 9' 0" & 9' 3".
Weight: 30 tons.
Seats 2nd:

E77100	E77105	E77110
E77101	E77106	E77111
E77102	E77107	E77112
E77103	E77108	E77113
E77104	E77109	E77114

SOUTH TYNESIDE
Motor Parcels Van

Body: 64' 5" × 9' 0" & 9' 3".
Weight: 49 tons.
Equipment: Four 250 h.p. English Electric traction motors.

E68000

NORTH TYNESIDE ARTICULATED TWIN UNITS

Motor Open Brake Second

Body: 55' 0" × 9' 0½" & 9' 3".
Combined weight with trailer: 54 tons 19 cwt.
Seats 2nd: 52.
Equipment: Two 154 h.p. Crompton Parkinson traction motors.

Driving Trailer Open Second

Body: 55' 0" × 9' 0½" & 9' 3".
Seats 2nd: 76.

Motor Coaches	Driving Trailers
E29101E	E29301E
E29102E	E29302E
E29103E	E29303E
E29104E	E29304E
E29105E	E29305E
E29106E	E29306E

E29107E	E29307E
E29108E	E29308E
E29109E	E29309E
E29110E	E29310E
E29111E	E29311E

Motor Open Brake Second

Body: 55′ 0″ × 9′ 0½″ & 9′ 3″.
Combined weight with trailer: 55 tons 7 cwt.
Seats 2nd: 52.
Equipment: Two 154 h.p. Crompton Parkinson traction motors.

Driving Trailer Open Second

Body: 55′ 0″ × 9′ 0½″ & 9′ 3″.
Seats 2nd: 60

Motor Coaches	Driving Trailers
E29113E	E29313E
E29114E	E29314E
E29115E	E29315E
E29116E	E29316E
E29117E	E29317E
E29118E	E29318E
E29119E	E29319E
E29120E	E29320E
E29121E	E29321E
E29122E	E29322E
E29123E	E29323E
E29124E	E29324E
E29125E	E29325E
E29126E	E29326E
E29127E	E29327E
E29128E	E29328E

Motor Open Brake Second

Body: 55′ 0″ × 9′ 0½″ & 9′ 3″.
Combined weight with trailer: 53 tons 12 cwt.
Seats 2nd: 52.
Equipment: Two 154 h.p. Crompton Parkinson traction motors.

Trailer Open Second

Body: 55′ 0″ × 9′ 0½″ & 9′ 3″.
Seats 2nd: 80.

Motor Coaches	Driving Trailers
E29129E	E29229E
E29130E	E29230E
E29131E	E29231E
E29132E	E29232E
E29133E	E29233E
E29134E	E29234E
E29135E	E29235E
E29136E	E29236E
E29137E	E29237E
E29138E	E29238E
E29139E	E29239E
E29140E	E29240E
E29141E	E29241E
E29142E	E29242E
E29143E	E29243E
E29144E	E29244E
E29145E	E29245E
E29146E	E29246E

Motor Open Brake Second

Body: 55′ 0″ × 9′ 0½″ & 9′ 3″.
Combined weight with trailer: 54 tons 6 cwt.
Seats 2nd: 52.
Equipment: Two 154 h.p. Crompton Parkinson traction motors.

Trailer Open Second

Body: 55′ 0″ × 9′ 0½″ & 9′ 3″.
Seats 2nd: 64.

Motor Coaches	Driving Trailers
E29147E	E29247E
E29148E	E29248E
E29149E	E29249E
E29150E	E29250E
E29151E	E29251E
E29152E	E29252E
E29153E	E29253E
E29154E	E29254E
E29155E	E29255E

E29156E	E29256E
E29157E	E29257E
E29158E	E29258E
E29159E	E29259E
E29160E	E29260E
E29161E	E29261E
E29162E	E29262E
E29163E	E29263E
E29164E	E29264E

Single Driving
Trailer Open Second

Body: 56' 6" × 9' 0¾" & 9' 3".
Weight: 26 tons 10 cwt.
Seats 2nd: 68.

E29376E	E29388E
E29387E	E29390E

Single Motor
Open Brake Second

Body: 59' 0" × 9' 0½" & 9' 3".
Weight: 47 tons 5 cwt.
Seats 2nd: 52.
Equipment: Two 154 h.p. Crompton Parkinson traction motors.

E29165E	E29166E

Motor Parcels Van

Body: 59' 0" × 9' 0½" & 9' 3".
Weight: 38 tons 15 cwt.
Equipment: Four 154 h.p. Crompton Parkinson traction motors.

E29467E	E29468E

Scottish Region

SYSTEM: 25 kV. A.C. OVERHEAD

GLASGOW SUBURBAN
THREE-CAR SETS

B.R. Standard design

Driving Trailer Open Second
Body: 63' 11⅝" × 9' 3" & 9' 3"
Weight: 34 tons.
Seats 2nd: 83.

SC75566	SC75578	SC75590
SC75567	SC75579	SC75591
SC75568	SC75580	SC75592
SC75569	SC75581	SC75593
SC75570	SC75582	SC75594
SC75571	SC75583	SC75595
SC75572	SC75584	SC75596
SC75573	SC75585	SC75597
SC75574	SC75586	SC75598
SC75575	SC75587	SC75599
SC75576	SC75588	SC75600
SC75577	SC75589	

Motor Open Brake Second

Body: 63' 6⅛" × 9' 3" & 9' 3".
Weight: 56 tons.
Seats 2nd: 70.
Equipment: Metropolitan-Vickers.

SC61481	SC61493	SC61505
SC61482	SC61494	SC61506
SC61483	SC61495	SC61507
SC61484	SC61496	SC61508
SC61485	SC61497	SC61509
SC61486	SC61498	SC61510
SC61487	SC61499	SC61511
SC61488	SC61500	SC61512
SC61489	SC61501	SC61513
SC61490	SC61502	SC61514
SC61491	SC61503	SC61515
SC61492	SC61504	

Driving Trailer Open Second

Body: 63′ 11⅝″ × 9′ 3″ & 9′ 3″.
Weight: 38 tons.
Seats 2nd: 83.

SC75601	SC75605	SC75609	SC75613	SC75621	SC75629
SC75602	SC75606	SC75610	SC75614	SC75622	SC75630
SC75603	SC75607	SC75611	SC75615	SC75623	SC75631
SC75604	SC75608	SC75612	SC75616	SC75624	SC75632
			SC75617	SC75625	SC75633
			SC75618	SC75626	SC75634
			SC75619	SC75627	SC75635
			SC75620	SC75628	

Southern Region

(Unit numbers to be seen on front and rear of each set)

SYSTEM: 750 VOLTS D.C. 3rd RAIL

TWO-CAR SETS
(2-BIL.)
Motor Brake Second (K)

Body: 62′ 6″ × 9′ 0″ & 9′ 3″.
Weight: 43 tons 10 cwt.
Seats 2nd: 56†.
　　　　52.
Equipment: Two 275 h.p. English Electric
traction motors.

Driving Trailer Composite (K)

Body: 62′ 6″ × 9′ 0″ & 9′ 3″.
Weight: 31 tons 5 cwt.
Seats 1st: 24.
　　　2nd: 32.

2001†	2017	2032	2047
2002†	2018	2033	2048
2003†	2019	2034	2049
2004†	2020	2035	2050
2005†	2021	2036	2051
2006†	2022	2037	2052
2007†	2023	2038	2053
2008†	2024	2039	2054
2009†	2025	2040	2055
2010†	2026	2041	2056*
2011	2027	2042	2057
2012	2028	2043	2058
2013	2029	2044	2059
2015	2030	2045	2060
2016	2031	2046	2061

2062	2084	2107	2130
2063	2085	2108	2132
2064	2086	2109	2133‡
2065	2087	2110	2134
2066	2088*	2111	2135
2067	2089	2112	2136
2068	2090	2113	2137
2069‡	2091	2114	2138
2070	2092	2115	2139
2071	2093	2116	2140
2072	2094	2117	2141
2073	2095	2118	2142
2074	2096	2120	2143
2075	2097	2121	2144
2076	2098	2122	2145
2077	2099	2123	2146
2078	2100†	2124	2147
2079	2101	2125	2148
2080	2103	2126	2149
2081	2104	2127	2150
2082	2105	2128	2151
2083	2106	2129	2152

*BIL Motor Coach and 1939 type HAL
Trailer.
‡BIL Motor Coach and post-war all steel
HAL Trailer.

TWO-CAR SETS
(2-HAL.)
1939-type
Motor Brake Second

Body: 62′ 6″ × 9′ 0″ & 9′ 3″.
Weight: 44 tons.
Seats 2nd: 70.

Equipment: Two 275 h.p. English Electric nose-suspended traction motors.

Driving Trailer Composite (K)
Body: 62' 6" × 9' 0" & 9' 3".
Weight: 32 tons.
Seats 1st: 18 or 24.
2nd: 40 or 32.

2601	2624	2648	2671
2602	2625	2649	2672
2603	2626	2650	2673
2604	2627	2651	2674
2605	2628	2652	2675
2606	2629	2653*	2676
2607	2630	2654	2677
2608	2631	2655	2678
2609	2632	2656	2679
2610	2633	2657	2681
2611	2634	2658	2682
2612	2635	2659	2683
2613	2636	2660	2684
2614	2637	2661	2685
2615	2638	2662	2686
2616	2639	2663	2687
2617	2640	2664	2688
2618	2641	2665	2689
2619	2642	2666	2690
2620	2643	2667	2691
2621	2644	2668	2692
2622	2645	2669	
2623	2647	2670	

*Post-war all steel Trailer.

TWO-CAR SETS (2-HAL.)
Post War all-steel type.

Motor Brake Second
Body: 62' 6" × 9' 0" & 9' 3".
Weight: 42 tons.
Seats 2nd: 84.
Equipment: Two 275 h.p. English Electric nose-suspended traction motors.

Driving Trailer Composite (K)
Body: 62' 6" × 9' 0" & 9' 3"

Weight: 31 tons.
Seats 1st: 18.
2nd: 40.

2693	2695	2697	2699
2694	2696	2698	

TWO-CAR SETS (2-HAL.)
Post War all-steel type.

Motor Brake Saloon Second
Body: 62' 6" × 9' 0" & 9' 3".
Weight: 39 tons.
Seats 2nd: 82.
Equipment: Two 275 h.p. English Electric traction motors.

Driving Trailer Composite (K)
Body: 62' 6" × 9' 0" & 9' 3".
Weight: 31 tons.
Seats 1st: 24.
2nd: 32.

2700

FOUR-CAR SETS (4-LAV.)
Motor Brake Second
Body: 62' 6" × 9' 0" & 9' 3".
Weight: 41 tons.
44 tons*.
45 tons†.
Seats 2nd: 70
Equipment: Two 275 h.p. Metropolitan-Vickers traction motors.
†*Two 275 h.p. English Electric traction motors.

Trailer Composite
Body: 62' 0" × 9' 0" & 9' 3".
Weight: 28 tons.
29 tons*.
Seats 1st: 16.
2nd: 70.

Trailer Composite (K)

Body: 62' 0" × 9' 0" & 9' 3".
Weight: 29 tons.
　　　　30 tons*.
Seats 1st: 30.
　　　2nd: 24.

Motor Brake Second

(As Above)

2921	2930	2939	2948
2922	2931	2940	2949
2923	2932	2941	2950
2924	2933	2942	2951
2925	2934	2943	2952
2926†	2935	2944	2953
2927	2936	2945	2954*
2928	2937	2946	2955*
2929	2938	2947	

†One motor coach of 1939 2-HAL type.
* 1939 Bullied units.

SIX-CAR SETS
(6-PUL.)

Gangwayed within set

Motor Saloon Brake Second

Body: 63' 6" × 9' 0" & 9' 5".
Weight: 59 tons.
Seats 2nd: 52.
Equipment: Four 225 h.p. B.T.H. traction motors.

Trailer Second (K)

Body: 63' 6" × 9' 0" & 9' 3".
Weight: 35 tons.
Seats 2nd: 68.

Trailer Composite (K)

Body: 63' 6" × 9' 0" & 9' 3".
Weight: 35 tons.
Seats 1st: 30.
　　　2nd: 24.

Trailer Composite
Pullman (L)

Body: 66' 0" × 8' 11½" & 8' 11½".
Weight: 43 tons.
Seats 1st: 12.
　　　2nd: 16.

Trailer Composite (K)

(As Above)

Motor Saloon Brake Second

(As Above)

3001	3006	3011	3016
3002	3007	3012	3017
3003*	3008	3013	3018
3004	3009	3014*	3019
3005	3010	3015	3020

*One PAN motor coach.
*1939 Kulked Units.

SIX-CAR SETS
(6-PAN.)

Gangwayed within set

Motor Saloon Brake Second

Body: 63' 6" × 9' 0" & 9' 5".
Weight: 59 tons.
Seats 2nd: 52.
Equipment: Four 225 h.p. Eng'ish Electric traction motors.

Trailer Second (K)

Body: 63' 6" × 9' 0" & 9' 3".
Weight: 31 tons 10 cwt.
Seats 2nd: 68.

Trailer First (K)

Body: 59' 0" × 9' 0" & 9' 3".
Weight: 31 tons.
Seats 1st: 42.

Trailer Pantry First (K)

Body: 63' 6" × 9' 0" & 9' 3".
Weight: 32 tons.
Seats 1st: 30.

Trailer Second (K)

(As Above)

Motor Saloon Brake Second

(As Above)

3021	3025	3029	3034
3022	3026†	3030	3035
3023	3027	3031	3036
3024	3028	3033	3037

† One PUL motor coach.

SIX-CAR SETS
(6-PUL.)
Gangwayed within set

Motor Saloon Brake Second

Body: 63' 6" × 9' 0" & 9' 5"
Weight: 57 tons.
   59 tons*.
Seats 2nd: { 56.
    { 52*.
Equipment: Four 225 h.p. B.T.H. traction motors.

Trailer Second (K)

Body: 59' 0" × 9' 0" & 9' 3".
Weight: 34 tons.
Seats 2nd: 56.

Trailer Composite (K)

Body: 59' 0" × 9' 0" & 9' 3".
Weight: 34 tons.
Seats 1st: 30.
  2nd: 16.

Trailer Composite Pullman (L)

Body: 66' 0" × 8' 11½" & 8' 11½".
Weight: 43 tons.
Seats 1st: 12.
  2nd: 16.

Trailer Composite
(As Above)

Motor Saloon Brake Second

Body: 63' 6" × 9' 0" & 9' 3".
Weight: 59 tons.
Seats 2nd: 52.
Equipment: Four 225 h.p. B.T.H. traction motors.

3041	3042	3043*

FIVE-CAR PULLMAN SETS
(5-BEL.)
All-Pullman
Gangwayed within set

Motor Brake Second Pullman (L)

Body: 66' 0" × 8' 11½" & 8' 11½".
Weight: 62 tons.
Seats 2nd: 48.
Equipment: Four 225 h.p. B.T.H. traction motors.

Trailer Second Pullman (L)

Body: 66' 0" × 8' 11½" & 8' 11½".
Weight: 39 tons.
Seats 2nd: 56.

Trailer Kitchen First Pullman (L)

Body: 66' 0" × 8' 11½" & 8' 11½".
Weight: 43 tons.
Seats 1st: 20.

Trailer First Pullman (L)
(As Above)

Motor Brake Second Pullman (L)
(As Above)

3051	3052	3053

FOUR-CAR SETS
(4-RES.)
Gangwayed throughout

Motor Saloon Brake Second

Body: 63' 6" × 9' 0" & 9' 4½".
Weight: 46 tons 10 cwt.
Seats 2nd: 52.
Equipment: Two 225 h.p. English Electric traction motors.

Trailer First (K)

Body: 63' 6" × 9' 0" & 9' 3".
Weight: 33 tons.
Seats 1st: 30.
  1st Dining: 12.

Trailer Kitchen Second (K)

Body: 63' 6" × 9' 0" & 9' 4½".
Weight: 35 tons.
Seats 2nd Dining: 36.

Motor Saloon Brake Second
(As Above)

3054	3059	3065	3069
3055	3061	3066	3070
3056	3062	3067	3071
3057	3064	3068	3072*

*Kitchen Second in this unit converted to Buffet Car, weight 35 tons.

FOUR-CAR SETS
(4-BUF.)

Gangwayed throughout

Motor Saloon Brake Second

Body: 63′ 6″ × 9′ 0″ & 9′ 4½″.
Weight: 46 tons 10 cwt.
Seats 2nd: 52.
Equipment: Two 225 h.p. English Electric traction motors.

Trailer Composite (K)

Body: 63′ 6″ × 9′ 0″ & 9′ 3″.
Weight: 32 tons 12 cwt.
Seats 1st: 30.
    2nd: 24.

Trailer Buffet (L)

Body: 63′ 6″ × 9′ 0″ & 9′ 3″.
Weight: 37 tons.
Seats Buffet: 26.

Motor Saloon Brake Second

(As Above)

3073	3077	3080	3083
3074	3078	3081	3084
3075	3079	3082	3085
3076			

FOUR-CAR SETS
(4-COR.)

Gangwayed throughout

Motor Saloon Brake Second

Body: 63′ 6″ × 9′ 0″ & 9′ 4½″.
Weight: 46 tons 10 cwt.
Seats 2nd: 52.
Equipment: Two 225 h.p. English Electric traction motors.

Trailer Second (K)

Body: 63′ 6″ × 9′ 0″ & 9′ 3″.
Weight: 32 tons 13 cwt.
Seats 2nd: 68.

Trailer Composite (K)

Body: 63′ 6″ × 9′ 0″ & 9′ 3″.
Weight: 32 tons 12 cwt.
    *33 tons.
Seats 1st: 30.
    2nd: 24
    16.*

Motor Saloon Brake Second

(As Above)

3101	3116	3131	3146
3102	3117	3132	3147
3103	3118	3133	3148
3104	3119	3134	3149
3105	3120	3135	3150
3106	3121	3136	3151
3107	3122	3137	3152
3108	3123	3138	3153
3109	3124	3139	3154
3110	3125	3140	3155
3111	3126	3141	3156
3112	3127	3142	3157
3113	3128	3143	3158*
3114	3129	3144	
3115	3130	3145	

FOUR-CAR SUBURBAN SETS (DOUBLE DECK)
(4-DD.)

Motor Brake Second

Body: 62′ 6″ × 9′ 0″ & 9′ 3″.
Weight: 39 tons.
Seats 2nd: Lower deck 55
    Upper deck 55 (*plus* 10 tip-up)
Equipment: Two 250 h.p. English Electric traction motors.

Trailer Second

Body: 62′ 0″ × 9′ 0″ & 9′ 3″.
Weight: 28 tons.
Seats 2nd: Lower deck 78.
    Upper deck 66 (*plus* 12 tip-up)

Trailer Second

(As Above)

Motor Brake Second

(As Above)

4001	4002

FOUR-CAR SUBURBAN SETS
(4-SUB.)

Motor Brake Second

Body: 62′ 6″ × 9′ 0″ & 9′ 3″.
Weight: 43 tons.
Seats 2nd: 102.
Equipment: Two 275 h.p. English Electric traction motors.

Trailer Second

Body: 62′ 0″ × 9′ 0″ & 9′ 3″.
Weight: 29 tons·
Seats 2nd: 132.

Trailer Second

Body: 62′ 0″ × 9′ 0″ & 9′ 3″
Weight: 29 tons.
Seats 2nd: 120.

Motor Brake Second

(As Above)

4101	4104	4107	4110
4102	4105	4108	
4103	4106	4109	

Motor Brake Second

Body: 62′ 6″ × 9′ 0″ & 9′ 3″.
Weight: 43 tons.
Seats 2nd: 96.
Equipment: Two 275 h.p. English Electric traction motors.

Trailer Second

Body: 62′ 0″ × 9′ 0″ & 9′ 3″.
Weight: 28 tons.
Seats 2nd: 108.

Trailer Second

Body: 62′ 0″ × 9′ 0″ & 9′ 3″.
Weight: 28 tons.
Seats 2nd: 120.

Motor Brake Second

(As Above)

4111	4114	4117	4120
4112	4115	4118	
4113	4116	4119	

Motor Brake Second
(Semi-Saloon)

Body: 62′ 6″ × 9′ 0″ & 9′ 3″.
Weight: 43 tons.
Seats 2nd: 84.
Equipment: Two 275 h.p. English Electric traction motors.

Trailer Second

Body: 62′ 0″ × 9′ 0″ & 9′ 3″.
Weight: 28 tons
Seats 2nd: 108.

Trailer Second
(Semi-Saloon)

Body: 62′ 0″ × 9′ 0″ & 9′ 3″
Weight: 28 tons.
Seats 2nd: 106.

Motor Brake Second
(Semi-Saloon)

(As Above)

4121	4124	4127	4130
4122	4125	4128	
4123	4126	4129	

Motor Saloon Brake Second

Body: 62′ 6″ × 9′ 0″ & 9′ 3″.
Weight: 39 tons.
Seats 2nd: 82.
Equipment: Two 250 h.p. English Electric traction motors.

Trailer Second

Body: 62′ 0″ × 9′ 0″ & 9′ 3″.
Weight: 28 tons.
Seats 2nd: 120.

Trailer Saloon Second

Body: 62′ 0″ × 9′ 0″ & 9′ 3″.
Weight: 28 tons.
Seats 2nd: 102.

Motor Saloon Brake Second

(As Above)

4277	4283	4289	4295
4278	4284	4290	4296
4279	4285	4291	4297
4280	4286	4292	4298
4281	4287	4293	4299
4282	4288	4294	

Motor Brake Second

Body: 56′ 11″ × 8′ 6″ & 9′ 0″.
Weight: 39 tons.
Seats 2nd: 90.
Equipment: Two 275 h.p. Metropolitan-Vickers traction motors.

Trailer Second

Body: 60′ 0″ × 8′ 6″ & 9′ 0′.
Weight: 27 tons.
Seats 2nd: 90.

Trailer Second
Body: 62′ 0″ × 9′ 0″ & 9′ 3″.
Weight: 28 tons.
Seats 2nd: 120.

Motor Brake Second
(As Above)

4301	4310†	4315	4323
4302	4311	4319	4324
4305	4314	4322	4325
4308			

† Unit 4310 has two 60-ft. 90-seat trailers.

Motor Brake Second
Body: 62′ 6″ × 8′ 6″ & 9′ 0″.
Weight:
Seats 2nd: 80.
Equipment: Two 275 h.p. English Electric traction motors.

Trailer Second
Body: 62′ 0″ × 8′ 6″ & 9′ 0″.
Weight:
Seats 2nd: 90.

Trailer Second
Body: 62′ 0″ × 9′ 0″ & 9′ 3″.
Weight:
Seats 2nd: 120.

Motor Brake Second
(As Above)

4326	4333	4340	4347
4328	4334	4341	4348
4329	4335	4343	4351†
4330	4337	4344	4352
4331	4338	4346	4353
4332	4339*		

*Unit 4339 has one motor brake second of the 4301-25 type.
†Unit 4351 has two 62-ft. 90 seat trailers.

Motor Brake Second
Body: 62′ 6″ × 9′ 0″ & 9′ 3″.
Weight: 43 tons.
Seats 2nd: 96
Equipment: Two 275 h.p. English Electric traction motors.

Trailer Second
Body: 62′ 0″ × 9′ 0″ & 9′ 3″
Weight: 28 tons.
Seats 2nd: 120.

Trailer Second
(As Above)

Motor Brake Second
(As Above)

4355	4358	4360	4362
4356	4359	4361	4363
4357			

Motor Brake Second
Body: 62′ 6″ × 9′ 0″ & 9′ 3″.
Weight: 43 tons.
Seats 2nd: 96.
Equipment: Two 275 h.p. English Electric traction motors.

Trailer Second
Body: 62′ 0″ × 9′ 0″ & 9′ 3″.
Weight: 28 tons.
Seats 2nd: 108.

Trailer Second
Body: 62′ 0″ × 9′ 0″ & 9′ 3″.
Weight: 28 tons.
Seats 2nd: 120.

Motor Brake Second
(As Above)

4364	4368	4371	4374
4365	4369	4372	4375
4366	4370	4373	4376
4367			

Motor Brake Second
Body: 62′ 6″ × 9′ 0″ & 9′ 3″.
Weight:
Seats 2nd: 96.
Equipment: Two 275 h.p. English Electric traction motors.

Trailer Second

Body: 62′ 0″ × 9′ 0″ & 9′ 3″.
Weight:
Seats 2nd: 108.

Trailer Saloon Second

Body: 62′ 0″ × 9′ 0″ & 9′ 3″.
Weight:
Seats 2nd: 102.

Motor Brake Second
(As Above)

4377

Motor Saloon Brake Second

Body: 62′ 6″ × 9′ 0″ & 9′ 3″.
Weight: 42 tons.
Seats 2nd: 82.
Equipment: Two 275 h.p. English Electric traction motors.

Trailer Second

Body: 62′ 0″ × 9′ 0″ & 9′ 3″.
Weight: 28 tons.
Seats 2nd: 120.

Trailer Saloon Second

Body: 62′ 0″ × 9′ 0″ & 9′ 3″.
Weight: 28 tons.
Seats 2nd: 102.

Motor Saloon Brake Second
(As Above)

4378	4381	4384	4387
4379	4382	4385	
4380	4383	4386	

Motor Saloon Brake Second

Body: 62′ 6″ × 9′ 0″ & 9′ 3″.
Weight: 39 tons.
Seats 2nd: 82.
Equipment: Two 250 h.p. English Electric traction motors.

Trailer Second

Body: 62′ 6″ × 9′ 0″ & 9′ 3″.
Weight: 28 tons.
Seats 2nd: 120.

Trailer Second
(As Above)

Motor Saloon Brake Second
(As Above)

| 4601 | 4603 | 4605 | 4607 |
| 4602 | 4604 | 4606 | |

Motor Saloon Brake Second

Body: 62′ 6″ × 9′ 0″ & 9′ 3″.
Weight: 39 tons.
Seats 2nd: 82.
Equipment: Two 250 h.p. English Electric traction motors.

Trailer Second

Body: 62′ 0″ × 9′ 0′ & 9′ 3 .
Weight: 28 tons.
27 tons.
Seats 2nd: 120.
108*.

Trailer Saloon Second

Body: 62′ 0″ × 9′ 0″ & 9′ 3″.
Weight: 26 tons.
28 tons.
Seats 2nd: 102.

Motor Brake Saloon Second
(As Above)

4621	4643	4665	4687
4622	4644	4666	4688*
4623	4645	4667	4689
4624	4646	4668	4690
4625	4647	4669	4691
4626	4648	4670	4692
4627	4649	4671	4693
4628	4650	4672	4694
4629	4651	4673	4695
4630	4652	4674	4696*
4631	4653	4675	4697
4632	4654	4676	4698
4633	4655	4677	4699
4634	4656	4678	4700
4635	4657	4679	4701
4636	4658	4680	4702
4637	4659	4681	4703
4638	4660	4682	4704
4639	4661	4683	4705
4640	4662	4684	4706
4641	4663	4685	4707
4642	4664	4686	4708

4709	4721	4733*	4744
4710	4722	4734	4745
4711	4723*	4735	4746
4712	4724	4736	4747
4713	4725	4737	4748
4714	4726	4738	4749
4715	4727	4739*	4750
4716	4728*	4740	4751
4717	4729	4741	4752
4718	4730	4742	4753
4719	4731	4743	4754
4720	4732		

FOUR-CAR SUBURBAN SETS (4-EPB.)

Motor Saloon Brake Second

Body: 62′ 6″ × 9′ 0″ & 9′ 3″.
Weight: 40 tons.
Seats 2nd: 82.
Equipment: Two 250 h.p. English Electric traction motors.

Trailer Second

Body: 62′ 0″ × 9′ 0″ & 9′ 3″.
Weight: 28 tons.
Seats 2nd: 120.
108*.

Trailer Saloon Second

Body: 62′ 0″ × 9′ 0″ & 9′ 3″.
Weight: 27 tons.
Seats 2nd: 102.

Motor Saloon Brake Second

(As Above)

5001	5013	5025	5036
5002	5014	5026	5037
5003	5015	5027	5038
5004	5016	5028	5039
5005*	5017	5029	5040
5006	5018	5030	5041
5007	5019	5031	5042
5009	5020	5032	5043
5010	5021	5033	5044
5011	5022	5034	5045
5012	5024	5035	5046

5047	5136	5178	5220*
5048	5137	5179	5221
5049	5138	5180	5222
5050	5139	5181	5223
5051	5140	5182	5224
5052	5141	5183	5225
5053	5142	5184	5226
5101	5143	5185	5227
5102	5144	5186	5228
5103	5145	5187	5229
5104	5146	5188	5230
5105	5147	5189	5231
5106	5148	5190	5232
5107	5149	5191	5233
5108	5150	5192	5234
5109	5151	5193	5235
5110	5152	5194	5236
5111	5153	5195	5237
5112	5154	5196	5238
5113	5155	5197	5239
5114	5156	5198	5240
5115	5157	5199	5241
5116	5158	5200	5242
5117	5159	5201	5243
5118	5160	5202	5244
5119	5161	5203	5245
5120	5162	5205	5246
5121	5163	5206	5247
5122	5164	5207	5248
5123	5165	5208	5249
5124	5166	5209	5250
5125	5167	5210	5251
5126	5168	5211	5252
5127	5169	5212	5253
5128	5170	5213	5254
5129	5171	5214	5255
5130	5172	5215	5256
5131	5173	5216	5257
5132	5174	5217	5258
5133	5175	5218	5259
5134	5176	5219	5260
5135	5177		

FOUR-CAR SUBURBAN SETS (4-EPB.)

B.R. Standard design

Motor Saloon Brake Second

Body: 63′ 11½″ × 9′ 0″ & 9′ 3″
Weight: 39 tons.
          40 tons.
Seats 2nd: 82.
Equipment: Two 250 h.p. English Electric
traction motors.

Trailer Second
(Semi-Compartment)

Body: 63′ 6″ × 9′ 0″ & 9′ 3″.
Weight: 29 tons.
Seats 2nd: 112.

Trailer Second
(Semi-Compartment)

(As Above)

Motor Saloon Brake Second

(As Above)

5301*	5315	5329	5343
5302*	5316	5330	5344
5303	5317	5331	5345
5304	5318	5332	5346
5305	5319	5333	5347
5306	5320	5334	5348
5307	5321	5335	5349
5308	5322	5336	5350
5309	5323	5337	5351
5310	5324	5338	5352
5311	5325	5339	5353
5312	5326	5340	5354
5313	5327	5341	5355
5314	5328	5342	5356

*Formed partly of S.R. type vehicles on
62′ underframes weights as 5001–5260.

TWO-CAR SETS
(2-HAP.)

Motor Brake Second
(Semi-Saloon)

Body: 62′ 6″ × 9′ 0″ & 9′ 3″.
Weight: 40. tons.
Seats 2nd: 84.
Equipment: Two 250 h.p. English
Electric traction motors.

Driving Trailer
Composite (K)

Body: 62′ 6″ × 9′ 0″ & 9′ 3″.

Weight: 32 tons.
Seats 1st 18.
      2nd: 38.

5601	5610	5619	5628
5602	5611	5620	5629
5603	5612	5621	5630
5604	5613	5622	5631
5605	5614	5623	5632
5606	5615	5624	5633
5607	5616	5625	5634
5608	5617	5626	5635
5609	5618	5627	5636

TWO-CAR
SUBURBAN SETS
(2-NOP.)

Motor Brake Second
(Semi-Saloon)

Body: 62′ 6″ × 9′ 0″ & 9′ 3″.
Weight: 40 tons.
Seats 2nd: 84.
Equipment: Two 250 h.p. English
Electric traction motors.

Driving Trailer Second
(Semi-Saloon)

Body: 62′ 6″ × 9′ 0″ & 9′ 3″.
Weight: 30 tons.
Seats 2nd: 94.

5651	5660	5669	5677
5652	5661	5670	5678
5653	5662	5671	5679
5654	5663	5672	5680
5655	5664	5673	5681
5656	5665	5674	5682
5657	5666	5675	5683
5658	5667	5676	5684
5659	5668		

TWO-CAR
SUBURBAN SETS
(2-EPB.)

B.R. Standard design

Motor Brake Second (Semi-Saloon)

Body: 63′ 11½″ × 9′ 0″ & 9′ 3″.
Weight: 40 tons.
Seats 2nd: 84.
Equipment: Two 250 h.p. English Electric traction motors.

Driving Trailer Second (Semi-Compartment)

Body: 63′ 11½″ × 9′ 0″ & 9′ 3″.
Weight: 30 tons.
　　　31 tons*
Seats 2nd: 102.

5701	5721	5741	5761
5702	5722	5742	5762
5703	5723	5743	5763
5704	5724	5744	5764
5705	5725	5745	5765
5706	5726	5746	5767
5707	5727	5747	5768
5708	5728	5748	5769
5709	5729	5749	5770
5710	5730	5750	5771
5711	5731	5751	5772
5712	5732	5752	5773
5713	5733	5753	5774
5714	5734	5754	5775
5715	5735	5755	5776
5716	5736	5756	5777
5717	5737	5757	5778
5718	5738	5758	5779
5719	5739	5759	5800*
5720	5740	5760	

TWO-CAR SETS (2-HAP.)

B.R. Standard design

Motor Brake Second (Semi-Saloon)

Body: 63′ 11½″ × 9′ 0″ & 9′ 3″
Weight: 40 tons.
Seats 2nd: 84.
Equipment: Two 250 h.p. English Electric traction motors.

Driving Trailer Composite (L)

Body: 63′ 11½″ × 9′ 0″ & 9′ 3″.
Weight: 30 tons.
Seats 1st: 19.
　　　2nd: 50.

6001	6028	6054	6080
6002	6029	6055	6081
6003	6030	6056	6082
6004	6031	6057	6083
6005	6032	6058	6084
6006	6033	6059	6085
6007	6034	6060	6086
6008	6035	6061	6087
6009	6036	6062	6088
6010	6037	6063	6089
6011	6038	6064	6090
6012	6039	6065	6091
6013	6040	6066	6092
6014	6041	6067	6093
6015	6042	6068	6094
6016	6043	6069	6095
6017	6044	6070	6096
6018	6045	6071	6097
6019	6046	6072	6098
6020	6047	6073	6099
6021	6048	6074	6100
6022	6049	6075	6101
6023	6050	6076	6102
6024	6051	6077	6103
6025	6052	6078	6104
6026	6053	6079	6105
6027			

FOUR-CAR SETS (4-BEP.)

B.R. Standard design
Gangwayed throughout

Motor Saloon Brake Second

Body: 64′ 6″ × 9′ 0″ & 9′ 3″.
Weight: 40 tons*.
　　　41 tons.
Seats 2nd: 56.
Equipment: Two 250 h.p. English Electric traction motors.

Trailer Composite (K)

Body: 64′ 6″ × 9′ 0″ & 9′ 3″.
Weight: 31 tons*.
33 tons.
Seats 1st : 24
2nd: 24

Trailer Buffet

Body: 64′ 6″ × 9′ 0″ & 9′ 3″.
Weight: 35 tons*.
36 tons.
Seats Buffet: 21.

Motor Saloon Brake Second

(As Above)

7001*	7004	7007	7010
7002*	7005	7008	7011
7003	7006	7009	7012

FOUR-CAR SETS
(4 CEP.)

B.R. Standard design

Gangwayed throughout

Motor Saloon Brake Second

Body: 64′ 6″ × 9′ 0″ & 9′ 3″.
Weight: 40 tons*.
41 tons.
Seats 2nd: 56.
Equipment: Two 250 h.p. English
Electric traction motors.

Trailer Composite (K)

Body: 64′ 6″ × 9′ 0″ & 9′ 3″.
Weight: 31 tons*.
33 tons.
Seats 1st: 24.
2nd: 24.

Trailer Second (K)

Body: 64′ 6″ × 9′ 0″ & 9′ 3″.
Weight: 31 tons*.
32 tons.
Seats 2nd: 64.

Motor Saloon Brake Second

(As Above)

7101*	7104*	7107	7110
7102*	7105	7108	7111
7103*	7106	7109	7112

7113	7124	7134	7144
7114	7125	7135	7145
7115	7126	7136	7146
7116	7127	7137	7147
7117	7128	7138	7148
7118	7129	7139	7149
7119	7130	7140	7150
7120	7131	7141	7151
7121	7132	7142	7152
7122	7133	7143	7153
7123			

Motor Luggage Van

Body: 64′ 6″ × 9′ 0″ & 9′ 3″.
Weight: 45 tons.
Equipment: Two 250 h.p. English
Electric traction motors.
Note: These vehicles can work
singly, hauling a limited load, or in
multiple with CEP type stock. They
are equipped with traction batteries
for working on non-electrified lines at
Dover and Folkestone.

COACH Nos.
S68001   S68002

WATERLOO & CITY
ONE- OR FIVE-CAR SETS

Motor Saloon Brake Second

Body: 47′ 0″ × 8′ 7¾″.
Weight:
Seats 2nd: 40.
Equipment: Two 190 h.p. English
Electric traction motors.

51	54	57	60
52	55	58	61
53	56	59	62

Trailer Saloon Second

Body: 47′ 0″ × 8′ 7¾″.
Weight: 18 tons 14 cwt.
Seats 2nd: 52.

71	75	79	83
72	76	80	84
73	77	81	85
74	78	82	86

Trains are formed of a single motor
car or up to five-car units comprising
two motor cars and three trailers.

Front cover: LNER Class K3 2-6-0 No 61880 near Islip. *Gerald T. Robinson*

Back cover, top: 'Warship' class No D600 *Active* at Penzance. *P. Thatcher*

Back cover, bottom: A 'Pullman' unit on a trial run, No 60099 leading.
MCCW

First published 1960
Reprinted 2004

ISBN 0 7110 3022 7

Published by Ian Allan Publishing

an imprint of Ian Allan Publishing Ltd, Hersham, Surrey, KT12 4RG.

Printed by Ian Allan Printing Ltd, Hersham, Surrey, KT12 4RG.

Code: 0401/B2